JUMBO

Book of

Logic Puzzles

The edition is published by Igloo Books Ltd

Henson Way, Telford Way Industrial Estate

Kettering, Northants, NN16 8PX

First published in 2005

Puzzle compilation, typesetting and design by:
Puzzle Press Ltd, http://www.puzzlepress.co.uk

Henson Way, Telford Way Industrial Estate

Kettering, Northants, NN16 8PX

info@igloo-books.com

ISBN 1-84561-210-8

Walking the Dog

To raise extra pocket-money, young Miles Trotter takes dogs for walks in the local park and his services are currently employed by five of his neighbours, who can't personally exercise their dogs every day. From the clues below, can you discover the number of the house at which each dog lives, the name of his owner and the number of times per week that Miles takes him for a run in the park?

1. Bonzo is taken to the park more often than Mr Carter's dog.

2. Mr Taylor lives at No 3. Miles takes Whisky to the park four times every week.

3. Miss French's dog goes to the park twice per week.

4. Pip (who belongs to Mrs Beale) goes to the park more often than the dog from house No 1, who doesn't get taken to the park just once per week.

5. Rusty (not Mr Taylor's dog) is taken for a run in the park five times every week.

6. The dog from No 2 gets taken out three times per week.

7. Mrs Morris doesn't live at No 5.

	House					Mrs Beale	Mr Carter	Miss French	Mrs Morris	Mr Taylor	Once	Twice	3 times	4 times	5 times
	No 1	No 2	No 3	No 4	No 5										
Bobby															
Bonzo															
Pip															
Rusty															
Whisky															
Once															
Twice															
3 times															
4 times															
5 times															
Mrs Beale															
Mr Carter															
Miss French															
Mrs Morris															
Mr Taylor															

Dog	House No	Owner	Times per week

Lost Property

Ivor Scruluce often mislays things and last week was no exception. Luckily, however, various members of the public noticed that he'd left things behind and ran after him, to give them back. What was left behind on each day, at which place and who returned his property to Ivor that very same day, before he'd realised it was missing?

1. Pete left the train two stations earlier than he had intended, chasing Mr Scruluce along the platform to return an item.

2. Ivor left his wallet behind (not on the train) later in the week than he forgot to pick up his house keys which had fallen from his pocket, but one day earlier in the week than the day on which he lost his watch (which also wasn't on the train).

3. John is the taxi driver who noticed that Ivor had forgotten his briefcase. He returned it earlier in the week than the day on which Ivor lost his car keys.

4. Lynda picked up something in the car park the day after Ivor's house keys were returned to him by Kenny.

5. Something was left behind in the waiting room of the doctor's surgery on Tuesday.

Day	Item	Place	Returner

Poetry Writers

Five friends recently entered a poetry writing competition. Each chose a different title for his or her piece and took a different length of time to compose it. Can you discover the full name of each poet, the title of his or her work and the amount of time he or she spent on its construction?

1. Mandy took two hours longer over her piece of work than the author of *Gentle Lady*, who spent longer writing a poem than the person surnamed Chester.

2. *Mark Of Cain* (coincidentally written by the man named Mark) took less time to write than Miss Holford's piece, which isn't entitled *Garden of Desire*.

3. George wrote *Capital Charisma* and the poet surnamed Willis penned a futuristic poem entitled *Final Frontiers* which, incidentally, won first prize in the competition.

4. The poet surnamed Jork took an hour longer to write an entry than Mrs Clayton spent at her creation.

	Chester	Clayton	Holford	Jork	Willis	Capital Charisma	Final Frontiers	Garden of Desire	Gentle Lady	Mark of Cain	7 hours	8 hours	9 hours	10 hours	11 hours
George															
Ingrid															
Mandy															
Mark															
Robert															
7 hours															
8 hours															
9 hours															
10 hours															
11 hours															
Capital Charisma															
Final Frontiers															
Garden of Desire															
Gentle Lady															
Mark of Cain															

Forename	Surname	Poem	Time taken

American Football

Five cousins recently took part in an American football match, playing for charity. Each came along wearing a different coloured shirt, sporting a different number (not necessarily related to the position played, since these were the only football shirts they possess). Each is a fan of a major football team; so find out which colour of shirt and number each player wore, as well as the name of the team he supports.

1. The cousin who wore the white shirt (which didn't have No 33 printed on it) doesn't support the Eagles.

2. The quarterback's shirt had a number ten higher than that on the blue shirt worn by the wide receiver.

3. The running back who supports the Jetstars wore a higher number than that on his cousin's orange shirt.

4. The Blue Sox supporter wore No 23 and the linebacker wore No 43.

5. The man in green supports the Dolphins and wore a number lower than that of the offensive linesman.

	No 13	No 23	No 33	No 43	No 53	Blue	Green	Orange	White	Yellow	Blue Sox	Dolphins	Eagles	Harlequins	Jetstars
Linebacker															
Off'sive linesman															
Quarterback															
Running back															
Wide receiver															
Blue Sox															
Dolphins															
Eagles															
Harlequins															
Jetstars															
Blue															
Green															
Orange															
White															
Yellow															

Position	Shirt number	Shirt colour	Team supported

Share & Share Alike

Five young women regularly borrow from and lend to one another. In fact, only yesterday, each lent and borrowed two different types of clothing, so that if one woman lent a coat, she didn't borrow a coat from anyone. Given that information, it's up to you to discover what each lent, who she lent to and what she borrowed!

1. The woman who borrowed a hat isn't Claire or Simone.

2. Claire lent a jumper to the woman (not Simone) who lent an item of clothing to Georgina.

3. Stephanie lent an item to the woman from whom Helen borrowed a skirt.

4. The woman who lent a coat didn't borrow a dress.

		Item lent					Lent to					Item borrowed				
		Coat	Dress	Hat	Jumper	Skirt	Claire	Georgina	Helen	Simone	Stephanie	Coat	Dress	Hat	Jumper	Skirt
Lender	Claire															
	Georgina															
	Helen															
	Simone															
	Stephanie															
Borrowed	Coat											
	Dress											
	Hat											
	Jumper											
	Skirt											
From	Claire											
	Georgina											
	Helen											
	Simone											
	Stephanie											

Lender	Item lent	Lent to	Item borrowed

School Daze

Perhaps the fact that there was a Founders' Day party with buns and ice-cream had something to do with the fact that the five children who feature in this puzzle were so keen to attend school, despite feeling unwell… However, each was promptly taken home again by one of the teachers! Can you discover every child's full name, together with his or her ailment and which teacher who took him or her home?

1. Mr O'Connor took home the girl (not Petunia) suffering from an earache. Neither Leon nor his cousin (whose surname is Crooke) was suffering from a fever or a headache.

2. The child surnamed Larkin (who wasn't taken home by Mrs Hale) had a very bad cold and couldn't stop sneezing.

3. Petunia wasn't the child who insisted on attending school despite running a very high fever, who was taken home again by Mr Ball.

4. Veronica Roberts had a terrible tummy ache (before the party started, so one couldn't blame the food!). She wasn't taken home by Mrs Hale or Miss Morton.

5. Norman's surname isn't Price.

	Crooke	Dillinger	Larkin	Price	Roberts	Cold	Earache	Fever	Headache	Tummy ache	Mr Ball	Mrs Hale	Miss Morton	Mr O'Connor	Mrs Warne
Hannah															
Leon															
Norman															
Petunia															
Veronica															
Mr Ball															
Mrs Hale															
Miss Morton															
Mr O'Connor															
Mrs Warne															
Cold															
Earache															
Fever															
Headache															
Tummy ache															

Pupil	Surname	Ailment	Teacher

Walking Week

Five people took hiking holidays in the gorgeous countryside surrounding the Lakes of Dunroamin last week. Where did each walk from and to and what was the total distance covered by each walker during their week's vacation?

1. Mel hiked from Gradbury. Herb walked forty-five miles to Tipton.

2. Graham (who began his journey in Awlford) wasn't the hiker who walked the furthest, finally arriving in Pip's Point.

3. The trip from Northwood to Mole End wasn't as long as that to Daw Creek, although it was further than was walked by Keith. Keith didn't start out from Bunston on his journey.

	From					To					Distance				
	Awlford	Bunston	Gradbury	Northwood	Southam	Daw Creek	Highwater	Mole End	Pip's Point	Tipton	40 miles	45 miles	49 miles	59 miles	66 miles
Graham															
Herb															
Keith															
Mel															
Wayne															
40 miles															
45 miles															
49 miles															
59 miles															
66 miles															
Daw Creek															
Highwater															
Mole End															
Pip's Point															
Tipton															

Hiker	From	To	Distance

They're Off!

Five horses and their riders competed in a fund-raising event for a local hospital. Using the clues below, can you determine the name of each horse's jockey, the colours every jockey wore and their finishing position.

1. The third jockey across the line wore purple.

2. Parmesan's rider wasn't dressed in orange.

3. The red silks were worn by Bob Bouncer, who didn't finish first.

4. Lance Lingfield and his mount came in fourth place.

5. Risky Business wasn't the horse that finished in second place.

6. Anthony Armstrong didn't wear yellow silks and didn't come in last.

7. Freshman's jockey wore green.

8. Martyn Mucklow, riding Mr Fisher, wasn't the second or fifth to cross the line.

9. The jockey in orange silks didn't ride Aardvark, who crossed the finish line first.

	Armstrong	Bouncer	Lingfield	Mucklow	Potterton	Green	Orange	Purple	Red	Yellow	1st	2nd	3rd	4th	5th
Aardvark															
Freshman															
Mr Fisher															
Parmesan															
Risky Business															
1st															
2nd															
3rd															
4th															
5th															
Green															
Orange															
Purple															
Red															
Yellow															

Horse	Jockey	Colour	Finished

Twin Sets

The six pairs of twins who feature in this puzzle have all been given two forenames apiece. Luckily, no boy has a second name which starts with the same letter as his first: in fact, every set of twins has names which begin with four different letters. Can you discover who is related to whom?

1. One boy's name is Simon Alan and one girl's name is Darlene Mary.

2. No girl is called Margaret Amelia and no boy is called Mark Stephen.

3. The girl whose second name is Dinah is the sister of the boy whose second name is Stephen, after their father.

4. One of the girls is Helen Lynne: she isn't the sister of the boy called Andrew Damian.

5. Margaret's brother's second name is Hubert, after their grandfather.

	Alan	Damian	Hubert	Lance	Michael	Stephen	Anna	Darlene	Helen	Louisa	Margaret	Sharon	Amelia	Dinah	Holly	Lynne	Mary	Susan
Andrew																		
David																		
Hector																		
Liam																		
Mark																		
Simon																		
Amelia																		
Dinah																		
Holly																		
Lynne																		
Mary																		
Susan																		
Anna																		
Darlene																		
Helen																		
Louisa																		
Margaret																		
Sharon																		

Boy	2nd name	Girl	2nd name

No Publicity, Please!

Although these writers are all proud of their works of fiction, they prefer to remain anonymous (perhaps understandably, considering their actual surnames!) and have assumed names (with forenames of the same sex as their own) under which they write. Can you discover every author's real forename and surname, together with the forename and surname under which he or she writes?

1. Gertie Ginsucker is not the woman whose works are better known to the public under her assumed name of Jane Reid.

2. Gwyneth has chosen Lizzie as an assumed forename.

3. Messrs Hollings & Carper have recently published the book written by the man who writes using the forename of Stanley and whose real surname is Grotwit.

4. Gerard's assumed surname is Soul.

5. The man surnamed Gadwhistle is better known to his readers by the surname Lovelace.

6. The author whose real surname is Gungho writes with an assumed surname of Harmony.

		Surname					Assumed Forename					Assumed Surname				
		Gadwhistle	Ginsucker	Gloop	Grotwit	Gungho	Arthur	Denise	Jane	Lizzie	Stanley	Gentle	Harmony	Lovelace	Reid	Soul
Forename	Griselda															
	Gertie															
	Godfrey															
	Gwyneth															
	Gerard															
Ass. surname	Gentle															
	Harmony															
	Lovelace															
	Reid															
	Soul															
Ass. forename	Arthur															
	Denise															
	Jane															
	Lizzie															
	Stanley															

Forename	Surname	Assumed forename	Assumed surname

Ins & Outs

Last Tuesday morning's post contained five bills and Bill Owen was at a loss as to how he was going to pay them all… However, by good fortune, Bill received money from five different sources, so was able to pay off his debts by the following Monday and still had some money left over. For what amount was each bill, with money from which source did he pay it and what was the amount of each windfall?

1. Money from only one source was used to pay any one bill, and any money left over was used for other expenses, such as day-to-day living.

2. The shares dividend netted Bill 20 Euros less than the cost of his gas bill, so obviously he paid another bill with the money from the shares dividend.

3. The money from the lottery win wasn't used to pay Bill's phone bill, which amounted to 100 Euros more than his garage bill.

4. The bonus Bill received from work amounted to either 70 Euros more or 90 Euros more than his lottery win.

5. The win of 180 Euros came as the result of a lucky bet on the horses in the 3.00pm race on Thursday and he used this money to pay a bill which amounted to 25 Euros less than the one which he paid with money from his shares dividend.

6. Surprisingly, the tax bill amounted to less than the electricity bill.

	Bill amount										Received				
	150 euros	175 Euros	200 Euros	250 Euros	300 Euros	Lottery win	Racing bet	Shares dividend	Sale of computer	Works bonus	180 Euros	190 Euros	260 Euros	280 Euros	310 Euros
Electricity															
Garage															
Gas															
Phone															
Tax															
180 Euros										
190 Euros										
260 Euros										
280 Euros										
310 Euros										
Lottery win					
Racing bet					
Shares dividend					
Sale of computer					
Works bonus					

Bill	Bill amount	Source	Received

Student Exchange

Five students at a Welsh university are taking part in a student exchange programme. From the clues, can you discover the full name of every student, what each is studying and the country to which each is going?

1. Megan is going to Denmark, but her friend Janet isn't going to Australia.

2. The man surnamed Jones is studying chemistry and is travelling further afield than Europe.

3. Gwynneth isn't the student surnamed Hann. The student surnamed Hann isn't studying computing or mathematics.

4. Hugh Boyd's fellow student is studying music and is travelling to Australia.

5. The woman going to Italy is studying computing, unlike the student surnamed Williams.

Student	Surname	Studying	Travelling to

Irresistible

Pauline works at the local bakery every Saturday morning, but spends nearly all of the money she earns there on cakes, pies and tarts! Over the past five Saturdays, she has purchased various quantities of the aforementioned goods, so use the clues to discover the numbers of each that she bought on every Saturday.

1. Pauline bought fewer tarts and one fewer pie on the second Saturday than she had purchased on the day when she bought nine cakes.

2. Eleven pies were bought on the same day (not the fourth Saturday) as she purchased one more cake (and two fewer tarts) than she bought on the fifth Saturday.

3. Eleven cakes were purchased on the day that she bought one more pie (and one more tart) than were purchased on another day.

4. One fewer pie was bought on the fifth Saturday than on the fourth Saturday.

5. On the third Saturday, Pauline bought one more pie than she had purchased on the first Saturday.

	7 cakes	8 cakes	9 cakes	11 cakes	12 cakes	6 pies	7 pies	9 pies	10 pies	11 pies	5 tarts	6 tarts	7 tarts	9 tarts	10 tarts
1st Saturday															
2nd Saturday															
3rd Saturday															
4th Saturday															
5th Saturday															
5 tarts															
6 tarts															
7 tarts															
9 tarts															
10 tarts															
6 pies															
7 pies															
9 pies															
10 pies															
11 pies															

Saturday	No of cakes	No of pies	No of tarts

Card Sharp

What is the face value and suit of each of the cards shown below? All twelve cards used below are of different values and together they total 81. Values of the cards are as per their numbers and ace=1, jack=11, queen=12 and king=13. No card is horizontally or vertically next to another of the same colour and there are four different suits in each horizontal row and three different suits in each vertical column.

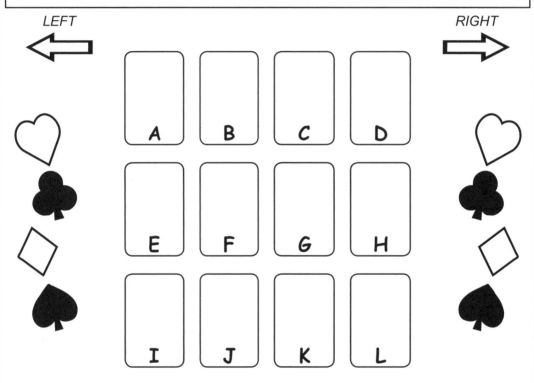

LEFT   RIGHT

1. Card H has a value either three higher or three lower than that of card J (which isn't directly next to the five of spades).

2. Card D has a value either two higher or two lower than that of card K.

3. Card L has a lower value than that of card C, but a higher value than that of card B (which isn't an ace).

4. The total of the three hearts is higher than the total of cards I and J, which aren't hearts. Card E isn't the king of diamonds.

5. Card F has a value three times that of card H, which is a spade.

6. The total value of cards D and H is the same as that of card A, which has a value two lower than that of card F.

Auntie's Present

Coincidentally, the first five customers in Laura's Gift Shop this morning were all young men who told her they wanted to purchase a present for an aunt's birthday. Every man bought a different gift and Laura wrapped them all in differently coloured sheets of paper. Can you discover who purchased each item, the name of his aunt and the colour of the paper in which each is gift-wrapped?

1. Jimmy's aunt will receive the gift in blue paper.

2. The present wrapped in silver paper is a vase, destined for one young man's Auntie Bessie. Keith hasn't an Aunt Bessie.

3. Paul's Aunt Madge won't receive the present wrapped in purple paper.

4. The gift wrapped in purple paper is a scented candle and won't be given to Aunt Caroline; nor will Aunt Caroline receive the silver-plated teapot.

5. Neither the decorative teapot nor the porcelain mug was bought by Stuart, whose present for his Aunt Judith is wrapped in pink paper.

	Jimmy	Keith	Paul	Richard	Stuart	Auntie Bessie	Aunt Caroline	Aunt Judith	Aunt Madge	Auntie Lesley	Blue	Pink	Purple	Red	Silver
Book															
Candle															
Mug															
Teapot															
Vase															
Blue															
Pink															
Purple															
Red															
Silver															
Auntie Bessie															
Aunt Caroline															
Aunt Judith															
Aunt Madge															
Auntie Lesley															

Item	Bought by	For	Paper colour

A Visit to Santa

Five children who were in the queue to see Santa Claus on Christmas Eve were each seen to be wearing a striped scarf. Every child was given a small gift by Father Christmas and came away delighted. You will be delighted to learn that the details of these children: their surnames, where each stood in the queue, the two colours of his or her scarf and the gift received, can be discovered by following the clues below!

1. Of the children who wore white in their scarves, one (not surnamed Bliss) was given a football, one (not Krimble) was given a packet of transfers and the other received a packet of coloured pencils.

2. One child (not surnamed Jolly) was given a box of wax crayons and was either fifth or tenth in the queue, as was another child, whose surname is Krimble.

3. The children surnamed Frost and Jolly both wore red in their scarves and visited Santa later than the child who came away with a colouring book.

4. In the queue to see Santa, one child whose scarf contains green was immediately next to and behind the other child whose scarf contains green.

5. The child surnamed Meek (who didn't get a football) saw Father Christmas later than the child (not Bliss) who was given a packet of transfers.

	Fourth	Fifth	Seventh	Ninth	Tenth	Blue/white	Blue/red	Blue/green	Green/white	Red/white	Colouring book	Football	Pencils	Transfers	Wax crayons
Bliss															
Frost															
Jolly															
Krimble															
Meek															
Colouring book															
Football															
Pencils															
Transfers															
Wax crayons															
Blue/white															
Blue/red															
Blue/green															
Green/white															
Red/white															

Surname	Position in queue	Scarf colours	Gift from Santa

Buttons, Coins & Stamps

For some reason only known to herself, Melanie keeps buttons, coins and stamps in her moneybox. However, she suspected her little sister of playing with the contents, extracting some and replacing others each day. Trying to catch her out, Melanie listed the quantities of buttons, coins and stamps over five successive days last week and on each day there were three different quantities. What were her findings?

1. On the three days that Melanie counted seven buttons, seven coins and seven stamps, she didn't also count one of any item.

2. On Monday she counted seven of something and on Friday she counted seven of something (although she didn't count seven buttons on Monday or Friday). Melanie counted fewer coins on Tuesday than she found on Friday.

3. On Wednesday she counted two coins together with more than one button. Melanie counted more than two stamps and more than one button on Thursday.

4. Melanie didn't find two of any item in her moneybox on Monday, although she did find fewer buttons than stamps on Monday.

5. On the day Melanie counted three coins she also counted five stamps, but not two buttons. Nor were two buttons counted on the same day as eight stamps.

	1 button	2 buttons	6 buttons	7 buttons	8 buttons	2 coins	3 coins	4 coins	5 coins	7 coins	1 stamp	2 stamps	5 stamps	7 stamps	8 stamps
Monday															
Tuesday															
Wednesday															
Thursday															
Friday															
1 stamp															
2 stamps															
5 stamps															
7 stamps															
8 stamps															
2 coins															
3 coins															
4 coins															
5 coins															
7 coins															

Day	Buttons	Coins	Stamps

Simple as A,B,C?

Each of the small squares in the grid below contains either A, B or C. Every row, every column and each of the two long diagonal lines of six squares contains exactly two of each letter. The information in the clues refers only to the squares in that row or column. To help you solve this problem, we've given as many clues as we think you'll need! Can you tell which letter should be placed into each square?

Across:

1. The Bs are somewhere between the Cs.

3. Reading from left to right, there isn't an A in the first square.

4. The Bs are next to each other.

5. The Bs are further right than the Cs.

6. The Cs are further right than the Bs.

Down:

1. The As are somewhere between the Bs.

3. The As are somewhere between the Bs.

5. The As are somewhere between the Bs.

6. The Bs are lower than the Cs.

	1	2	3	4	5	6
1						
2						
3						
4						
5						
6						

Dressing in the Dark

As a result of an electrical fault in the Sparks family residence, the five children who got up extremely early this morning all ended up in odd socks and wearing a jumper which belonged to one of the others. See if you can gain a little light from the clues below to discover whose jumper each wore and the colour of the socks on each child's right and left foot.

1. Malcolm wore a jumper belonging to one of his sisters. The sock he wore on his right foot was the same colour as the sock worn on the left foot by the child (not Philip) who wore Malcolm's jumper.

2. Joanne wore Iain's jumper. The sock on her right foot was the same colour as the sock worn on the left foot by the child (not Philip) who wore Joanne's jumper.

3. One child wore a white sock on the right foot and a red sock on the left foot.

4. The child who wore Philip's jumper wore a blue sock on the right foot and a grey sock on the left foot. Suzanne's right sock was the same colour as Philip's left sock (which wasn't blue or beige).

	Jumper					Right foot					Left foot				
	Iain's	Joanne's	Malcolm's	Philip's	Suzanne's	Beige	Blue	Grey	Red	White	Beige	Blue	Grey	Red	White
Iain															
Joanne															
Malcolm															
Philip															
Suzanne															
Left foot Beige															
Blue															
Grey															
Red															
White															
Right foot Beige															
Blue															
Grey															
Red															
White															

Child	Jumper	Right foot	Left foot

Marrying Ages

There are five husbands and wives in this puzzle, any of whom may be the same age, or older or younger than their spouses – to whom they have been married for, well, ages! Can you marry the clues below in order to discover not only each husband and wife pair, but also their respective ages?

1. Geri is two years younger than Lucille.

2. John (whose wife is younger than Frank's) is two years older than Frank.

3. One woman's husband is two years younger than Terry, whose wife is two years older than Yolande (who isn't married to John).

4. Lucille's husband is four years younger than Kathy's husband.

5. Adam is two years younger than his wife (who isn't the oldest of the five women).

6. Gordon (whose wife isn't the youngest of the five women) is two years older than Annette's husband.

	Annette	Geri	Kathy	Lucille	Yolande	His age 58	60	62	66	68	Her age 58	60	62	66	68
Adam															
Frank															
Gordon															
John															
Terry															
His age 58															
60															
62															
66															
68															
Her age 58															
60															
62															
66															
68															

Husband	Wife	His age	Her age

Working Parts

All forty of the actors and actresses on the books of theatrical agent Ivor Bitpart are currently working, appearing in five different plays. Can you discover the running time of each play, together with the number of men and women in each play, for whom Ivor Bitpart managed to secure work?

1. The play with four women runs for five minutes longer than *Eglantine*, in which more than one woman has a part.

2. The play with three men is five minutes shorter than the one with three women.

3. More than one woman appears in both *Devil's Task* and the play which runs for 105 minutes.

4. The play in which five women have rôles runs for five minutes longer than *Devil's Task*, which hasn't seven men in its cast.

5. *Lucinda's Diary* runs for five minutes longer than the play which has two fewer men than *Time Matters*, which is ten minutes longer than the play in which six men have a rôle.

	90 minutes	95 minutes	105 minutes	110 minutes	115 minutes	3 men	4 men	5 men	6 men	7 men	1 woman	2 women	3 women	4 women	5 women
Devil's Task															
Eglantine																
The First Post																
Lucinda's Diary																
Time Matters																
1 woman															
2 women															
3 women															
4 women															
5 women															
3 men															
4 men															
5 men															
6 men															
7 men															

Play	Running time	No of men	No of women

Sum Code

In this puzzle, every letter of the alphabet represents a different number from 1 to 26. The sums below will help you to crack the code and if any letter does not appear, its value is that remaining once the rest of the puzzle is complete. The only arithmetical signs used in this puzzle are '–' (minus), 'x' (times) and '+' (plus).

A	B	C	D	E	F	G	H	I	J	K	L	M

N	O	P	Q	R	S	T	U	V	W	X	Y	Z

1	2	3	4	5	6	7	8	9	10	11	12	13

14	15	16	17	18	19	20	21	22	23	24	25	26

1. E = G x Z
2. E x E = N + O
3. H = Q – T
4. L – R = Z
5. S = H + J
6. O = X + R
7. Q + T = W
8. M = F + H

9. U + A = P x P
10. Z + A = L + D
11. B x B = O – 1
12. J = Z x P
13. J + 1 = V x G
14. C x E = U
15. B x I = K x C

Play Time

Five plays are currently being staged in different theatres across town, each with a late afternoon matinée followed by an early evening performance. There is at least a fifteen-minute break between the end of the matinée and the start of the early evening performance (which, incidentally, features a different cast). What are the times and the length of each production?

1. *Wall Street Crush* runs for a shorter time than the play with an evening performance beginnning at 7.10pm.

2. The curtain rises at both 3.45pm and 6.45pm at one theatre, but not that showing *High Tune*.

3. The curtain falls at 8.45pm on the evening performance of *Sunlight Express*, which runs for thirty fewer minutes than *Dogs*, the afternoon matinée of which starts at 4.15pm.

4. *Hello Molly* runs for twenty minutes less time than the play which starts at 4.10pm.

5. No matinée ends at 6.20pm.

	Matinée					Evening					1 hour 50 mins	2 hours 10 mins	2 hours 15 mins	2 hours 30 mins	2 hours 45 mins
	3.45pm	3.50pm	3.55pm	4.10pm	4.15pm	6.30pm	6.45pm	7.00pm	7.10pm	7.15pm					
Dogs															
Hello Molly															
High Tune															
Sunlight Express															
Wall Street Crush															
1 hour 50 mins															
2 hours 10 mins															
2 hours 15 mins															
2 hours 30 mins															
2 hours 45 mins															
6.30pm															
6.45pm															
7.00pm															
7.10pm															
7.15pm															

Play	Matinée	Evening	Running length

Flying Fingers

Five women who work for the Temps Galore employment agency each undertook various tests last week, to determine her speed at data entry, shorthand and typing. Can you discover just how fast each woman is in each of these three skills? NB – Data entry is calculated in 'strokes per minute' (spm) and shorthand and typing are calculated in 'words per minute' (wpm).

1. Hannah's data entry speed is 20spm faster than Lynda's and Lynda's shorthand speed is 20wpm faster than Hannah's.

2. Mary types at 15wpm faster than the woman whose data entry speed is 90spm.

3. Julia types and writes shorthand at the same number of words per minute.

4. Karen's data entry speed is 20spm slower than that of the woman who types at 70wpm.

5. Mary's shorthand speed is 10wpm faster than Hannah's.

6. The five women are: the one with a data entry speed of 120spm, the one with a shorthand speed of 70wpm, the one who types at 60wpm, the one with a shorthand speed of 80wpm and the one who types at 70wpm.

	Data entry 70spm	80spm	90spm	100spm	120spm	Shorthand 70wpm	75wpm	80wpm	90wpm	100wpm	Typing 50wpm	55wpm	60wpm	70wpm	75wpm
Hannah															
Julia															
Karen															
Lynda															
Mary															
Typing 50wpm															
55wpm															
60wpm															
70wpm															
75wpm															
Shorthand 70wpm															
75wpm															
80wpm															
90wpm															
100wpm															

Woman	Data entry	Shorthand	Typing

Placed in Work

Because of their skills at data entry, shorthand and typing, the women who took part in the tests featured in the previous puzzle had no trouble finding employment and every day last week, one was placed in work by an agent at Temps Galore. You'll need some of the information from the answer to the previous puzzle to solve this one and discover where each woman was placed, by which agent and on which day.

1. The woman with the fastest shorthand speed was given a job two days after Terry successfully placed someone in work.

2. On Thursday, James met a request for someone with *minimum* speeds of 80wpm shorthand and 65wpm typing.

3. P J Willis requested the fastest data entry clerk and one of the women was placed here the day before Clarice found work at Ink-Mart for the slowest typist.

4. Pauline placed one of the women in work at Cooper's the day before someone was given a job at Smith & Brown.

	Cooper's	Ink-Mart	P J Willis	Smith & Brown	Tringle & Co	Clarice	James	Pauline	Simon	Terry	Monday	Tuesday	Wednesday	Thursday	Friday
						Agent									
Hannah															
Julia															
Karen															
Lynda															
Mary															
Monday															
Tuesday															
Wednesday															
Thursday															
Friday															
Clarice															
James															
Pauline															
Simon															
Terry															

Woman	Company	Agent	Day placed

Patchwork

Each piece in the patchwork square below is decorated with a letter of the alphabet: A, B, C, D, E, F or G. In each horizontal row, vertical column and long diagonal line of seven smaller pieces there are seven different letters: some are already in place. Can you discover which letter fits in every piece? There is only one correct solution to this puzzle – if you take a wrong path along the way, you won't finish the quilt!

1. The letter in piece 29 is the same as that in piece 49.

2. The letter in piece 34 is different to that in piece 38.

3. The letter in piece 14 is the same as that in piece 45.

4. The letter in piece 33 is the same as that in piece 42.

5. The letter in piece 15 is the same as that in piece 41, but different to the letter which is in piece 12.

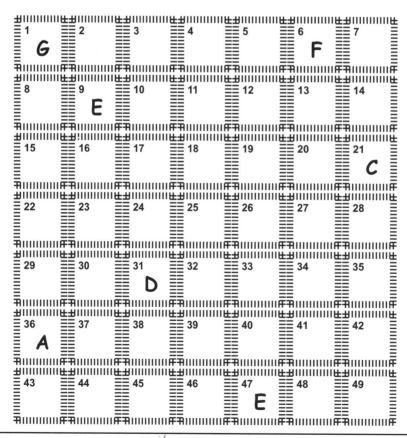

Paying for Their Mistakes

The waiters and waitresses at the local restaurant were surprised last week when, despite making unfortunate mistakes, each was left a tip by a forgiving customer! Our tip to you is to scan through the clues below, making no mistakes, in order to discover the number of the table at which each waiter or waitress served, together with his or her blunder and the tip which he or she received despite this.

1. The customer whose piping hot coffee was spilt over him (although not by Martin) was still kind enough to leave the apologetic waiter or waitress a tip of £1.20.

2. The cold vegetables (which weren't actually meant to be cold, but which had been left standing for too long) weren't served by Angela, who received a larger tip than was left by the customers whose order was completely muddled.

3. Martin served the couple at table 2 and received a smaller tip than Cora.

4. The diners at table 14 left a tip of £1.50.

5. The person (not Cora) who attended the diners at table 7 was given a larger tip than Daniel, who dropped the cutlery.

6. The person who dipped a thumb deeply into the soup received the £1.80 tip.

7. Elizabeth didn't serve the customers who were at table 20.

	Table No 2	Table No 7	Table No 14	Table No 20	Table No 24	Cold vegetables	Dropped cutlery	Muddled order	Spilt coffee	Thumb in soup	£1.20	£1.30	£1.50	£1.80	£2.00
Angela															
Cora															
Elizabeth															
Daniel															
Martin															
£1.20															
£1.30															
£1.50															
£1.80															
£2.00															
Cold vegetables															
Dropped cutlery															
Muddled order															
Spilt coffee															
Thumb in soup															

Waiter/waitress	Table No	Mistake	Tip

Day Excursions

George is a coach driver for a British company specialising in day-trips for tourists. Last week he was assigned to take a different professional or hobby group to a different location every day. Can you discover the day on which each group was taken out by George, together with their nationality and the place they visited (the latter of which is not necessarily connected to their professions or hobbies)?

1. The party from New Zealand took their excursion on Friday.

2. Wednesday's excursion was taken by the group of amateur historians (who weren't from Russia).

3. The party of Swedish teachers didn't take Saturday's trip to the Tower of London.

4. The party who visited the Royal Horticultural Society's gardens at Wisley went out later in the week than those who visited Windsor Castle.

5. On the day before George drove a group of journalists to see Canterbury Cathedral, he took out a party of Americans.

6. George took out a party of police officers the day after the trip to Hampton Court (which wasn't on Friday).

	Tuesday	Wednesday	Thursday	Friday	Saturday	American	Australian	New Zealanders	Swedish	Russian	Canterbury Cath	Hampton Court	Tower of London	Windsor Castle	Wisley Gardens
Birdwatchers															
Historians															
Journalists															
Police officers															
Teachers															
Canterbury Cath															
Hampton Court															
Tower of London															
Windsor Castle															
Wisley Gardens															
American															
Australian															
New Zealanders															
Swedish															
Russian															

Profession/hobby	Day	Nationality	Visited

Hair's to Success

In an effort to boost their morale before their final examinations, five girls each visited the local hairdresser and beautician. It obviously worked wonders, because each did extremely well, earning a first class pass. Can you work out the hair details relating to every girl, in terms of style and length, as well as colour, together with the mark she achieved in the examination?

1. Opal didn't do as well in the examination as the girl with dark blonde hair (which isn't short).

2. Naomi, whose hair is neither wavy nor light in colour, achieved a mark two percentage points lower than that obtained by the girl with ginger hair.

3. Opal's long hair isn't light blonde. She achieved a mark two percentage points higher than that of Lorinda, whose hair is of the same length as Naomi's.

4. Marilyn, whose hair is straight, achieved a mark two percentage points lower than that obtained by Pamela.

	Curly/short	Straight/long	Straight/medium	Wavy/long	Wavy/medium	Dark blonde	Dark brown	Ginger	Light blonde	Light brown	89%	91%	93%	97%	99%
Lorinda															
Marilyn															
Naomi															
Opal															
Pamela															
89%															
91%															
93%															
97%															
99%															
Dark blonde															
Dark brown															
Ginger															
Light blonde															
Light brown															

Girl	Style/length	Colour	Mark

Figure It Out

Each of the thirty-six squares in the grid is filled with a single digit number from 1 to 9 – each of those numbers being used four times. Use the clues to complete the square, bearing in mind that the same number must not appear in two adjacent (touching) squares in any row across or column down. If the same number is used more than once in any row across or column down it is stated in the relevant clue.

Across:

1. Two 4s. The only odd number is 9.

2. Two 8s.

3. Consecutive numbers placed in order.

4. The only even number is 6.

5. Two 9s. No 8.

6. Two 1s. Two 7s.

Down:

1. Two 1s. Two 2s.

2. Total twenty-two.

3. Two 3s.

4. Total thirty-nine.

5. Two 8s. No 3.

6. Consecutive numbers placed in order.

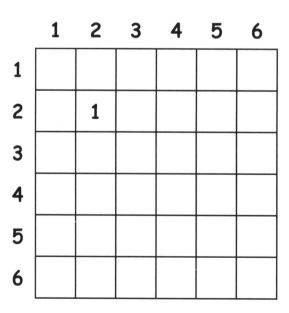

Throwing Pots

Five would-be potters have had various attempts at making things, all of which cracked in the kiln or suffered some other mishap during their construction. However, last week each was successful and made something which turned out good enough to give as a present to one of their relatives. What did each person make, after how many attempts and who received the object as a gift?

1. One woman made a rather lopsided plate for her niece. Another would-be potter succeeded in shaping a mug (complete with handle) at only the third shot.

2. The person who produced the somewhat droopy-looking vase wasn't Miss Adams. The person who made the jug proudly presented it to a father-in-law.

3. Mr Turner made something for his mother, in fewer attempts than it took Mrs Vole to make something.

4. The people who had two and five (or five and two!) tries at making a successful piece were the person who made the bowl and the woman who gave her work to her cousin.

5. Mr Gordon had one fewer attempt than the person (not Miss Adams) who presented something to a son.

	Bowl	Jug	Mug	Plate	Vase	2 attempts	3 attempts	4 attempts	5 attempts	6 attempts	Cousin	Father-in-law	Mother	Niece	Son
Miss Adams															
Mrs Bright																
Mr Gordon																
Mr Turner																
Mrs Vole																
Cousin											
Father-in-law											
Mother											
Niece											
Son											
2 attempts					
3 attempts					
4 attempts					
5 attempts					
6 attempts					

Potter	Item	No of attempts	Presented to

Speech Day

Every year on Founder's Day, St John's School invites a prominent scientist from a major university to come and speak to its pupils. Over a given period of five years (as listed in the grid below), who was the speaker, in which 'ology' does he specialise and to which university is he attached?

1. Dr Allwood didn't address the pupils of St John's in 2002 or 2003. The man from Camford University (who isn't Dr Myers) didn't speak to the school in 2001.

2. The lexicologist (who didn't visit St John's in 2004) addressed the school in a later year than Professor Toft's visit, but an earlier year than that of the man from Newchester University.

3. Dr Barker visited St John's in a later year than the climatologist, who spoke the year after the anthropologist from Wale University.

4. The psychologist visited the school the year after the man from St Ann's University, who spoke to the pupils of St John's in a later year than the one who gave a lecture on his specialised subject: sociology.

	Dr Allwood	Dr Barker	Dr Myers	Professor Ling	Professor Toft	Anthropology	Climatology	Lexicology	Psychology	Sociology	Camford	Hervard	Newchester	St Ann's	Wale
2001															
2002															
2003															
2004															
2005															
Camford											
Hervard											
Newchester											
St Ann's											
Wale											
Anthropology						
Climatology						
Lexicology						
Psychology						
Sociology						

Year	Speaker	'Ology'	University

Travelling About

Five sales representatives each visited three towns on different days (Monday to Friday inclusive) last week, none going to more than one town per day and no town being visited by more than one sales representative per day. Can you work out the day on which every representative visited each town?

1. Norman went to Marwell later in the week than his trip to Abbeyville.

2. Gordon went to Abbeyville earlier in the week than Ann travelled to Richford (which wasn't on the same day as David's visit to Marwell).

3. Lynette went to Richford on the same day that Norman went to Marwell.

4. Lynette went to Marwell earlier in the week than Norman's trip to Richford.

5. Norman went to Richford on the day that Ann went to Abbeyville, which was the day before David went to Richford.

6. David went to Abbeyville on the day that Gordon travelled to Richford.

7. Lynette went to Richford the day before her trip to Abbeyville.

		Abbeyville					Marwell					Richford				
		Monday	Tuesday	Wednesday	Thursday	Friday	Monday	Tuesday	Wednesday	Thursday	Friday	Monday	Tuesday	Wednesday	Thursday	Friday
	Ann															
	David															
	Gordon															
	Lynette															
	Norman															
Richford	Monday															
	Tuesday															
	Wednesday															
	Thursday															
	Friday															
Marwell	Monday															
	Tuesday															
	Wednesday															
	Thursday															
	Friday															

Representative	Abbeyville	Marwell	Richford

Dominological

A standard set of twenty-eight dominoes has been laid out as shown. One is already in position, to give you a start. Can you draw in the edges of the rest? The check-box is provided as an aid to solving.

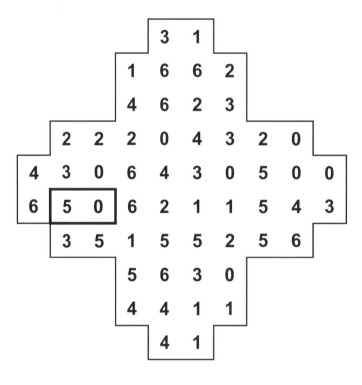

```
              3   1
          1   6   6   2
          4   6   2   3
      2   2   2   0   4   3   2   0
  4   3   0   6   4   3   0   5   0   0
  6   5   0   6   2   1   1   5   4   3
      3   5   1   5   5   2   5   6
          5   6   3   0
          4   4   1   1
              4   1
```

0 – 0		1 – 1		2 – 3		3 – 6	
0 – 1		1 – 2		2 – 4		4 – 4	
0 – 2		1 – 3		2 – 5		4 – 5	
0 – 3		1 – 4		2 – 6		4 – 6	
0 – 4		1 – 5		3 – 3		5 – 5	
0 – 5	✓	1 – 6		3 – 4		5 – 6	
0 – 6		2 – 2		3 – 5		6 – 6	

Sow What?

Five neighbouring gardeners today sowed one type of flower, one type of herb and one type of vegetable. Each neighbour sowed seeds of plants beginning with three different letters of the alphabet, none of which is the same as the initial letter of his or her forename. Can you discover what each sowed today?

1. Laura didn't sow carrots or chives and Martin didn't sow parsnips.

2. Neither of the people who sowed carrots and spinach seeds also sowed the parsley seeds.

3. The neighbour who sowed chives lives next door to the one who sowed parsnips.

4. Three of the neighbours are: the one who sowed heliotropes, the one who sowed mint and the one who made a sowing of cabbages.

5. Three of the neighbours are: the one who sowed beetroot seed, the one who sowed mint and the one who made a sowing of carnations.

6. Three of the neighbours are: the one who sowed parsley seed, the one who sowed cabbages and the one who made a sowing of marigolds.

7. Two of the neighbours are: the one who sowed chives, the one who sowed parsnips.

	Carnations	Heliotrope	Marigolds	Sunflowers	Violets	Chives	Lovage	Mint	Parsley	Sage	Beetroot	Cabbages	Carrots	Parsnips	Spinach
Chris															
Laura															
Martin															
Olivia															
Sandy															
Beetroot															
Cabbages															
Carrots															
Parsnips															
Spinach															
Chives															
Lovage															
Mint															
Parsley															
Sage															

Neighbour	Flowers	Herbs	Vegetables

The Same Old Story

Mitch picked up five western novels at a book sale last month, but (sadly) all turned out to have the same plot, revolving around ranches, rustlers, bandits, heroic cowhands and the illegal sales of liquor and firearms – together with a fair sprinkling of sheriffs, saloons and shoot-outs! From the clues below, can you work out the title of each author's book, together with the name of its hero and villain?

1. Marshal Matt Kirby opposes and finally defeats Mexican bandido Robbie Gomez, but not in *Texas Tightspot*. Neither *Gunfighter* nor *Showdown* was written by Ray Rogers, whose hero has a three-letter forename.

2. Rancher Ben Varmint is the creation of an author whose surname starts with a letter which occurs earlier in the alphabet than that of his hero's surname.

3. Steve Dodge's book has a villain with a military title, unlike *Showdown* (which wasn't penned by Dave Shyan).

4. Neither *Texas Tightspot* nor *Frontier Town* has Bob Bailey or Joe Appleton as its hero. Nor does *Frontier Town* or *Texas Tightspot* feature ex-Confederate Cavalry officer Major Klink, who isn't opposed by Bob Bailey or Joe Appleton in any of the books.

5. Tim Carson's hero isn't the tough-but-honest cowhand Luke Rock.

6. Reformed rustler Bob Bailey isn't the hero of *The Last Stand*.

[Logic grid with rows: Alan Wayne, Dave Shyan, Ray Rogers, Steve Dodge, Tim Carson; Ben Varmint, Captain Prior, Eddie Walker, Major Klink, Robbie Gomez; Bob Bailey, Glen Derrick, Joe Appleton, Luke Rock, Matt Kirby. Columns: Frontier Town, Gunfighter, Showdown, Texas Tightspot, The Last Stand; Hero: Bob Bailey, Glen Derrick, Joe Appleton, Luke Rock, Matt Kirby; Villain: Ben Varmint, Captain Prior, Eddie Walker, Major Klink, Robbie Gomez]

Author	Title	Hero	Villain

Always a Bridesmaid...

At a reunion of former pupils of Puzzleton School two years ago, Jenny was asked to be bridesmaid at five of her friends' weddings, which took place last year. Since all of the weddings took place in different countries, Jenny managed to fit in five short holidays at the same time! Can you discover the name of each friend's husband, together with the country and the month of last year in which they were married?

1. Jenny travelled to Spain for one friend's marriage to John, which took place later in the year than that in Greece.

2. Megan was married in June. Tina didn't marry Peter.

3. Joanna's wedding wasn't the last of the five, but it did take place later in the year than Brenda's, for which Jenny travelled to Portugal.

4. The Albanian wedding was earlier in the year than the one in Portugal.

5. Sally married Philip two months before Jenny's youngest friend was married (although not to Vernon).

6. Vernon wasn't at the wedding which took place in France in October.

	John	Peter	Philip	Richard	Vernon	Albania	France	Greece	Portugal	Spain	January	March	June	August	October
Brenda															
Joanna															
Megan															
Sally															
Tina															
January															
March															
June															
August															
October															
Albania															
France															
Greece															
Portugal															
Spain															

Friend	Husband	Country	Month of wedding

Playing Card Bingo

Every Thursday night, the local Darby & Joan Club holds prize competitions, one of which is Playing Card Bingo. This week's winning card is shown below. Can you determine the order in which the cards on it were called?

Values of cards are as shown and ace=1, jack=11, queen=12 and king=13.

1. The card called fifth is of the same suit as (and has a value either one higher or one lower than) the card called eleventh, which is directly next to and right of the card called twelfth. The card called twelfth has a higher value than and is either directly above or directly below the card called seventh.

2. The card called tenth is of the same suit as the card called last, which is directly next to and right of the card called sixth. Card H was called directly after card A.

3. The card called eighth is in the same horizontal row as (and further right than) the card called thirteenth.

4. The card called third is of the same suit as (but in a different horizontal row to) the card called ninth. The card called ninth has a higher value than (and is directly next to and right of) the card called fourteenth.

1st	2nd	3rd	4th	5th
6th	7th	8th	9th	10th
11th	12th	13th	14th	15th

LEFT ←   RIGHT →

	A	B	C		D		E	F	G
	K♥	3♠	6♣		9♥		5♣	10♦	7♠
	J♠	2♣		9♦	4♣	Q♦	10♥		8♠	J♦
	H	I		J	K	L	M		N	O

Spending Sprees

Five women had fairly modest spending sprees last Saturday. Use the clues below to discover each woman's surname, how much she spent and the name of the shop from which she made her purchases.

1. Vera shopped in Supa-Bargain and Verna shopped in Bymoor & Sons.

2. Verna (who isn't Mrs Yenn) spent more than Miss Doller (who shopped in Purse-busters).

3. Money-mall attracted the custom of Mrs Sheckle, who spent less than Venetia.

4. Mrs Franks spent more than at least one other woman, although she didn't spend as much as Victoria.

5. Victoria Pounde didn't spend $60.

	Doller	Franks	Pounde	Sheckle	Yenn	$20	$30	$40	$50	$60	Bymoor & Sons	Money-mall	Purse-busters	Supa-Bargain	Wall et Cie
Valerie															
Venetia															
Vera															
Verna															
Victoria															
Bymoor & Sons															
Money-mall															
Purse-busters															
Supa-Bargain															
Wall et Cie															
$20															
$30															
$40															
$50															
$60															

Shopper	Surname	Amount spent	Shop

Magazine Gifts

This morning, these five women bought magazines, having been enticed by the different products taped to the covers – and each of the products looked so attractive that every woman convinced herself she really wanted it! At what time today did each buy her magazine, how much did it cost and what was attached to the front?

1. Either Louise or Magda paid the highest amount, for the magazine which had the 'revitalising' face mask taped to the front.

2. The magazine with a small phial of bath oil taped to the cover was bought at either 10.05am or 10.35am.

3. The latest magazine to be purchased (by either Patsy or Sheena) wasn't the cheapest. The magazine offering the free sample of eye-shadow wasn't purchased at 9.35am.

4. Of the two women who bought magazines before 10 o'clock, one got the lip liner and the other paid $2.00.

5. Either Sheena or Julia paid $2.00. Sheena bought a magazine exactly one hour later than Julia had made her purchase.

6. Louise's choice of magazine cost twenty cents more than Julia's. Julia wasn't the first of the five women to buy a magazine.

	9.05am	9.35am	10.05am	10.35am	11.05am	$1.80	$1.90	$2.00	$2.20	$2.40	Bath oil	Eye-shadow	Face mask	Lip liner	Shampoo
Julia															
Louise															
Magda															
Patsy															
Sheena															
Bath oil															
Eye-shadow															
Face mask															
Lip liner															
Shampoo															
$1.80															
$1.90															
$2.00															
$2.20															
$2.40															

Purchaser	Time	Price	Gift

Signs of the Times

The Puzzlebrough Times newspaper carries a daily astrology feature in its pages and the five women who appear in this puzzle are all avid followers of their fate, as predicted in the paper. Can you discover the full name of each woman, together with her occupation and her star-sign?

1. Miss Thomson (who wasn't born under the sign of Taurus) isn't the nurse. The woman (not Lou) whose star-sign is Aries isn't Mrs Roberts or Miss Gold. Neither the chemist nor the cook was born under the sign of Aries.

2. Neither Beth nor Lou was born under the signs of Taurus or Cancer. Mrs Wise is neither the chemist nor the nurse.

3. Delia is neither Miss Gold nor Miss Thomson. Lou wasn't born under the sign of Aquarius. The woman whose star-sign is Aquarius isn't a teacher.

4. Neither the woman born under the sign of Aquarius nor the woman born under the sign of Taurus is Tricia. Tricia is neither the teacher nor Mrs Wise, who is taller than the teacher. Neither Mrs Roberts nor Mrs Wise is a cook.

5. Rowena is neither the teacher nor the hairdresser. Neither the teacher nor the hairdresser was born under the sign of Cancer. The woman born under the sign of Cancer is neither Tricia nor Rowena.

	Gold	Poitier	Roberts	Thomson	Wise	Chemist	Cook	Hairdresser	Nurse	Teacher	Aquarius	Aries	Taurus	Gemini	Cancer
Beth															
Delia															
Lou															
Rowena															
Tricia															
Aquarius															
Aries															
Taurus															
Gemini															
Cancer															
Chemist															
Cook															
Hairdresser															
Nurse															
Teacher															

Forename	Surname	Occupation	Star-sign

Mis-cakes

The tea-shop in the village of Trayford is excellent, but the waitresses, whilst remembering tea orders correctly, invariably bring the customer a different type of cake to that which he or she ordered. Over a ten-minute period yesterday afternoon, for example, five people were given cake ordered by one of the others. Can you discover what each ordered and received, together with the type of tea each drank?

1. Samantha received ginger cake instead of the slice of succulent carrot cake she had been waiting for.

2. The customer drinking Earl Grey tea had hoped to get a slice of Swiss roll filled with raspberry jam and cream, but didn't! The one who ordered Lapsang Souchong was somewhat disappointed to receive the carrot cake.

3. The customer who received the Madeira cake had ordered whatever was given to the person who wanted ginger cake.

4. Kylie (who didn't drink Assam or Ceylon tea) received whatever Dave had ordered.

5. Judy wasn't the person who drank Assam tea and ordered the piece of cake which was given to Wayne.

6. The customer who drank Darjeeling tea was given the cake that Wayne had ordered.

	Ordered					Received					Assam	Ceylon	Darjeeling	Earl Grey	Laps S'chong
	Carrot	Chocolate	Ginger	Madeira	Swiss roll	Carrot	Chocolate	Ginger	Madeira	Swiss roll	Assam	Ceylon	Darjeeling	Earl Grey	Laps S'chong
Dave															
Judy															
Kylie															
Samantha															
Wayne															
Assam															
Ceylon															
Darjeeling															
Earl Grey															
Lapsang S'chong															
Received Carrot															
Chocolate															
Ginger															
Madeira															
Swiss roll															

Customer	Ordered	Received	Tea

Simple as A,B,C?

Each of the small squares in the grid below contains either A, B or C. Every row, every column and each of the two long diagonal lines of six squares contains exactly two of each letter. The information in the clues refers only to the squares in that row or column. To help you solve this problem, we've given as many clues as we think you'll need! Can you tell which letter should be placed into each square?

Across:

1. The Bs are further right than the As.

2. The Cs are further right than the Bs.

3. The Bs are somewhere between the As.

4. The As are next to one another.

5. The Cs are somewhere between the As.

6. The Bs are further right than the Cs.

Down:

1. The Bs are somewhere between the As.

2. No two squares containing the same letter are next to one another.

3. Each C is immediately next to and above an A.

4. The As are lower than the Bs.

5. The Cs are next to one another.

6. Each B is immediately next to and below an A.

```
        1   2   3   4   5   6
      ┌───┬───┬───┬───┬───┬───┐
   1  │   │   │   │   │   │   │
      ├───┼───┼───┼───┼───┼───┤
   2  │   │   │   │   │   │   │
      ├───┼───┼───┼───┼───┼───┤
   3  │   │   │   │   │   │   │
      ├───┼───┼───┼───┼───┼───┤
   4  │   │   │   │   │   │   │
      ├───┼───┼───┼───┼───┼───┤
   5  │   │   │   │   │   │   │
      ├───┼───┼───┼───┼───┼───┤
   6  │   │   │   │   │   │   │
      └───┴───┴───┴───┴───┴───┘
```

Rugby Strips

Five local rugby teams aren't doing so well this season, but what they lack in talent they make up for in the variety of the strips they have adopted. Tackle the clues below in order to discover the colour of the shirts, shorts and socks which the members of each team wear.

1. Either The Green Men or The Wanderers wear orange shirts. The players in the other of these two teams wear green shirts.

2. The Lemmings team isn't the one whose players wear beige shirts and yellow socks; nor do The Lemmings' team members wear brown shorts.

3. Either The Green Men or The Tigers kit out their team in the grey shorts and blue socks. The players in the other of these two teams wear white socks.

4. Players in The Bulls wear plain black shorts.

5. The members of one team dress in red shirts and matching red socks.

6. The team whose members wear green socks don't have shirts or shorts in green or brown.

7. The members of the team kitted out in blue socks don't have blue shirts.

	Shirts					Shorts					Socks				
	Beige	Blue	Green	Orange	Red	Black	Brown	Green	Grey	White	Blue	Green	Red	White	Yellow
The Bulls															
The Green Men															
The Lemmings															
The Tigers															
The Wanderers															
Socks — Blue															
Socks — Green															
Socks — Red															
Socks — White															
Socks — Yellow															
Shorts — Black															
Shorts — Brown															
Shorts — Green															
Shorts — Grey															
Shorts — White															

Team	Shirts	Shorts	Socks

Where There's a Will...

Lord Moneyman of Weigh recently passed on to a higher plane, leaving gifts of money and one other bequest from his personal effects to each of the five women in his employ: his nurse, his housekeeper, his cook, his maid and his, er, 'masseuse'. Use the clues to discover how much money and which other item/s were left to the women, together with the number of years each had worked for Lord Moneybags.

1. Jean had been in Lord Moneyman's employ for two years longer than the woman (not Georgina) who has been left Lord Moneyman's entire collection of priceless Ming vases. The latter has been left £20,000 more than Jean, whose title of 'masseuse' always led to gossip and raised eyebrows below stairs!

2. The woman who will inherit the 17th-century bedstead plus £150,000 worked for Lord Moneyman for three years longer than the one who will inherit his silver plus £120,000.

3. Deborah was in Lord Moneyman's service for two fewer years than Babs, who has been handed the keys to his lordship's vintage Rolls-Royce motor car.

	£100,000	£120,000	£150,000	£180,000	£200,000	Bedstead	Ming vases	Paintings	Rolls-Royce	Silver	4 years	5 years	6 years	7 years	8 years
Babs															
Deborah															
Georgina															
Jean															
Rosie															
4 years															
5 years															
6 years															
7 years															
8 years															
Bedstead															
Ming vases															
Paintings															
Rolls-Royce															
Silver															

Employee	Money	Other	Length of service

A Lucky Escape

Full of bravado, five men challenged one another to spend a night alone at Haunted House, which certainly lived up to its name! Every man was left there by the other four at ten o'clock and each made his getaway before midnight: the witching hour… However, not wishing to appear 'weak', each gave a different excuse for leaving. On which night did each stay, at what time did he leave and what was his excuse?

1. Dougal left twenty minutes earlier than the man who said he needed to go home because of a toothache.

2. The man left behind on Tuesday stayed for more than ten minutes longer than Carl, who stayed exactly ten minutes longer than the man stricken by a mysterious stomach upset.

3. Tom stayed at the house on Wednesday. Sean wasn't the man who managed to stay in the house for the longest period of time.

4. One man left at 11.20pm on Monday night.

5. The man who left at 11.45pm claimed that he had a dust allergy, which was causing him difficulty in breathing.

6. The man left behind on Thursday night told the others that he had only left due to the onset of a severe migraine.

	Monday	Tuesday	Wednesday	Thursday	Friday	11.15pm	11.20pm	11.25pm	11.35pm	11.45pm	Dust allergy	Earache	Migraine	Stomach upset	Toothache
Carl															
Dougal															
Sean															
Tom															
Wesley															
Dust allergy															
Earache															
Migraine															
Stomach upset															
Toothache															
11.15pm															
11.20pm															
11.25pm															
11.35pm															
11.45pm															

Name	Night	Time left	Excuse

Sum Code

In this puzzle, every letter of the alphabet represents a different number from 1 to 26. The sums below will help you to crack the code and if any letter does not appear, its value is that remaining once the rest of the puzzle is complete. The only arithmetical signs used in this puzzle are '–' (minus), 'x' (times) and '+' (plus).

?

A	B	C	D	E	F	G	H	I	J	K	L	M

N	O	P	Q	R	S	T	U	V	W	X	Y	Z

?

?

1	2	3	4	5	6	7	8	9	10	11	12	13

14	15	16	17	18	19	20	21	22	23	24	25	26

?

1. U x X = H
2. V + V = Y + Z
3. Z = B + G
4. D – X = R
5. X = I x W
6. C + J = N
7. D = G x G
8. N + Q = O

9. A = I + Z
10. B + B = Y
11. L = O + G
12. X + A = H
13. P + S = F + N
14. K = G + R
15. M + C = P
16. T = E + C + C + C

Close Finish

Every January, three-year-old thoroughbred racehorses compete for the prestigious Queen Adelaide Cup and this year's race was a close one, with five horses crossing the finishing line almost together. Can you discover the name of the horse in each of the listed finishing positions, together with the name of its owner and rider?

1. The winner was ridden by neither Sam Dawson nor Will Parton (who didn't ride Abracadabra).

2. Les Cotter's mount finished either second or fourth. Springwood finished either first or fourth.

3. Rob O'Connor's mount finished two places ahead of either Jon Keymer's or Lady Hayes's horse, but two places behind either Wayward Lass or Rosie Dawn.

4. Dusty Miller rode either Lady Hayes's horse or James Rasir's horse, the latter of which was neither first nor second to finish.

5. Springwood belongs to either James Rasir or Jon Keymer.

6. Wayward Lass was either first or second to finish and was ridden by either Sam Dawson or Rob O'Connor.

7. Rob O'Connor rode either Lady Hayes's or Ann Bridges' horse.

	Runner					Owner					Rider				
	Abracadabra	Rosie Dawn	Springwood	Striker	Wayward Lass	Ann Bridges	Prince Felip	Lady Hayes	Jon Keymer	James Rasir	Les Cotter	Sam Dawson	Dusty Miller	Rob O'Connor	Will Parton
First															
Second															
Third															
Fourth															
Fifth															
Les Cotter															
Sam Dawson															
Dusty Miller															
Rob O'Connor															
Will Parton															
Ann Bridges															
Prince Felip															
Lady Hayes															
Jon Keymer															
James Rasir															

Position	Runner	Owner	Rider

Close Cousins

Five cousins live within half a mile of one another, in different closes (or cul-de-sacs). Every girl is of a different age and lives in a house with a different number, so use the clues below to discover their ages and respective addresses.

1. In both Tennyson Close and Wordsworth Close there are nine houses, so the highest numbered houses in these closes is No 9.

2. Pamela lives at No 11 and is older than Katie, but younger than the girl who lives at No 2. The girl who lives at No 2 isn't two years older than Katie.

3. Susan lives in Keats Close in a house with a lower number than that of the girl who is two years older than the girl (not Katie) who lives in Wordsworth Close.

4. Diane (who doesn't live at No 8) is three years younger than the girl who lives in Shelley Close.

5. The twelve-year-old lives at No 7. The youngest girl doesn't live at No 4.

	11 years old	12 years old	13 years old	14 years old	15 years old	No 2	No 4	No 7	No 8	No 11	Byron Close	Keats Close	Shelley Close	Tennyson Cl	Wordsworth Cl
Cora															
Diane															
Katie															
Pamela															
Susan															
Byron Close															
Keats Close															
Shelley Close															
Tennyson Cl															
Wordsworth Cl															
No 2															
No 4															
No 7															
No 8															
No 11															

Cousin	Age	House No	Close

Tasty Treats

The vending machine at Littleton Railway Station dispenses chocolate bars of different brands and sizes for varying amounts of money. Which colour of button would you need to press and how much money would you have to feed into the machine, in order to obtain each bar – and what does each bar contain as a filling? To find out, just follow the clues… or visit Littleton Railway Station, of course!

1. The Whooper bar contains chewy treacle toffee.

2. The Jingle bar contains hazelnuts and sells for six cents more than the bar dispensed when the green button is pressed, but for a lower price than the cost of a Yum-Yum.

3. A Bingo bar can be obtained by pressing the blue button, for a higher price than that of the bar (not Scrummy) which contains biscuit pieces.

4. The bar containing peanuts is dispensed when the orange button is pressed.

5. A Yum-Yum bar isn't released when the red button is pressed.

	Blue	Green	Orange	Red	White	85 cents	88 cents	91 cents	94 cents	97 cents	Biscuit	Caramel	Hazelnuts	Peanuts	Toffee
Bingo															
Jingle															
Scrummy															
Whooper															
Yum-Yum															
Biscuit															
Caramel															
Hazelnuts															
Peanuts															
Toffee															
85 cents															
88 cents															
91 cents															
94 cents															
97 cents															

Brand	Button colour	Price	Filling

Animal Antics

Young Brendan drew pictures of five different animals and then cut each into four pieces: head, body, legs and tail, rearranging them so that each new picture contains parts of four different animals. Can you discover the make-up of the new pictures?

1. The legs of the cat are now attached to the body of the horse.
2. The horse's tail is in the same picture as the kangaroo's head.
3. The lion's head is now attached to the kangaroo's body.
4. The legs of the lion are in the same picture as the tail of the mouse.

		Body					Legs					Tail				
		Cat	Horse	Kangaroo	Lion	Mouse	Cat	Horse	Kangaroo	Lion	Mouse	Cat	Horse	Kangaroo	Lion	Mouse
Head	Cat															
	Horse															
	Kangaroo															
	Lion															
	Mouse															
Tail	Cat															
	Horse															
	Kangaroo															
	Lion															
	Mouse															
Legs	Cat															
	Horse															
	Kangaroo															
	Lion															
	Mouse															

Head	Body	Legs	Tail

Card Sharp

What is the face value and suit of each of the cards shown below? All twelve cards used below are of different values and together they total 82. Values of the cards are as per their numbers and ace=1, jack=11, queen=12 and king=13. No card is horizontally or vertically next to another of the same colour and there are four different suits in each horizontal row and three different suits in each vertical column.

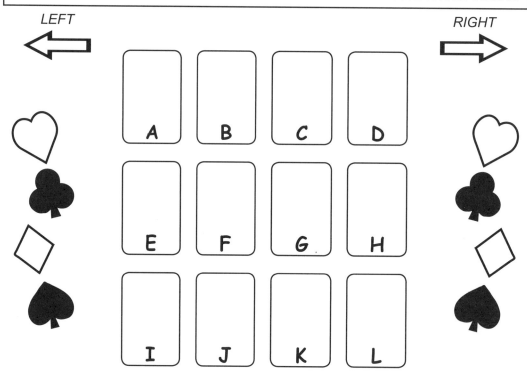

1. There is no ace of spades nor eight of hearts in the cards laid out above.

2. The three of hearts is on the same horizontal line as the two of clubs.

3. Card K has a value one lower than that of card H which, in turn, has a value one lower than that of card E.

4. Card I has a higher value than that of card F, but a lower value than that of card A.

5. Card B (which isn't directly next to and above a diamond) has half the value of card C (which isn't directly next to and above a spade).

6. Card G (which is directly above a diamond) has a value one higher than that of card L, but three times that of card D (which isn't a spade).

A Weighty Matter

Five friends decided to get into shape for summer and attended the local slimming club. They all exercise regularly and have followed the slimming club's advice on diet, so every woman has lost weight and is delighted. Can you discover each one's full name, together with her weight before attending and her weight today?

1. Currently, Lucille weighs 100kg.

2. Abigail (who isn't Mrs Williams) weighs more than 92kg.

3. The woman whose weight was 110kg has lost eleven kilogrammes to date.

4. Mrs Denby used to weigh 106kg.

5. The woman who used to weigh 101kg is now four kilogrammes lighter than Polly Crowe.

6. Francesca Stafford has lost precisely ten kilogrammes.

	Crowe	Denby	Norton	Stafford	Williams	Before 101kg	106kg	109kg	110kg	115kg	Today 92kg	96kg	99kg	100kg	105kg
Abigail															
Francesca															
Lucille															
Marian															
Polly															
Today 92kg															
96kg															
99kg															
100kg															
105kg															
Before 101kg															
106kg															
109kg															
110kg															
115kg															

Slimmer	Surname	Before	Today

Yachting

Five of the yachts taking part in the annual Sydney to New York race are skippered by former winners of the race, who are all hopeful of a second victory. Can you work out the names of their boats, together with the names of the men acting as grinder and trimmer on each?

1. Malcolm Evans skippers the yacht (not with a two-word name) on which Bill Hayes is the grinder.

2. *Golden Ghost* is the vessel on which Hank Jones is the trimmer but Tim Weston isn't the grinder. Nor does Tim Weston work alongside Jeff Thynne.

3. Roy Collins was delighted when Bob Naylor decided to join his crew.

4. Fred Grant is the grinder on the boat named *Ariadne*.

5. Don Stack isn't the grinder on the yacht skippered by Johnnie Bristow.

6. Jack Cooke and Liam Oates are sailing together on one of the yachts, but this isn't the *Mirabelle*, which is skippered by Ken McTavish.

Skipper	Yacht	Grinder	Trimmer

Ages & Ages

Mr & Mrs Boult have five daughters and five sons-in-law, all ten of whom have birthdays this month! Who is married to whom and what are their respective ages?

1. The husband of the woman (not Geraldine) aged 33 is one year younger than the husband of the oldest woman.

2. Geoff's wife Judy is one year younger than Caroline, whose husband is younger than Milton.

3. Geraldine's husband isn't the oldest of the five men.

4. Raymond's wife is one year younger than Derek's wife.

5. Henry's wife is one year older than Josephine.

6. Henry is either one year older or one year younger than Josephine's husband.

| | Daughter's age | | | | | | | | | | Son-in-law's age | | | | |
	32	33	35	36	37	Derek	Geoff	Henry	Milton	Raymond	35	36	37	38	39
Andrea															
Caroline															
Geraldine															
Josephine															
Judy															
35															
36															
37															
38															
39															
Derek															
Geoff															
Henry															
Milton															
Raymond															

Happy Birthday

Daughter	Daughter's age	Son-in-law	Son-in-law's age

A Busy Week

Every weekday last week, Kevin had an appointment in the morning, another in the afternoon and each evening he had a date with a different woman, whom he bored almost to tears with details of his morning and afternoon activities. Can you discover exactly what was in Kevin's diary?

1. Two days before his date with Kerry (which wasn't on Friday), Kevin had an appointment to collect a suit from his tailor, which he subsequently wore on his date that evening.
2. Wanting to look his best for Katya (who he didn't see on Tuesday), Kevin visited the barber's shop for a shave and haircut four hours before he dated her.
3. On Monday, Kevin attended a job interview (not that he has very much time to work, it seems!).

4. Kevin utterly bored Kathy with details of the finer points of ju-jitsu, a lesson on which he had attended the same day as his date with her.
5. Kevin visited his aunt for her birthday party on the same day as that of his French lesson, which was earlier in the week than his date with Kristel.
6. On the evening he saw Kim, Kevin was still suffering the effects of his trip to the dentist that afternoon. The very next day, he saw his chiropodist.

	Morning					Afternoon					Date with				
	Doctor	Tailor	French less.	Interview	Ju-jitsu less.	Aunt's party	Barber	Chiropodist	Dentist	Optician	Kathy	Katya	Kerry	Kim	Kristel
Monday															
Tuesday															
Wednesday															
Thursday															
Friday															
Kathy															
Katya															
Kerry															
Kim															
Kristel															
Aunt's party															
Barber															
Chiropodist															
Dentist															
Optician															

Day	Morning	Afternoon	Date with

Patchwork

Each piece in the patchwork square below is decorated with a letter of the alphabet:
A, B, C, D, E, F or G. In each horizontal row, vertical column and long diagonal line
of seven smaller pieces there are seven different letters: some are already in place.
Can you discover which letter fits in every piece? There is only one correct solution
to this puzzle – if you take a wrong path along the way, you won't finish the quilt!

1. The letter in piece 2 is the same as that in piece 47.

2. The letter in piece 18 is the same as that in piece 30.

3. The letter in piece 19 is the same as that in piece 29.

4. The letter in piece 28 is the same as that in piece 33.

5. The letter in piece 26 is the same as that in piece 42.

6. The letter in piece 12 is different to the letter which is in piece 41.

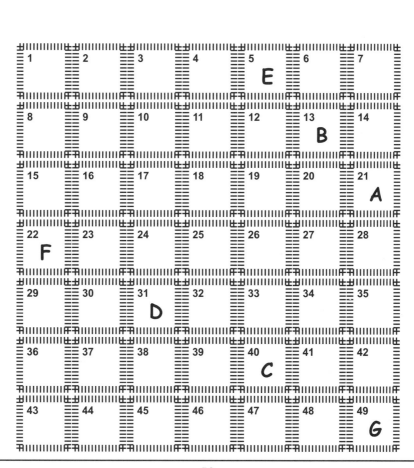

Shopping List

What is the surname of each of the five women in this puzzle and which (humanly!) edible and non-edible items did she have on her shopping list this morning? No woman bought more than one edible or non-edible item, every woman managed to buy the two items on her list and no woman bought the same as any other woman.

1. Belinda didn't have eggs on her shopping list and Margaret didn't buy the baking tray.

2. Either Belinda or Margaret is Miss Braden, who bought either a can of hairspray or a can of wax polish (for putting a shine on her wooden furniture).

3. The woman (not Miss Atkins or Miss Braden) who bought meat is either Greta or Margaret.

4. Mrs Simpson didn't buy any vegetables today.

5. Patsy bought either the hairspray or a toothbrush, but didn't buy vegetables or eggs.

6. The woman (not Miss Atkins or Mrs Trotter) who bought the shoe polish also bought either fish or vegetables.

7. Ruth's sister is Mrs Rather, who bought either bread or eggs, together with one of the cans of polish.

Shopper	Surname	Edible	Non-edible

A Lot in Common

The five men who feature in this puzzle work together and were surprised by the facts which emerged in a recent discussion: although the actual dates are different, they share in common with one another a birthday month, a wedding anniversary month and a month in which their first child was born. Can you discover on which date in the given months each fact applies to the five men?

1. Frank isn't the man whose birthday is on 30th June, whose wedding was on 19th July and whose first child was born exactly two years, one month and two days after he got married.

2. The man whose eldest child was born on 14th August has his wedding anniversary later in July than Tom and his birthday later in June than Dave (whose birthday is exactly one week after Tom's).

3. Tom married earlier in July than Dave.

4. The man married on 10th July (who became a father exactly one week before Barry) celebrates his birthday later in June than Barry (whose wedding anniversary is later in July than Frank's).

	Birthday					Wedding					1st child				
	14th June	15th June	22nd June	29th June	30th June	7th July	10th July	17th July	19th July	26th July	1st August	8th August	14th August	21st August	23rd August
Barry															
Dave															
Frank															
Simon															
Tom															
1st August															
8th August															
14th August															
21st August															
23rd August															
7th July															
10th July															
17th July															
19th July															
26th July															

Man	Birthday	Wedding	1st child

Dominological

A standard set of twenty-eight dominoes has been laid out as shown. One is already in position, to give you a start. Can you draw in the edges of the rest? The check-box is provided as an aid to solving.

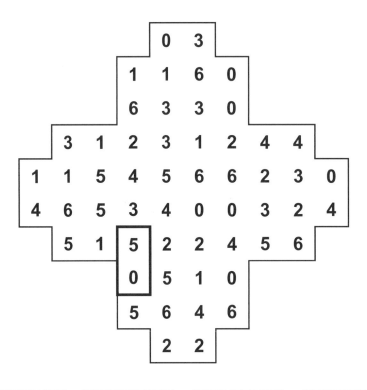

0 - 0		1 - 1		2 - 3		3 - 6	
0 - 1		1 - 2		2 - 4		4 - 4	
0 - 2		1 - 3		2 - 5		4 - 5	
0 - 3		1 - 4		2 - 6		4 - 6	
0 - 4		1 - 5		3 - 3		5 - 5	
0 - 5	✓	1 - 6		3 - 4		5 - 6	
0 - 6		2 - 2		3 - 5		6 - 6	

Drink Problem

Each of five families has a favourite type of fizzy drink and last week they shopped on different days (thus making possible this puzzle!). Can you discover each family's preference, together with the quantity of cans each bought and the day of the week on which they shopped?

1. One family bought forty-two cans of orangeade later in the week than the family who bought forty-four cans of their favourite drink.

2. One more can of fizzy blackcurrant drink was purchased by the Phelps family than by the Tyson family, who shopped the day before the Phelps family.

3. One fewer can was purchased on Wednesday by the Brooks family than the quantity of cans of cola bought by one of the other families.

4. Three fewer cans of cherryade (a fizzy drink which is flavoured with cherry juice) were purchased than the number of cans of lemonade bought by one of the five families.

5. The Martin family shopped two days later in the week than the Andrews family.

	Blackcurrant	Cherryade	Cola	Lemonade	Orangeade	40 cans	41 cans	42 cans	43 cans	44 cans	Tuesday	Wednesday	Thursday	Friday	Saturday
Andrews family															
Brooks family																
Martin family																
Phelps family																
Tyson family																
Tuesday											
Wednesday											
Thursday											
Friday											
Saturday											
40 cans					
41 cans					
42 cans					
43 cans					
44 cans					

Family	Favourite	Quantity	Shopping day

Turning the Tables

The neighbours who appear in this puzzle have all been busy this morning, painting their bird-tables, of all things! Every man chose a different colour and has placed his table in a different position on his lawn. What is the name of the man living in each of the named houses, where is his bird-table and what is its colour?

1. Either the white bird-table or the yellow bird-table is on Frank's lawn, on either the west or south side.

2. Dean's bird-table is on either the south or east side of his lawn.

3. The bird-table on the north side of a lawn is at either Condor Cottage or Finchley house. The bird-table on the east side of a lawn is at either Condor Cottage or Eagles' Lair and was painted by either Dean or Ivor.

4. The bird-table at Martins' Roost belongs to either Dean or Lance and was painted either green or yellow.

5. Either Dean or Frank lives at Parrot Park, where the bird table is either brown or green.

6. Brian lives at either Condor Cottage or Eagles' Lair.

7. The man who painted his bird-table brown placed it either in the centre or on the north side of his lawn.

	Brian	Dean	Frank	Ivor	Lance	North	South	East	West	Centre	Black	Brown	Green	White	Yellow
Condor Cottage															
Eagles' Lair															
Finchley House															
Martins' Roost															
Parrot Park															
Black															
Brown															
Green															
White															
Yellow															
North															
South															
East															
West															
Centre															

House name	Man	Position	Colour

Chat Lines

The eight people who feature in this puzzle made telephone calls to different relatives last night. Everyone made just one call and each spoke for a different length of time. Try to dial up the correct solution!

1. Felicity's call was one minute shorter than that made by whoever rang a father.

2. The conversation (not Joseph's) with a brother lasted for two fewer minutes than the one which Deirdre made to her cousin.

3. Edward's conversation (not with either of his parents) was one minute longer than Irma's, but shorter than the one someone had with an aunt.

4. Of the conversations lasting ten and fifteen minutes, one was to a grandfather and the other was made by Katherine.

5. Graham's conversation was longer than Joseph's but shorter than Lynne's.

6. Someone's conversation was three minutes shorter than the one to someone's mother which, in turn, was shorter than that made by someone to a sister, which didn't last for thirteen minutes.

	Aunt	Brother	Cousin	Father	Grandfather	Mother	Sister	Uncle	5 minutes	6 minutes	8 minutes	10 minutes	12 minutes	13 minutes	15 minutes	16 minutes
Deirdre																
Edward																
Felicity																
Graham																
Irma																
Joseph																
Katherine																
Lynne																
5 minutes									
6 minutes									
8 minutes									
10 minutes									
12 minutes									
13 minutes									
15 minutes									
16 minutes									

Caller	Relative	Time

Christmas Dinner

Five families living next door to one another in Yule Terrace have already planned what they will be eating for their main meal on Christmas Day! Can you discover the menu at each household?

1. The man at number 2 Yule Terrace makes a superb pea and ham soup and intends to serve this on Christmas Day.

2. Tomato soup will be followed by duck at one household and game soup will be followed with roast pork at another household. The roast pork will not, however, be followed by pavlova or Christmas pudding.

3. Mushroom soup followed by roast beef will be served at one household, but not number 3 Yule Terrace.

4. Neither the family at number 4 Yule Terrace nor their neighbours who will eat roast beef will follow their main course with fruit salad.

5. Christmas pudding will be eaten at number 3 Yule Terrace and roast turkey will be followed by profiteroles at number 1 Yule Terrace.

	Soup					Meat					Sweet				
	Asparagus	Game	Mushroom	Pea/ham	Tomato	Beef	Duck	Goose	Pork	Turkey	Fruit salad	Mince pies	Pavlova	Profiteroles	Xmas pudding
1 Yule Terrace															
2 Yule Terrace															
3 Yule Terrace															
4 Yule Terrace															
5 Yule Terrace															
Fruit salad															
Mince pies															
Pavlova															
Profiteroles															
Xmas pudding															
Beef															
Duck															
Goose															
Pork															
Turkey															

Address	Soup	Meat course	Sweet course

A Short Respite

Whilst waiting for their business partners to join them for dinner in their hotel, five businesswomen attending a conference sat in the bar, taking a respite from work by reading newspapers and enjoying a pre-dinner drink. Which newspaper was each reading, what had she to drink and at what time did her partner arrive?

1. Barbara wasn't the woman reading the *Daily Times*, who drank lager and whose business partner arrived ten minutes before Madge's.

2. The woman (not Madge or Tammy) with red wine met her business partner earlier than the partner of Phoebe (who doesn't drink lager or martini).

3. The woman who enjoyed reading the *Night Mail* (especially its business section) met her business partner thirty minutes earlier than Brenda's partner arrived.

4. The woman who read the *Evening Extra* met her partner at eight o'clock precisely.

5. The woman reading the *Daily Courier* sipped a martini whilst she waited.

6. Tammy's business partner arrived earlier than Phoebe's, but later than the partner of the woman who drank a vodka and tonic before dinner.

	Daily Courier	Daily News	Daily Times	Evening Extra	Night Mail	Lager	Martini	Red wine	Spritzer	Vodka and tonic	7.30pm	7.40pm	7.50pm	8.00pm	8.10pm
Barbara															
Brenda															
Madge															
Phoebe															
Tammy															
7.30pm											
7.40pm											
7.50pm											
8.00pm											
8.10pm											
Lager						
Martini						
Red wine						
Spritzer						
Vodka and tonic						

Businesswoman	Newspaper	Drink	Partner's time

No 66

Figure It Out

Each of the thirty-six squares in the grid is filled with a single digit number from 1 to 9 – each of those numbers being used four times. Use the clues to complete the square, bearing in mind that the same number must not appear in two adjacent (touching) squares in any row across or column down. If the same number is used more than once in any row across or column down it is stated in the relevant clue.

Across:

1. Two 9s. Total forty-four.

2. Two 1s.

3. Consecutive numbers placed in order.

4. Two 2s. No 9.

5. Total thirty-nine.

6. Two 1s. Two 4s.

Down:

1. Two 1s. Total sixteen.

2. Two 2s. No 6.

3. Two 7s.

4. No 5.

5. Consecutive numbers placed in order.

6. Two 8s.

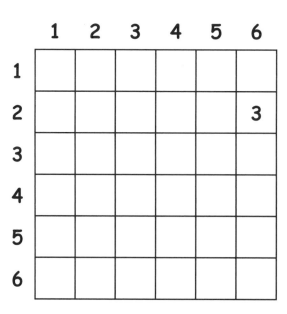

Broken Dreams

> *Daniel is having some sleepless nights just recently, since there are five newly-born babies in flats neighbouring his own, which is number 44. Use the clues to discover the name of the infant in each flat, together with that of its mother (also suffering from lack of sleep) and how many times each baby woke Daniel last week.*

1. Sandra's baby cried two more times than Simon, who lives in a flat with a number three higher than that of baby Bart and his mother.

2. Melinda's flat number is higher than that of the woman whose baby daughter Gabrielle woke Daniel eight times last week.

3. Doreen has a baby which woke Daniel either one or two more times than Ginny's infant managed.

4. Ginny's flat has a higher number than the flat in which Christopher lives with his mum.

5. Young Glenda woke Daniel four more times than Edna's baby managed.

	Bart	Christopher	Gabrielle	Glenda	Simon	Doreen	Edna	Ginny	Melinda	Sandra	4 times	6 times	8 times	9 times	10 times
Flat No 41															
Flat No 42															
Flat No 43															
Flat No 45															
Flat No 46															
4 times															
6 times															
8 times															
9 times															
10 times															
Doreen															
Edna															
Ginny															
Melinda															
Sandra															

Flat No	Baby	Mother	No of times

Fruit & Nut Case

Five of the Kindergarten's Reception Class brought two different things (fruits and nuts) this morning, for their teacher's nature table. See if you can discover their full names as well as the items they presented for the class to admire.

1. Neither the child surnamed Beeton nor Deborah (whose surname isn't Beeton or Wood) brought acorns for the nature table. Neither Della nor Deborah brought elderberries. Neither Debbie nor Mitch brought along blueberries or sloes.

2. The children surnamed Yates and Chester didn't bring rosehips for the table.

3. The blackberries weren't brought by the children who presented acorns and beechnuts. Della (whose surname isn't Chester) didn't bring the blueberries.

4. Mitch (whose surname isn't Chester or Yates) didn't bring rosehips or elderberries.

5. The child surnamed Beeton didn't bring the elderberries. The one who did gather elderberries didn't bring hazelnuts for the nature table.

6. Neither Fiona nor the child surnamed Wood (not Fiona) brought hazelnuts or walnuts to school. Kenny (whose surname isn't Mellard or Wood) didn't bring the blueberries.

7. The child who brought the hazelnuts isn't surnamed Beeton or Mellard.

	Beeton	Chester	Mellard	Wood	Yates	Blackberries	Blueberries	Elderberries	Rosehips	Sloes	Acorns	Beechnuts	Chestnuts	Hazelnuts	Walnuts
Della															
Deborah															
Fiona															
Kenny															
Mitch															
Acorns																
Beechnuts																
Chestnuts																
Hazelnuts																
Walnuts																
Blackberries																
Blueberries																
Elderberries																
Rosehips																
Sloes																

Child	Surname	Fruit	Nuts

Home Sweet Home

The five couples in this puzzle have just bought their very first homes, in neighbouring properties in the same street in Lochburgh, Scotland. Can you discover the number of the house purchased by each, together with its price and special feature not shared by any of the other houses in the street?

1. Mr & Mrs Smith bought the house selling for the lowest price, which has a lower number than the one sold for £138,000, but a higher number than the house purchased by Mr & Mrs Myers.

2. Mr & Mrs Giles have just purchased the house with a garage, which has a lower number than the one sold for £750 more than that (not number 18) with the tiled patio area.

3. The house with a conservatory cost £2,000 more than that bought by the Lloyds.

4. Number 15 wasn't sold for £136,500.

5. Number 19 (which wasn't purchased by Mr & Mrs Lloyd) doesn't have a greenhouse.

6. Number 18 wasn't sold for exactly £2,000 more than the price paid for number 17.

	No 15	No 16	No 17	No 18	No 19	£136,000	£136,500	£137,250	£138,000	£138,500	Conservatory	Double glazing	Garage	Greenhouse	Patio
Mr & Mrs Bates															
Mr & Mrs Giles															
Mr & Mrs Lloyd															
Mr & Mrs Myers															
Mr & Mrs Smith															
Conservatory															
Double glazing															
Garage															
Greenhouse															
Patio															
£136,000															
£136,500															
£137,250															
£138,000															
£138,500															

Couple	House No	Price	Feature

Partners

The Valentine Dating Agency has had many success stories, matching people with their ideal partners, of whom the happy couples below are good examples. Can you discover who the agency matched with whom, where they first met and the mutually shared interest which drew them together?

1. Dick (who is an ardent fishing enthusiast) met his ideal partner for the first time at the bus station – obviously an appropriate place from which to begin their joint journey in life!

2. Philately (stamp-collecting to you and me!) is the interesting hobby shared by Martina and Eddie.

3. Delores first met her partner in the local café, where they spent a considerable amount of time discussing their interest over coffee.

4. The woman who first met her partner in a bar isn't Oona, whose passion in life is theology.

5. The couple who first met at the bandstand in the park are interested in botany. Theo has no interest in either botany or archaeology.

6. Cynthia and Stan have just announced their intention to marry and are eternally grateful to the Valentine Dating Agency for bringing them together.

Grid columns: Cynthia, Delores, Martina, Oona, Petula, Bar, Bus station, Café, Library, Park, Archaeology, Botany, Fishing, Philately, Theology

Grid rows: Andy, Dick, Eddie, Stan, Theo, Archaeology, Botany, Fishing, Philately, Theology, Bar, Bus station, Café, Library, Park

Man	Woman	Place	Interest

Armchair Sportspersons

Five sports fanatics (of the armchair variety!) religiously tune in to view their three favourite sports, whenever they are able to do so. To discover each person's different first, second and third favourite TV sports, just race through the clues below.

1. Deanna isn't the person whose second favourite TV sport is cricket and whose third favourite is football.

2. Arthur never watches football on television and Deanna never watches snooker on television.

3. Neither Teresa nor Vincent is the person whose second favourite TV sport is snooker and whose third favourite is boxing.

4. The person whose favourite TV sport is tennis places football as second favourite.

5. Teresa's favourite TV sport is different to Vincent's second favourite.

6. Vincent isn't the person whose favourite TV sport is cricket and whose second favourite is tennis.

	Favourite					Second favourite					Third favourite				
	Boxing	Cricket	Football	Snooker	Tennis	Boxing	Cricket	Football	Snooker	Tennis	Boxing	Cricket	Football	Snooker	Tennis
Deanna															
Arthur															
Paul															
Teresa															
Vincent															
Third Boxing															
Third Cricket															
Third Football															
Third Snooker															
Third Tennis															
Second Boxing															
Second Cricket															
Second Football															
Second Snooker															
Second Tennis															

Viewer	Favourite	Second favourite	Third favourite

Cents Collection

Cheryl is feeling rather short-changed this week, having spent five dollars last week, contributing to the presents for work colleagues. To whose collection did she give on each day, how much did she donate and what is the reason for each collection?

1. Cheryl donated fifty cents towards a birthday present for the human resources manager two days after a collection was made for the receptionist (who is leaving to have a baby) but the day before the collection was made for the firm's delivery driver.

2. Cheryl donated twenty cents less to the collection for the driver than she gave to the collection which toured the offices on Tuesday.

3. The administrator is not the person who is about to get married.

4. The largest amount was given by Cheryl to the collection for the administrator two days before she gave one dollar towards a 'get well soon' card and gift for the colleague who has recently been hospitalised.

	Administrator	Driver	HR manager	Receptionist	Wages clerk	$0.50	$0.80	$1.00	$1.20	$1.50	Baby	Birthday	Get well soon	Marriage	Retirement
Monday															
Tuesday															
Wednesday															
Thursday															
Friday															
Baby															
Birthday															
Get well soon															
Marriage															
Retirement															
$0.50															
$0.80															
$1.00															
$1.20															
$1.50															

Day	For	Amount	Reason

Sleeping Arrangements

The five people in this puzzle have bed linen in a variety of colours, some of which do not go together very well… Can you discover the colour of each person's duvet, pillowcases and sheets?

1. Jeffrey's pillowcases are of the same colour as Yuri's sheets; and Yuri's duvet cover is of the same colour as Clarice's sheets.

2. Clarice's duvet cover isn't white. The orange duvet cover isn't on the same bed as the green sheets.

3. The green pillowcases are on the same bed as the beige sheets; and the pink sheets are on the same bed as the yellow duvet cover.

4. Leonora's duvet cover is of the same colour as Moira's pillowcases; and Moira's sheets are of the same colour as Clarice's pillowcases.

5. The white duvet cover is not on the same bed as the yellow sheets.

6. The blue duvet cover is not on the same bed as the blue pillowcases.

	Duvet					Pillowcases					Sheets				
	Blue	Orange	Purple	White	Yellow	Beige	Blue	Green	Pink	Purple	Beige	Green	Orange	Pink	Yellow
Clarice															
Jeffrey															
Leonora															
Moira															
Yuri															
Sheets Beige															
Green															
Orange															
Pink															
Yellow															
P'cases Beige															
Blue															
Green															
Pink															
Purple															

Sleeper	Duvet	Pillowcases	Sheets

Sum Code

In this puzzle, every letter of the alphabet represents a different number from 1 to 26. The sums below will help you to crack the code and if any letter does not appear, its value is that remaining once the rest of the puzzle is complete. The only arithmetical signs used in this puzzle are '–' (minus), 'x' (times) and '+' (plus).

?

A	B	C	D	E	F	G	H	I	J	K	L	M

N	O	P	Q	R	S	T	U	V	W	X	Y	Z

?

?

1	2	3	4	5	6	7	8	9	10	11	12	13

14	15	16	17	18	19	20	21	22	23	24	25	26

?

1. C = R x P

2. K = B x B

3. T = Z x Q

4. M = V x S

5. E = I x Q

6. N = R x S

7. T + B = C

8. B + C = Y

9. D + P = N

10. G + H = W

11. Z + J = A

12. G + R = X

13. V x V = F – L

14. The value of Y is one higher than that of K

15. O has a lower value than U

Many Hands...

…make light work, or so the saying goes. The five housewives in this puzzle all helped one another with spring cleaning last week. Each helped one other woman and none was, in turn, helped by the woman to whom she'd lent a hand. On which day was each woman's cleaning effort, who helped her and which room did they tackle together?

1. Jolene's dining room was thoroughly cleaned with the help of Tanya.

2. Jolene helped another woman with cleaning on Friday.

3. Midge helped Cissy clean a room on Tuesday, but this wasn't Cissy's kitchen or lounge.

4. Midge's cleaning day was on Monday, when she was assisted by Davina.

5. The bathroom was cleaned later in the week than the kitchen.

6. The cellar was cleaned out on Wednesday.

	Monday	Tuesday	Wednesday	Thursday	Friday	Cissy	Davina	Jolene	Midge	Tanya	Bathroom	Cellar	Dining room	Kitchen	Lounge
Cissy															
Davina															
Jolene															
Midge															
Tanya															
Bathroom															
Cellar															
Dining room															
Kitchen															
Lounge															
Cissy															
Davina															
Jolene															
Midge															
Tanya															

Columns grouped: Helper (Cissy, Davina, Jolene, Midge, Tanya); left block (Helper) labels the bottom rows.

Housewife	Day	Helped by	Room

On the Run

After a hold-up at the local bank, a gang of robbers got away with $450,000. However, they didn't disable the CCTV cameras, so the police know exactly who they are… Without the help of these pictures, you'll need the clues below to discover the full name of each felon and the part he played in the robbery, together with the amount he received for taking part (a detail not yet known to the police!).

1. Conrad (Connie to his friends) received $40,000 more than Mr Check, who acted as gunman, terrorising the innocent bystanders and staff by waving a shotgun at them.

2. Lonnie received $40,000 more than Ronnie, whose surname has exactly five letters.

3. Mr Swindler didn't act as the safe-blower or the driver and received less than one fifth of the total haul.

4. Mr Forge doesn't drive.

5. Donnie Blank isn't the man who acted as planner, who masterminded the whole robbery and received the largest share of the takings.

	Blank	Cash	Check	Forge	Swindler	Driver	Gunman	Look-out	Planner	Safe-blower	$50,000	$70,000	$90,000	$110,000	$130,000
Connie															
Donnie															
Johnnie															
Lonnie															
Ronnie															
$50,000															
$70,000															
$90,000															
$110,000															
$130,000															
Driver															
Gunman															
Look-out															
Planner															
Safe-blower															

Robber	Surname	Part played	Amount received

Fast Food

Mrs Parker takes in paying guests at her home and currently has five men staying with her. Each has the same thing for breakfast every morning, takes the same amount of time to consume his food and leaves the house at the same time each day: and these details are different for all five men. Can you use the clues to discover the times involved, listed against each man's chosen breakfast?

1. The man who chooses waffles for breakfast comes down for his meal directly before (and leaves an hour later than) the one who eats eggs and bacon, who takes one minute longer over his meal than the man who has waffles.

2. The man who eats at eight o'clock takes seventeen minutes over his meal. The one who takes sixteen minutes leaves half-an-hour earlier than the one who has boiled eggs.

3. The man who breakfasts at 7.30am leaves directly before whoever eats kedgeree.

4. The man who eats kippers each morning comes down for his meal earlier than (and leaves the house directly before) the man who spends the least time eating.

	Eaten at					12 minutes	13 minutes	14 minutes	16 minutes	17 minutes	9.30am	10.00am	11.00am	11.30am	12.00 noon
	6.30am	7.30am	8.00am	8.30am	9.00am										
Boiled eggs															
Eggs and bacon															
Kedgeree															
Kippers															
Waffles															
9.30am															
10.00am															
11.00am															
11.30am															
12.00 noon															
12 minutes															
13 minutes															
14 minutes															
16 minutes															
17 minutes															

Breakfast	Eaten at	Time taken	Leaves at

Playing Card Bingo

Every Thursday night, the local Darby & Joan Club holds prize competitions, one of which is Playing Card Bingo. This week's winning card is shown below. Can you determine the order in which the cards on it were called?

Values of cards are as shown and ace=1, jack=11, queen=12 and king=13.

1. The card called fourth is directly next to and left of the card called seventh.
2. Card D was called immediately after card G. Card I wasn't called immediately after card A.
3. The card called thirteenth is directly above the card called twelfth, which has a value one higher than that of the card called eleventh.
4. The card called eighth is directly above the card called third, which is of the same value as that of the card called sixth, which is of the same suit as the card called second.
5. The card called fourteenth has a value one higher than that of the first card called, which has a value one higher than that of the last card to be called.

1st	2nd	3rd	4th	5th
6th	7th	8th	9th	10th
11th	12th	13th	14th	15th

LEFT ←   RIGHT →

A	B	C		D	E	F		G	H
K ♦	7 ♣	9 ♦		4 ♠	A ♣	J ♡		5 ♠	6 ♣
2 ♡		A ♠	10 ♦	J ♣		5 ♦	6 ♡	9 ♠	
I		J	K	L		M	N	O	

Honeymooning Couples

Five couples from across the world are on their honeymoon at the exclusive (and reassuringly expensive) Starlight Plaza Hotel. Can you pair up each man with his wife, the day they arrived at the hotel and the country in which they live?

1. Pete and his wife are from the United States of America; they didn't arrive at the hotel on Friday.

2. Jack isn't from Denmark. Nor is Jack married to Suzie, who arrived (from Australia) with her new husband on Wednesday.

3. Dave and his wife arrived on Saturday and have a room above that shared by Ellen and her husband.

4. Mee-Ling and her husband arrived from Japan on Thursday.

5. Amanda and her husband arrived two days before Lee and his wife checked into the hotel.

	Amanda	Ellen	Mee-Ling	Suzie	Wendy	Tuesday	Wednesday	Thursday	Friday	Saturday	Australia	Denmark	Ireland	Japan	USA
Dave															
Hugh															
Jack															
Lee															
Pete															
Australia																
Denmark																
Ireland																
Japan																
USA																
Tuesday																
Wednesday																
Thursday																
Friday																
Saturday																

Husband	Wife	Arrived on	From

Laps & Stops

A certain make of car took all five leading places at the Conte Marlow rally, until engine troubles forced an early retirement. Use the clues below to discover the unique design on the bonnet of each differently coloured vehicle (for once the cars aren't in the colours of their corporate sponsor), as well as the number of laps and how many times each had to pull into the pits before finally retiring from the race.

1. The gold car made two more pit stops than the yellow vehicle.

2. Of the five cars in this puzzle, the one painted with the picture of the globe made the fewest number of pit stops.

3. The black car made two more pit stops than the car which completed seventeen laps before retiring from the race.

4. The red car made one more pit stop than the car with red stars.

5. The car painted with pink swirls completed one more lap than the red car (which wasn't decorated with green stars).

6. The car sporting a design of white stripes completed one fewer lap than the car which made four pit stops.

7. The yellow car made more pit stops than the car which completed one fewer lap than the black car.

	Green stars	Globe	Pink swirls	Red stars	White stripes	14 laps	15 laps	17 laps	18 laps	19 laps	3 pit stops	4 pit stops	5 pit stops	6 pit stops	7 pit stops
Black															
Blue															
Gold															
Red															
Yellow															
3 pit stops															
4 pit stops															
5 pit stops															
6 pit stops															
7 pit stops															
14 laps															
15 laps															
17 laps															
18 laps															
19 laps															

Car colour	Design	No of laps	No of pit stops

Lost & Found

The five absent-minded people who appear in this puzzle all lost things last week, which five eagle-eyed youngsters then found. On which day did each child find something, what was it and to whom does it belong? (You'll be pleased to hear that all of the children are honest and very quickly returned their finds to the rightful owners, for which they received a small reward.)

1. Lucien didn't find anything on Friday.

2. The watch was found earlier in the week than the pocket calculator, which had inadvertently been left on a bus.

3. The book wasn't found on Thursday. Nor did Willow find a book.

4. Billy found something (not an umbrella) which had been lost by Mr Barlow. This was earlier in the week than the find of a fountain pen.

5. On Tuesday, Harry found something (not an umbrella) which doesn't belong to Mr Thomas.

6. Neither Lucien nor Tina discovered the item belonging to Mr Porter, which was found two days after the umbrella.

7. Miss Cooke gave one child a small reward for returning the item found on Friday.

	Monday	Tuesday	Wednesday	Thursday	Friday	Book	Calculator	Pen	Umbrella	Watch	Mr Barlow	Miss Cooke	Mrs Jarvis	Mr Porter	Mr Thomas
Billy															
Harry															
Lucien															
Tina															
Willow															
Mr Barlow															
Miss Cooke															
Mrs Jarvis															
Mr Porter															
Mr Thomas															
Book															
Calculator															
Pen															
Umbrella															
Watch															

Finder	Day	Item	Owner

A Likely Story

After a recent robbery, five men were taken in for questioning by the police. Each gave his name as 'John Smith' (not very helpful), but of more interest to the police was that each man sported something looking both new and rather expensive… There is no point in listing five John Smiths here, so can you identify the suspects by age, height, item in question and who he said gave it to him for Christmas last year?

1. The man aged forty is one inch taller than the one who said his item was a gift from his grandfather. The tallest suspect didn't say that his item was given to him by his mother.

2. The man aged thirty-four is one inch shorter than the one sporting Rayban sunglasses. The man who said his item was from his girlfriend is two inches taller than the one sporting a chunky silver identity bracelet (with no name on it, of course!).

3. The man with the gold signet ring on his finger is older than (but not as tall as) the man who said his item was given to him by an auntie.

4. The man with the solid gold wristwatch is four years younger and one inch shorter than the suspect who said his item had been given to him by his uncle.

5. The suspect who said his item came from his mother is older and taller than the one with a silver locket.

	Height					Gold ring	Gold watch	Silver bracelet	Silver locket	Sunglasses	Auntie	Girlfriend	Grandfather	Mother	Uncle
	5' 8"	5' 9"	5' 10"	6' 0"	6' 1"										
Age 32															
34															
36															
40															
42															
Auntie															
Girlfriend															
Grandfather															
Mother															
Uncle															
Gold ring															
Gold watch															
Silver bracelet															
Silver locket															
Sunglasses															

Age	Height	Item	Present from

Old School Ties

Five old friends who lost touch when they left primary school recently met again at their old school reunion party. They got to talking about their secondary education and what you can discover from the clues below is their full names, who went to which secondary school and the colour of his old (secondary school) tie.

1. Red was not one of the colours in the tie worn by pupils at Bell Hill school.

2. Mr Cameron attended Hill Rise School. His tie had one colour in common with that worn by the pupils at St Christophe's Secondary School and another colour in common with that worn by Benny.

3. Mr Shaw's tie was black with purple stripes. Clifford (who isn't Mr Shaw) attended Denne Road School and his tie had no colours in common with that worn by Robbie.

4. Joe Bush's tie had one colour in common with that worn by Robbie; and Robbie's tie also had one colour in common with Mr Dickins's old school tie. None of these three men attended East Park School.

	Bush	Cameron	Dickins	Shaw	Smythe	Bell Hill	Denne Road	East Park	Hill Rise	St Christophe's	Black/purple	Blue/red	Green/black	Purple/blue	Red/white
Benny															
Clifford															
Joe															
Mike															
Robbie															
Black/purple															
Blue/red															
Green/black															
Purple/blue															
Red/white															
Bell Hill															
Denne Road															
East Park															
Hill Rise															
St Christophe's															

Forename	Surname	Secondary school	School tie colours

Patchwork

Each piece in the patchwork square below is decorated with a letter of the alphabet: A, B, C, D, E, F or G. In each horizontal row, vertical column and long diagonal line of seven smaller pieces there are seven different letters: some are already in place. Can you discover which letter fits in every piece? There is only one correct solution to this puzzle – if you take a wrong path along the way, you won't finish the quilt!

1. The letter in piece 2 is the same as the letter in piece 13.

2. The letter in piece 3 is the same as the letter in piece 12.

3. The letter in piece 20 is the same as the letter in piece 7.

4. The letter in piece 31 is the same as the letter in piece 49.

5. The letter in piece 33 is the same as the letter in piece 37.

6. The letter in piece 11 is not a D and the letter in piece 14 is not an E.

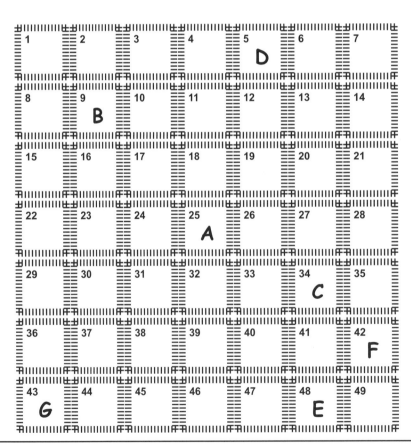

Presidential Residences

There are five blocks of flats in Presidents' Place (shown in the map below), each identical, apart from being named after different presidents of the United States of America. What is the name of each block and how many men and women live there?

1. One fewer woman lives in Carter Court than in block B, which has the most men.

2. There is one more woman living in Kennedy Court than at the block in which forty-four men live.

3. Two more women live in Clinton Court than in Lincoln Court, which is directly next to and is identified by a letter later in the alphabet than that depicting Clinton Court. More men live in Clinton Court than in Lincoln Court.

4. More men live in the block where there are forty-four women than in Bush Court (which isn't D or E on the map below).

5. Carter Court (which doesn't house the fewest women) is next to the block which houses the highest number of women and which is identified by a later letter of the alphabet than that depicting Carter Court.

	Bush Court	Carter Court	Clinton Court	Kennedy Court	Lincoln Court	40 men	41 men	42 men	44 men	45 men	43 women	44 women	46 women	47 women	48 women
Block A															
Block B															
Block C															
Block D															
Block E															
43 women															
44 women															
46 women															
47 women															
48 women															
40 men															
41 men															
42 men															
44 men															
45 men															

Block	Name	No of men	No of women

Multiple Births

Mrs Greenwood gave birth to her five children (two boys and three girls) during the 1990s, each on a different date of a different month in successive years. When were they born, exactly?

1. None of the children was born on 14th September. Stephen wasn't born on the 15th of any month. Stephen is older than the child who celebrates a birthday on the 17th July.

2. The youngest of Mrs Greenwood's five children is either Danny or Stephen and was born on the 16th of a month.

3. Danny wasn't born in October.

4. The child born in 1995 celebrates a birthday two months before that of the child born in 1993 (whose birth date is one lower than Naomi's).

5. Christine wasn't born in 1994.

6. Naomi was the first of Mrs Greenwood's five children.

7. Louisa was born in June.

	13th	14th	15th	16th	17th	June	July	August	September	October	1992	1993	1994	1995	1996
Christine															
Danny															
Louisa															
Naomi															
Stephen															
1992															
1993															
1994															
1995															
1996															
June															
July															
August															
September															
October															

Child	Birth date	Birth month	Birth year

Simply Cricket

No 87

Five friends took part in a charity cricket match last Saturday, each batting in turn with six other players whose details do not appear in this puzzle (batsman number 1 was first and number 11 last, so number 1 was highest in the batting order). Which man batted in each of the given positions, how many runs did he make and how was he sent out in the first innings?

1. Ambrose scored either five more or nine more runs than batsman number 5.

2. Des scored one more run than Roger, who was given out after the 'obstruction' of a fielder, although none of the other players could understand this decision.

3. The batsman who was 'caught out' when he spooned an easy catch to the fielder at square leg was two higher in the batting order than the man who scored a total of eleven runs, who was 'run out' following a brilliant throw from long on.

4. The batsman given out 'lbw' (leg before wicket) scored fewer runs than batsman number 3.

5. Willie (not the batsman who was 'stumped') appeared two lower in the batting order than Roger.

6. Batsman number 2 made more than five runs.

	Ambrose	Des	Jamie	Roger	Willie	5 runs	6 runs	10 runs	11 runs	15 runs	Caught out	Lbw	Obstruction	Run out	Stumped
No 2															
No 3															
No 5															
No 6															
No 8															
Caught out															
Lbw															
Obstruction															
Run out															
Stumped															
5 runs															
6 runs															
10 runs															
11 runs															
15 runs															

Batting order	Batsman	No of runs	How out

Love Stories

Penn & Hollis, publishers, have just brought out five new titles in their 'Love Stories' series, each set in a different city of the world, as reflected in the title of every story; and each being a tale of love, followed by despair, followed by happiness! Can you discover not only the full name of the author, but also the full title of his or her novel?

1. Angela Hammond's story isn't set in London or Sydney.

2. One book is entitled *Waiting In New York*.

3. Luke, the author surnamed Walsh and the writer who penned the story set in London are three different people. Ursula (whose surname isn't Walsh) didn't set her story in London.

4. The story set in Wellington was written by Mark.

5. The author surnamed Brooker (not Steven) wrote the book with a title which begins with *Steamy In*.

6. Mr Findlay's tale is set in Adelaide, unlike the one which begins *Adoration In*.

7. No book has the title *Adoration in London* or *Passion in Adelaide*.

	Brooker	Findlay	Hammond	Packer	Walsh	Adoration In	Passion In	Steamy In	Waiting In	Wedding In	Adelaide	London	New York	Sydney	Wellington
Angela															
Luke															
Mark															
Steven															
Ursula															
Adelaide															
London															
New York															
Sydney															
Wellington															
Adoration In															
Passion In															
Steamy In															
Waiting In															
Wedding In															

Title of novel — First part / Second part

Author	Surname	First part of title	Second part of title

War Heroes

Bill Tompkins recently put together his family tree and was pleasantly surprised to learn that five of his great-uncles had all played active parts in the First World War, receiving decorations for bravery. Can you discover the award received by each, in which year he was decorated and in which branch of the services each had enlisted?

1. The DSO (Distinguished Service Order) was awarded to one of Bill's great-uncles two years after Henry (who served in the Cavalry) received his medal.

2. The great-uncle who won the Military Cross wasn't the first of the five men to be decorated.

3. Bill's great-uncle Albert was in the Guards.

4. The officer in the RFC (Royal Flying Corps) was decorated in 1916.

5. The DCM (Distinguished Conduct Medal) was awarded to one of Bill's uncles in 1917, but not the man who served in the Artillery. Bill's great-uncle George didn't serve in the Infantry.

6. The man who served in the Guards received either the Victoria Cross or the Military Cross.

7. William Tompkins was the last of the five men to receive an award, which wasn't the Military Cross or the Victoria Cross.

	1914	1915	1916	1917	1918	DCM	DSO	Military Cross	Military Medal	Victoria Cross	Artillery	Cavalry	Guards	Infantry	RFC
Albert															
Frederick															
George															
Henry															
William															
Artillery															
Cavalry															
Guards															
Infantry															
RFC															
DCM															
DSO															
Military Cross															
Military Medal															
Victoria Cross															

Great-uncle	Award	Year decorated	Served in

About Time!

Jayne isn't normally a clock-watcher, but she did notice yesterday that four of the five clocks in her house were showing the wrong time (her wristwatch was accurate, as was one of the clocks, but the other four clocks were either running slow or fast). Can you discover the room in which each listed piece is located, the time at which Jane looked at it (and corrected it where necessary) and how inaccurate it was?

1. The clock in the dining room was put right later than the one in the study.

2. The clock in the lounge was found to be accurate at the time Jayne looked at it.

3. The carriage clock was found to be running slow, as was the grandfather clock (which was put right earlier than the bedroom alarm clock).

4. The wall-clock was put right one hour earlier than the clock in the hall, which was found to be running fast.

5. The cuckoo-clock was wrong by seven minutes.

6. The last clock which Jayne adjusted was found to be twelve minutes slow.

	Bedroom	Dining room	Hall	Lounge	Study	6.30pm	7.00pm	8.00pm	8.30pm	9.30pm	Accurate	7 mins fast	12 mins fast	7 mins slow	12 mins slow
Alarm clock															
Carriage clock															
Cuckoo-clock															
Grandfather clock															
Wall-clock															
Accurate															
7 mins fast															
12 mins fast															
7 mins slow															
12 mins slow															
6.30pm															
7.00pm															
8.00pm															
8.30pm															
9.30pm															

Clock	Location	Time checked	Inaccuracy

Sticky Treats

The five schoolboys who appear in this puzzle were each given a handful (or two!) of toffees by their respective teachers, as a reward for coming top of the class in their favourite subjects! Can you discover not only how many toffees each lad received, but also his favourite subject (in which he had excelled) and his least favourite subject (in which he achieved the lowest grade in his class)?

1. Of the five boys: one's favourite subject is English (and his least favourite is mathematics); one's least favourite subject is history; one's favourite subject is art; one is Adam; and one received a total of eight toffees from his teacher.

2. Of the five boys: one (not Graeme) was given the smallest quantity of toffees; one is Rupert (who isn't the boy given ten toffees); one was given six toffees; one's favourite subject is physics; and one's least favourite subject is French (although his favourite subject isn't art or geography).

3. Of the five boys: one (not Graeme or Rupert) was given the largest quantity of toffees; one is Mark; one was given four more toffees than Mark; one's least favourite subject is literature; and one came top of the class in chemistry.

4. Of three of the boys: one is Graeme; one is Francis; and one was given ten toffees by his teacher.

	4 toffees	6 toffees	8 toffees	10 toffees	12 toffees	Art	Chemistry	English	Geography	Physics	English	French	History	Literature	Maths
						Favourite					**Least favourite**				
Adam															
Francis															
Graeme															
Mark															
Rupert															
English (Least fav.)															
French															
History															
Literature															
Maths															
Art (Favourite)															
Chemistry															
English															
Geography															
Physics															

Schoolboy	No of toffees	Favourite	Least favourite

Figure It Out

Each of the thirty-six squares in the grid is filled with a single digit number from 1 to 9 – each of those numbers being used four times. Use the clues to complete the square, bearing in mind that the same number must not appear in two adjacent (touching) squares in any row across or column down. If the same number is used more than once in any row across or column down it is stated in the relevant clue.

Across:

1. Two 3s, one of which is next to a 6. Two 9s.

2. Two odd and four even numbers.

3. Two 5s are the only odd numbers.

4. Consecutive numbers placed in order.

5. Two 7s, neither of which is next to the 4 which appears in this row.

6. Two 1s. Two 9s. Total thirty.

Down:

1. Two 8s are the only even numbers.

2. Total thirty-nine.

3. Two 1s are the only odd numbers. Two 6s.

4. Two 9s. Total thirty-seven.

5. Two odd and four even numbers.

6. Two 2s.

	1	2	3	4	5	6
1						
2						
3						
4						
5						
6					1	

All Shapes & Sizes

Shopkeepers tend to describe the proportions of the five friends below as 'unusual' when explaining why they having nothing in stock which will fit… However, each woman was delighted when, on her last shopping trip into town, she finally found an item for which she'd been looking for some considerable time. What item did each woman buy, from which shop and what is every woman's specific 'problem'?

1. The woman with odd-sized feet was very pleased to come across an odd-sized pair of trainers to fit her! She isn't Maisie, who shopped in Deal & Marsh.

2. Maisie isn't petite. The woman who is both tall and slim wasn't looking for a dress – so didn't buy one!

3. Nicky didn't buy a pair of trainers and has never shopped in either B T Nolan or Corbett's.

4. The woman who is both petite and slim didn't shop in Geckle & Sons; and neither of the slim women bought a jacket.

5. The woman who found what she was looking for whilst shopping in B T Nolan isn't petite.

6. Wilma (who isn't slim) managed to find just what she was looking for in The Supplier.

7. The coat was bought by Fleur, who isn't slim.

	Coat	Dress	Jacket	Trainers	Trousers	Corbett's	Deal & Marsh	Geckle & Sons	B T Nolan	The Supplier	Odd-sized feet	Petite and plump	Petite and slim	Tall and plump	Tall and slim
Fleur															
Maisie															
Nicky															
Victoria															
Wilma															
Odd-sized feet															
Petite and plump															
Petite and slim															
Tall and plump															
Tall and slim															
Corbett's															
Deal & Marsh															
Geckle & Sons															
B T Nolan															
The Supplier															

Shopper	Item	Shop	'Problem'

Food for Thought

At five of the houses in Sandwich Street, a traditional Sunday lunch is served every week. Your task is to digest the information below, in order to discover the type of soup with which the family living at each address started their meal last Sunday lunchtime, the roast meat which followed the soup and the milk pudding which then followed the main course. A plan showing the layout of the houses is below.

1. Asparagus soup was served at the home of the family which lives directly next to and between two other families: those who ate roast pork and those who tucked into semolina pudding after their meal.

2. One family had minestrone soup to start, followed by roast duck; another had both vegetable soup and semolina pudding. These two families live next door to one another. The home-made leek and potato soup wasn't served at No 9, nor did the family at No 9 eat sago or tapioca pudding.

3. The family who tucked into the milky rice pudding have a house with a number four higher than that where French onion soup was supped, but lower than that where the roast chicken was carved.

4. The family which tucked into roast beef last Sunday didn't start with asparagus soup or finish with sago pudding.

	Asparagus	French onion	Leek/potato	Minestrone	Vegetable	Beef	Chicken	Duck	Lamb	Pork	Macaroni	Rice	Sago	Semolina	Tapioca
No 1															
No 3															
No 5															
No 7															
No 9															
Macaroni															
Rice															
Sago															
Semolina															
Tapioca															
Beef															
Chicken															
Duck															
Lamb															
Pork															

Houses: 1 3 5 7 9

House No	Soup	Meat	Milk pudding

Rudely Awoken

Although last Tuesday night's thunderstorm was localised and of fairly short duration, it woke these five people from extremely pleasant dreams, to which they were unable to return… No dreaming for you, however, as you work through the clues below to find each one's surname, the time he or she was so rudely awoken and the nature of the dream he or she had been enjoying up until that time.

1. Of the two people who awoke earliest, one is surnamed Nye and the other dreamt of a holiday in which he or she was lazing on a tropical beach… some hope!

2. Neil isn't the person surnamed O'Brien, who was woken later than Harry. One of the three men who feature in this puzzle dreamt he had inherited a fortune from an elderly aunt (he actually hasn't any aunts, so there's no chance of his dream becoming reality!).

3. The person surnamed Hilton dreamt of his or her forthcoming wedding.

4. Olga (whose surname isn't O'Brien) woke five minutes later than Neil (whose surname isn't Masters or Standish).

5. Scott was woken five minutes earlier than Harry.

6. Harry's dream was either about an inheritance or becoming the star of a major new Hollywood film.

7. The person surnamed Masters dreamt of moving into a brand new house.

	Hilton	Masters	Nye	O'Brien	Standish	2.35am	2.40am	2.45am	2.55am	3.00am	Film stardom	Holiday	Inheritance	New house	Wedding
Harry															
Marjorie															
Neil															
Olga															
Scott															
Film stardom															
Holiday															
Inheritance															
New house															
Wedding															
2.35am															
2.40am															
2.45am															
2.55am															
3.00am															

Dreamer	Surname	Time	Dreaming about

Simple as A,B,C?

Each of the small squares in the grid below contains either A, B or C. Every row, every column and each of the two long diagonal lines of six squares contains exactly two of each letter. The information in the clues refers only to the squares in that row or column. To help you solve this problem, we've given as many clues as we think you'll need! Can you tell which letter should be placed into each square?

Across:

1. The Cs are further left than the As.

2. The As are further right than the Bs.

3. Any three consecutive squares contain three different letters.

4. The As are somewhere between the Cs.

5. The Bs are somewhere between the As.

6. The Cs are next to one another.

Down:

1. The As are somewhere between the Bs.

2. The Bs are somewhere between the Cs.

3. The As are higher than the Cs.

5. Each C is immediately next to and below a B.

6. The Bs are lower than the As.

Strippers!

Five women who work in the same office each took off a different day last week, in order to strip the wallpaper from a room in her house, ready for redecorating at the weekend. Can you discover the day on which each stripped, the length of time she spent doing so and the room in which she worked?

1. Sally isn't the woman who took exactly four hours (not a minute longer!) to strip away the wallpaper in her bathroom.

2. Selina's day off was two days later in the week than that taken by the woman who spent one hour less time stripping her walls than Simone, who is redecorating her lounge.

3. Monday wasn't Sonia's day away from the office.

4. The woman (not Selina) who is redecorating her conservatory was off work the day after Sue, who spent two hours longer at her task than the woman who stripped walls on Monday.

5. The woman who stripped wallpaper on Tuesday isn't redecorating her kitchen.

	Monday	Tuesday	Wednesday	Thursday	Friday	4 hours	4½ hours	5 hours	6 hours	6½ hours	Conservatory	Bathroom	Bedroom	Kitchen	Lounge
Sally															
Selina															
Simone															
Sonia															
Sue															
Conservatory											
Bathroom											
Bedroom											
Kitchen											
Lounge											
4 hours					
4½ hours					
5 hours					
6 hours					
6½ hours					

Woman	Day off work	Time taken	Room

Teaming Up

Carla and Dean love to play cards with their friends in the evenings. Last week they found two other couples to play with, on five successive evenings. Can you team up the four names of the husband and wife couples who joined Carla and Dean on different evenings?

1. On one of the evenings, Phil sat next to Dana.

2. Neither Ian nor Bruce was present when Betsy sat next to Hank.

3. On Monday evening, Jeff came along with his wife Antonia, who chatted to Miles.

4. Caroline sat next to Alison on Tuesday evening.

5. On the evenings that Josie and Stephanie played cards with Carla and Dean, Dana and Jessica did not.

6. Ian sat next to Stephanie during one of the games sessions, but this wasn't the evening on which Frederick sat next to Laura.

7. Roseanne and Clive have never met one another.

		First wife					Second husband					Second wife				
		Betsy	Caroline	Dana	Jessica	Roseanne	Bernard	Clive	Hank	Jeff	Phil	Alison	Antonia	Josie	Laura	Stephanie
First husband	Bruce															
	Frederick															
	Ian															
	Miles															
	Ted															
Second wife	Alison															
	Antonia															
	Josie															
	Laura															
	Stephanie															
Second husband	Bernard															
	Clive															
	Hank															
	Jeff															
	Phil															

First husband	First wife	Second husband	Second wife

Art Students

Five art students of widely varying ages are currently making charcoal sketches in the Little Puzzleton History Museum. Can you discover their ages, together with the item each is drawing and the section of the museum in which it is located?

1. The artist sketching the flagon is forty-six years of age.

2. Although Sharon isn't twenty-two years old, she is younger than Thomas.

3. The suit of armour in the Tudor section of the museum is being sketched by an artist who is eight years older than the person in the Indian section of the museum, but younger than Arthur, who is putting together a series of sketches of the pots displayed at the museum.

4. Steve is sketching in the Egyptian Room and is older than both Pamela and Pamela's cousin, who is busy sketching a rather fine sword on display in the Victorian section of the museum.

	22 years old	30 years old	38 years old	46 years old	54 years old	Armour	Flagon	Jewellery	Pots	Sword	Egyptian	Indian	Roman	Tudor	Victorian
Arthur															
Pamela															
Sharon															
Steve															
Thomas															
Egyptian															
Indian															
Roman															
Tudor															
Victorian															
Armour															
Flagon															
Jewellery															
Pots															
Sword															

Artist	Age	Sketching	Section

Card Sharp

What is the face value and suit of each of the cards shown below? All twelve cards used below are of different values and together they total 80. Values of the cards are as per their numbers and ace=1, jack=11, queen=12 and king=13. No card is horizontally or vertically next to another of the same colour and there are four different suits in each horizontal row and three different suits in each vertical column.

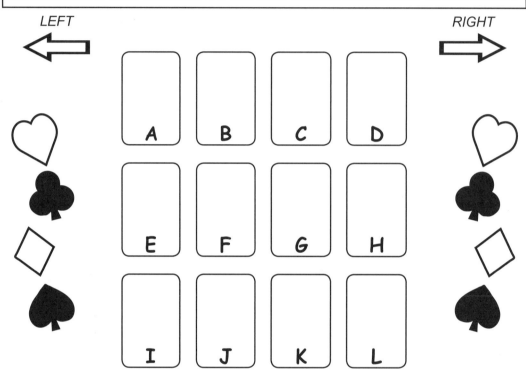

1. Card C has a value one lower than that of card B, which has a value half that of card A.
2. Card G has a value one lower than that of card F, which has a value half that of card E.
3. Card F has a value one lower than that of card C, which has a value half that of card L, which has a value three higher than that of card I.
4. Card I (which isn't a diamond) has a value two higher than that of card C.
5. The value of card K is the difference between the values of cards I and J. Card J has a higher value than that of card H.
6. There is no three of spades on the table. However, there is a king of clubs on the table, but it isn't next to and above a diamond.

Every One a Winner

Five friends were lucky enough to win the National Lottery last week – not BIG wins, you understand, but enough to bring a smile to the face… Each had three correct numbers on her lottery ticket, winning $10. Can you discover every woman's three 'lucky' numbers, listed in the grid in the order in which she chose them?

1. The number which Henrietta chose first was the same as Ariadne's second choice, which was higher than Wilhelmina's second number.

2. The number which Henrietta chose second was the same as Wilhelmina's first number.

3. The number which Henrietta chose third (which wasn't 45) was the same as the second number chosen by Jacqueline.

4. Pamela's second choice of number was lower than her third, which was different to Henrietta's first number.

5. Wilhelmina's third number was the same as Jacqueline's first number and Pamela's second number.

	First					Second					Third				
	12	16	20	41	45	16	20	36	37	45	12	20	36	41	45
Ariadne															
Henrietta															
Jacqueline															
Pamela															
Wilhelmina															
Third 12															
Third 20															
Third 36															
Third 41															
Third 45															
Second 16															
Second 20															
Second 36															
Second 37															
Second 45															

Player	First number	Second number	Third number

Long Live Love

Romance isn't dead! Last St Valentine's Day, five men gave their respective girlfriends jewellery as well as another gift and a card. To discover what each lucky woman received (and from whom) just follow the clues below.

1. Neither of the two women who received flowers was given a pair of earrings.

2. Kate's boyfriend Eric didn't give her a brooch.

3. Valentina received a gold bracelet from her boyfriend: he isn't Clifford, who gave lilies to the love of his life. Nor did Valentina receive the roses or the bottle of wine.

4. On St Valentine's Day, Bella received a diamond ring from her boyfriend, when she consented to marry him!

5. Jo didn't receive the necklace, nor is she the woman given both a brooch and a scented candle.

6. Nigel didn't present his girlfriend with either the candle or the bracelet. Frank wasn't the man who presented his girlfriend with a box of chocolates.

Woman	Jewellery	Other gift	Boyfriend

No 103

Dominological

A standard set of twenty-eight dominoes has been laid out as shown. One is already in position, to give you a start. Can you draw in the edges of the rest? The check-box is provided as an aid to solving.

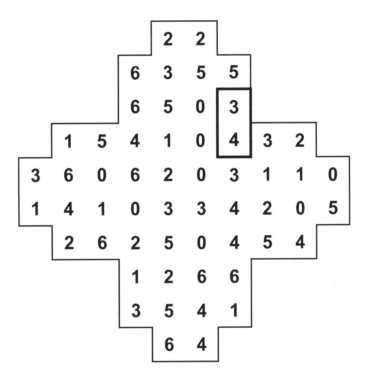

0 – 0		1 – 1		2 – 3		3 – 6	
0 – 1		1 – 2		2 – 4		4 – 4	
0 – 2		1 – 3		2 – 5		4 – 5	
0 – 3		1 – 4		2 – 6		4 – 6	
0 – 4		1 – 5		3 – 3		5 – 5	
0 – 5		1 – 6		3 – 4	✓	5 – 6	
0 – 6		2 – 2		3 – 5		6 – 6	

105

No 104

In The Garden

Five gardening enthusiasts made the most of the good weather last week. What is each gardener's full name, how many hours did each spend digging in his or her garden and on which day did he or she work?

1. Either Lisa or Peter is the person who dug in the garden on Monday, whose surname is either Mower or Trowell.
2. Boris worked in his garden on either Tuesday or Friday and spent either two or three hours digging. Either the person surnamed Forke or the person surnamed Mower worked in the garden on Thursday.
3. Either John or Lisa is the gardener surnamed Raikes, who spent either three or three-and-a-half hours digging on Wednesday.
4. Either Peter or Boris is the person who worked in the garden on Tuesday, whose surname is either Mower or Raikes.
5. The gardener who was digging on Tuesday spent either three-and-a-half or four hours at the task.
6. The person surnamed Spayde spent either two-and-a-half or three hours digging and worked in his or her garden either the day before or the day after whoever spent two hours digging.

	Forke	Mower	Raikes	Spayde	Trowell	2 hours	2½ hours	3 hours	3½ hours	4 hours	Monday	Tuesday	Wednesday	Thursday	Friday
Boris															
Cathy															
John															
Lisa															
Peter															
Monday															
Tuesday															
Wednesday															
Thursday															
Friday															
2 hours															
2½ hours															
3 hours															
3½ hours															
4 hours															

Gardener	Surname	Time digging	Day

Write On

Five would-be authors entered a contest, in which each had to write an essay of between 1,000 and 2,000 words. Hundreds of others entered the competition, however, but the works submitted by these five authors were all ranked in the top fifty, which they didn't consider to be too bad for a first attempt at writing. On which subject did each write, of how many words was each essay and how was it ranked?

1. The essay on the subject of birds of the world wasn't written by Dick. The one of 1,320 words was ranked one place higher than Dick's piece (which contained more words than the essay on the subject of international commerce).

2. The essay on the subject of global travel contained twenty fewer words than the one (not on birds or commerce) submitted by Mike.

3. Lucy's attempt contained more words than the one on the subject of the theatre, which contained twenty more words than the essay ranked in thirty-third position.

4. The essay sent in by Hugh (which contained twenty more words than the one on music) achieved a rating more than two places higher than Fenella's work.

	Birds	Commerce	Music	Theatre	Travel	1,250 words	1,270 words	1,290 words	1,320 words	1,340 words	28th	29th	31st	32nd	33rd
Dick															
Fenella															
Hugh															
Lucy															
Mike															
28th															
29th															
31st															
32nd															
33rd															
1,250 words															
1,270 words															
1,290 words															
1,320 words															
1,340 words															

Contestant	Subject	No of words	Ranking

No 106

Sum Code

In this puzzle, every letter of the alphabet represents a different number from 1 to 26. The sums below will help you to crack the code and if any letter does not appear, its value is that remaining once the rest of the puzzle is complete. The only arithmetical signs used in this puzzle are '–' (minus), 'x' (times) and '+' (plus).

?

A	B	C	D	E	F	G	H	I	J	K	L	M

N	O	P	Q	R	S	T	U	V	W	X	Y	Z

?

?

1	2	3	4	5	6	7	8	9	10	11	12	13

14	15	16	17	18	19	20	21	22	23	24	25	26

?

1. A x A = L + G
2. C x C = U
3. J x H = P + R
4. W – K = N
5. G + L = E + Z
6. S + J = P – Y
7. E x C = Z x B
8. D + U = Z + E

9. G x F = D + U
10. O + X = V
11. S x K = Z + E
12. K x R = M
13. D + U = R + P
14. Q has a higher value than T
15. O has a higher value than I

Back to School

The five couples in this puzzle have all decided to undertake evening classes at the newly-opened college in town. Every husband is in the same class as his wife but, typical of logic puzzles, no two couples are studying the same thing! By studying the clues below, can you discover which couple (husband, wife and surname) is studying each of the listed subjects?

1. Either Kay or Anne is the woman studying accounting, whose surname is either Lind or Ross.

2. Either James or Kelvin is Mr Lind and either James or Thomas is Mr Ross.

3. Either Kay or Doreen is the woman studying computing, whose surname is either Lind or Muckle.

4. Mr & Mrs Packard didn't enrol for the literature classes. Mandy isn't Mrs Packard.

5. Anne's husband is either Stuart or Grant.

6. Kelvin is studying either painting or Spanish and his surname is either Lind or White.

7. Stuart is studying either literature or Spanish.

8. Either Doreen or Gill is Mrs Ross.

	Grant	Kelvin	James	Stuart	Thomas	Anne	Doreen	Gill	Kay	Mandy	Lind	Muckle	Packard	Ross	White
Accounting															
Computing															
Literature															
Painting															
Spanish															
Lind															
Muckle															
Packard															
Ross															
White															
Anne															
Doreen															
Gill															
Kay															
Mandy															

Subject	Husband	Wife	Surname

Brothers

This puzzle concerns five brothers who look nothing like one another. Each was born in a different month, has a different colour hair to that of the other four and is of a different height. Can you determine the details relating to every man?

1. The brother with jet black hair is one inch shorter than Tommy.

2. The brother with blond hair is taller than the one whose birthday is in July.

3. Malcolm's birthday is later in the year than that of a brother who is one inch shorter than the man with ginger hair.

4. The man with ginger hair celebrates his birthday one month earlier in the year than that of the man (not Abraham) with brown hair.

5. The brother born in November is one inch taller than the one with brown hair, but shorter than the brother with ginger hair.

6. Raymond celebrates his birthday one month after that of the man who is one inch shorter than the brother with grey hair.

	July	August	October	November	December	Black	Blond	Brown	Ginger	Grey	5' 7"	5' 8"	5' 9"	5' 11"	6' 0"
Abraham															
Malcolm															
Raymond															
Tommy															
Walter															
5' 7"										
5' 8"										
5' 9"										
5' 11"										
6' 0"										
Black					
Blond					
Brown					
Ginger					
Grey					

Brother	Month of birth	Hair colour	Height

No 109

European Holidays

Each of five couples have taken holidays in Europe this year. Every couple has a different number of children (one couple has no children), so can you discover not only the country in which they holidayed and the type of accommodation in which they stayed, but also how many children (if any) accompanied them on their trip?

1. Mr & Mrs Green, who didn't holiday in Belgium, have more children than Mr & Mrs Gray, who stayed in a guesthouse and who may (or may not!) be the couple who have no children at all.

2. Greece was not the destination chosen by the couple who have three children.

3. A farmhouse holiday was chosen by the family with the most children.

4. The couple who booked a holiday in a caravan didn't visit Greece or Portugal.

5. The couple (not Mr & Mrs Green) who booked a week's stay in a tent on a campsite in southern France aren't Mr & Mrs Black, who have one child.

6. Mr & Mrs Brown holidayed in Italy and have twice as many children as Mr & Mrs White.

	Belgium	France	Greece	Italy	Portugal	Caravan	Farmhouse	Guesthouse	Hotel	Tent	0 children	1 child	2 children	3 children	4 children
Mr & Mrs Black															
Mr & Mrs Brown															
Mr & Mrs Green															
Mr & Mrs Gray															
Mr & Mrs White															
0 children															
1 child															
2 children															
3 children															
4 children															
Caravan															
Farmhouse															
Guesthouse															
Hotel															
Tent															

Couple	Country	Accommodation	No of children

Cold Comfort

According to Mrs Frost, it doesn't seem to matter how cold it gets, there's always a neighbour outside doing something vital, whilst you curl up by the fire, doing no more than feeling guilty! Which neighbour was outside last week on the listed days, what was he doing and what was the temperature at the time?

1. Mr I C Wynde was painting his fence whilst Mrs Frost watched, from the comfort of her very warm lounge.

2. A temperature of -1°C was recorded on the day Mr Shivra worked, which was the day after the temperature fell to -3°C and when Mrs Frost could distinctly hear the sound of firewood being chopped.

3. On Saturday, Mrs Frost saw Mr Sheik washing his car – with cold water!

4. It was two degrees warmer on the day that Mr Hardy mended his shed roof than the recorded temperature on Wednesday of last week.

	Mr Hardy	Mr Shivra	Mr Sheik	Mr Tufnut	Mr Wynde	Chopping firewood	Mending shed roof	Painting fence	Sweeping paths	Washing car	-1°C	-2°C	-3°C	-4°C	-5°C
Tuesday															
Wednesday															
Thursday															
Friday															
Saturday															
-1°C															
-2°C															
-3°C															
-4°C															
-5°C															
Chopping firewood															
Mending roof															
Painting fence															
Sweeping paths															
Washing car															

Day	Neighbour	Activity	Temperature

Simple as A,B,C?

Each of the small squares in the grid below contains either A, B or C. Every row, every column and each of the two long diagonal lines of six squares contains exactly two of each letter. The information in the clues refers only to the squares in that row or column. To help you solve this problem, we've given as many clues as we think you'll need! Can you tell which letter should be placed into each square?

Across:

1. The Bs are somewhere between the Cs.

3. Any three consecutive squares contain three different letters.

4. The Bs are further right than the As.

6. Each C is immediately next to and right of an A.

Down:

2. The Bs are lower than the Cs.

4. One B is immediately next to and above one of the Cs and the other B is immediately next to and below the other C.

6. The As are somewhere between the Bs.

```
      1   2   3   4   5   6
   ┌───┬───┬───┬───┬───┬───┐
 1 │   │   │   │   │   │   │
   ├───┼───┼───┼───┼───┼───┤
 2 │   │   │   │   │   │   │
   ├───┼───┼───┼───┼───┼───┤
 3 │   │   │   │   │   │   │
   ├───┼───┼───┼───┼───┼───┤
 4 │   │   │   │   │   │   │
   ├───┼───┼───┼───┼───┼───┤
 5 │   │   │   │   │   │   │
   ├───┼───┼───┼───┼───┼───┤
 6 │   │   │   │   │   │   │
   └───┴───┴───┴───┴───┴───┘
```

Costume Conundrum

Over the Hallowe'en period, five costumes were hired out to friends, each of whom patronised a different hire shop. Can you discover the name of the shop which hired out each of the listed costumes, together with the time it was collected and the time it was returned the very next day?

1. The costume from Choose Who was returned ten minutes later than the Darth Vader outfit, which didn't come from Katy's Hire.

2. The person who hired a costume earliest was the first to return a costume, although he/she kept it for longer than the person who had hired from the shop called Witching Hour.

3. The witch costume was returned half an hour before the mummy costume.

4. The person who hired the Frankenstein's monster costume returned it ten minutes earlier than the return of the outfit to Katy's Hire. Katy's Hire loaned a costume to someone directly before the visit made to Witching Hour.

5. The costume returned at eleven o'clock to the Party Shop was hired out later than the costume from the Choose Who shop.

	Choose Who	Dressage	Katy's Hire	Party Shop	Witching Hour	10.20am	10.30am	10.50am	11.10am	11.20am	10.30am	11.00am	11.20am	11.30am	11.40am
						Hired out					**Returned**				
Darth Vader															
Dracula															
Frankenstein															
Mummy															
Witch															
Returned 10.30am															
11.00am															
11.20am															
11.30am															
11.40am															
Hired out 10.20am															
10.30am															
10.50am															
11.10am															
11.20am															

Costume	Shop	Hired out	Returned

Construction Conundrum

Cath and Pete are furnishing their new home and, in order to save money, decided to buy five sets of self-assembly furniture. Unfortunately, not all of the screws needed for construction were contained in each box, so they had to provide more. How much did they pay for each item, how many pieces were provided and how many extra screws did they need to use in order to put it together?

1. The kit containing bar stools for the kitchen cost less than $70. It consisted of the highest number of pieces, but didn't need the highest number of extra screws.

2. The item priced at $72 (which needed fourteen extra screws) consisted of one fewer piece than the item which cost $70.

3. There were more pieces contained in the kit used to construct the bed than in the one (not the table kit) where twelve screws were missing.

4. The most expensive kit didn't need the highest number of screws to be provided by the couple.

5. The wardrobe kit had two more pieces than the bookcase kit.

6. The cheapest item required fewer screws to complete than either the wardrobe or the bar stools.

7. No kit required a number of extra screws exactly divisible by the number of pieces it contained.

	$65	$68	$70	$72	$73	6 pieces	7 pieces	8 pieces	9 pieces	10 pieces	12 screws	14 screws	15 screws	20 screws	21 screws
Bar stools															
Bed															
Bookcase															
Table															
Wardrobe															
12 screws										
14 screws										
15 screws										
20 screws										
21 screws										
6 pieces					
7 pieces					
8 pieces					
9 pieces					
10 pieces					

Item	Price	No of pieces	No of extra screws

Split Personalities

Photographs of five famous people were each cut into four pieces (head, body, legs and feet) and then reassembled so that each new picture contains parts of four different personalities. Can you discover the make-up of the new pictures?

1. Kate Winslet's head is now in the same picture as Bob Geldof's legs.

2. Tom Hanks's body (which isn't topped by Liz Hurley's head) is in the same picture as Bob Geldof's feet.

3. Tom Hanks's legs are in a different picture to Bob Geldof's head.

4. Bob Geldof's body isn't topped by Tom Hanks's head.

5. Kate Winslet's legs are now attached to Kylie Minogue's body.

6. Kylie Minogue's legs don't end in Liz Hurley's feet.

		Body					Legs					Feet				
		Bob Geldof	Tom Hanks	Kylie	Liz Hurley	Kate Winslet	Bob Geldof	Tom Hanks	Kylie	Liz Hurley	Kate Winslet	Bob Geldof	Tom Hanks	Kylie	Liz Hurley	Kate Winslet
Head	Bob Geldof															
	Tom Hanks															
	Kylie															
	Liz Hurley															
	Kate Winslet															
Feet	Bob Geldof															
	Tom Hanks															
	Kylie															
	Liz Hurley															
	Kate Winslet															
Legs	Bob Geldof															
	Tom Hanks															
	Kylie															
	Liz Hurley															
	Kate Winslet															

Head	Body	Legs	Feet

Double Orders

Each of the five children in this puzzle had a bowl of cereal for breakfast this morning, together with a drink. When they all returned from school, every child was feeling a little peckish, so had another bowl of cereal (different to that which he or she had eaten in the morning). Can you discover what the different children had for breakfast and as an after-school snack?

1. The child who ate Wheeties for breakfast had a bowl of Krispo after school.

2. Emma wasn't the child who drank coffee in the morning and ate a bowl of Brownies in the afternoon.

3. The child who drank a glass of water with his or her Brownies at breakfast time is either Patrick or Thomas.

4. Emma didn't eat Cococrunch or Crumbler for breakfast.

5. The child who had a glass of milk ate Cococrunch for breakfast, but not Crumbler as an after-school snack.

6. Patrick drank either milk or tea for breakfast.

7. The child who drank coffee didn't eat a bowl of Crumbler for breakfast.

8. Dean (who never drinks coffee) didn't have a bowl of Crumbler for his breakfast.

Child	Breakfast	Drink	After school

Patchwork

Each piece in the patchwork square below is decorated with a letter of the alphabet: A, B, C, D, E, F or G. In each horizontal row, vertical column and long diagonal line of seven smaller pieces there are seven different letters: some are already in place. Can you discover which letter fits in every piece? There is only one correct solution to this puzzle – if you take a wrong path along the way, you won't finish the quilt!

1. The letter in piece 1 is the same as that in piece 42.

2. The letter in piece 13 is the same as that in piece 33.

3. The letter in piece 15 is the same as that in piece 48.

4. The letter in piece 14 is different to that in piece 34.

5. The letter in piece 23 is different to that in piece 31.

6. The letter in piece 28 is different to that in piece 44.

7. The letter in piece 9 is the same as that in piece 45 but different to the letter which is in piece 19.

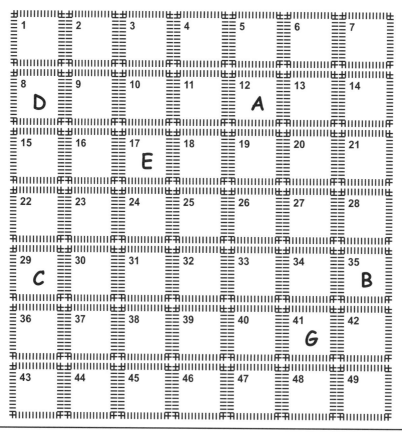

Readers

There being nothing worth watching on TV (as usual!) last night, silence reigned over the Reader family's home, as everyone settled down to read a book. During the course of the evening, each member of the family fetched drinks for everyone, using a marker to keep his or her place in the book being read. What was each reading, what colour is his or her bookmarker and what type of drink did he or she fetch?

1. Jennifer (who didn't get up to make the coffee) has a green bookmarker, unlike the person reading the autobiography.

2. The person who read the western novel used the yellow bookmarker.

3. When it came to Sharon's turn to fetch the drinks, she placed her red bookmarker in the pages of a whodunnit.

4. Arthur got up to make tea for everyone.

5. The person who fetched the lager has a grey bookmarker.

6. Pauline read the biography of a political leader and fetched a glass of home-made lemonade for each person.

	Autobiography	Biography	Romance	Western	Whodunnit	Black	Green	Grey	Red	Yellow	Chocolate	Coffee	Lager	Lemonade	Tea
Arthur															
Jennifer															
Pauline															
Sharon															
Tommy															
Chocolate															
Coffee															
Lager															
Lemonade															
Tea															
Black															
Green															
Grey															
Red															
Yellow															

Family member	Type of book	Bookmarker	Drink fetched

Electrical Switches

At the local electrical goods shop, customers select the goods they wish to purchase and are then given a ticket, which they exchange for the item. However, five customers who shopped there yesterday each received one another's goods. What was each person's ticket number, what did he or she decide to buy and what was each given instead?

1. The holder of ticket number 123 received Stella's iron.

2. The holder of ticket number 126 got whatever Sam had paid for, which wasn't the coffee percolator or the kettle.

3. Ian's ticket number was one lower than that held by the person who was looking forward to receiving the coffee percolator, but who actually got whatever Pippa had purchased.

4. The kettle should have been given to the person with ticket number 124, however the holder of this ticket was presented with an electric drill.

	Ticket 123	Ticket 124	Ticket 125	Ticket 126	Ticket 127	Alarm clock	Drill	Iron	Kettle	Percolator	Alarm clock	Drill	Iron	Kettle	Percolator
						Bought					**Received**				
Cordelia															
Ian															
Pippa															
Sam															
Stella															
Received Alarm clock															
Drill															
Iron															
Kettle															
Percolator															
Bought Alarm clock															
Drill															
Iron															
Kettle															
Percolator															

Customer	Ticket No	Bought	Received

Bottling Out

Each of the five women in this puzzle has been shopping for a party she's holding this Saturday night. However, they all got rather carried away, buying far more than they intended, as a result of which they're having trouble carrying the goods away! How many bottles of beer, spirits and wine has each woman purchased?

1. Nancy has bought two more bottles of wine than Mary, who has bought more bottles of spirits than Fiona, who has bought more bottles of beer than June.

2. June has bought more bottles of wine than Amanda, who has bought more bottles of spirits than Nancy, who has bought more bottles of beer than Mary.

3. Amanda has bought four more bottles of wine than Nancy, who has bought six more bottles of spirits than Mary, who has bought ten more bottles of beer than Fiona.

	Beer					Spirits					Wine				
	15 bottles	20 bottles	25 bottles	30 bottles	35 bottles	2 bottles	4 bottles	6 bottles	10 bottles	12 bottles	5 bottles	7 bottles	9 bottles	13 bottles	15 bottles
Amanda															
Fiona															
June															
Mary															
Nancy															
Wine 5 bottles															
Wine 7 bottles															
Wine 9 bottles															
Wine 13 bottles															
Wine 15 bottles															
Spirits 2 bottles															
Spirits 4 bottles															
Spirits 6 bottles															
Spirits 10 bottles															
Spirits 12 bottles															

Shopper	Beer	Spirits	Wine

Weekend Away

Five travel advisors working at a newly-opened travel agency sold their first customers short breaks to five different European cities. Can you discover who served each client, together with the destination and the cost of the holiday?

1. The weekend break in Madrid was the cheapest holiday.

2. Mr Bishop (who wasn't served by Richard) bought the most expensive package.

3. Mrs Carter spent £100 more than Mr Ford.

4. The holiday which Martina sold to Mr Wilton cost more than Miss Anderson's break in Paris, which wasn't sold to her by Dennis.

5. Louise arranged a weekend in Rome for one customer.

6. Richard's client bought a break in Stockholm.

	Dennis	Gina	Louise	Martina	Richard	Lisbon	Madrid	Paris	Rome	Stockholm	£199	£205	£249	£299	£305
Miss Anderson															
Mr Bishop															
Mrs Carter															
Mr Ford															
Mr Wilton															
£199															
£205															
£249															
£299															
£305															
Lisbon															
Madrid															
Paris															
Rome															
Stockholm															

6. Richard's client bought a break in Stockholm.

Customer	Advisor	City	Cost

Little Wagers

Each of five little boys decided to race his 'pet of the moment' against the other four boys' pets. Can you discover what 'pet' each has, together with its name and the position in which it finished the race?

1. George raced his snail (can one race a snail?), which didn't finish in fourth position.

2. Neither the snail nor the garden slug is called Horace.

3. Timmy has named his 'pet' Nora: no-one knows why.

4. One of the five boys has a little black ant by the name of Digger. ,

5. Colin's 'pet' has the name Bilbo. Bilbo finished one place ahead of Speedy.

6. Joe's 'pet' (not an ant) came second in the race; only just being beaten by the ladybird.

	Ant	Caterpillar	Ladybird	Slug	Snail	Bilbo	Digger	Horace	Nora	Speedy	First	Second	Third	Fourth	Fifth
Colin															
George															
Joe															
Timmy															
Will															
First															
Second															
Third															
Fourth															
Fifth															
Bilbo															
Digger															
Horace															
Nora															
Speedy															

Boy	'Pet'	Pet's name	Position

Treading the Boards

Five actors who are cousins each have rôles in plays at different theatres. Even though the scripts are remarkably similar, every play differs from the others in that it has a different number of performances per week. Perhaps because they are all so similar, these plays are not doing very well and all five cousins have taken on part-time work to supplement their incomes. Can you discover the facts?

1. The cousin in the play with the highest number of performances per week treads the boards of the Gaeity Theatre.

2. John isn't the man who appears in eight shows per week (who has a part-time job as a shoe salesman). Neither Jeff (who works as a jobbing gardener between shows) nor John is the man at the Alhambra Theatre.

3. The man who works as a delivery driver performs once more per week than the cousin appearing at the Old Mill Theatre.

4. Jason's cousin has a part-time job as a waiter and gives two more performances every week than Jack, who is currently appearing at the Albion Theatre.

	4 performances	5 performances	6 performances	8 performances	9 performances	Jack	Jason	Jeff	John	Jude	Chef	Driver	Gardener	Salesman	Waiter
Albion Theatre															
Alhambra Theatre															
Criterion Theatre															
Gaeity Theatre															
Old Mill Theatre															
Chef															
Driver															
Gardener															
Salesman															
Waiter															
Jack															
Jason															
Jeff															
John															
Jude															

Theatre	Performances	Actor	Part-time job

No 123

At the Sales

Stacey's Department Store recently held a stock-clearance sale, with reductions of up to fifty per cent on some of its items. Every one of the shoppers in this puzzle took advantage of the sale to purchase something he or she wouldn't otherwise have been able to afford. Which department did each buy from, on which floor of the Stacey's building is it situated and what percentage saving did each shopper make?

1. The kitchenware department is on the second floor, above the floor where Jill saved ten per cent more than Conrad's saving.

2. The department on the fifth floor had the highest percentage reduction on its prices and the menswear department (which isn't on the third floor) had the lowest percentage reduction on its prices.

3. Hannah bought household linen. Sue shopped on the fourth floor of Stacey's.

4. The department on the third floor was patronised by Conrad.

5. Robert made a saving of forty per cent, which was ten per cent more than the reduction on the goods in the stationery department.

	Kitchenware	Leatherwear	Menswear	Linen	Stationery	First floor	Second floor	Third floor	Fourth floor	Fifth floor	10%	20%	30%	40%	50%
Conrad															
Hannah															
Jill															
Robert															
Sue															
10%															
20%															
30%															
40%															
50%															
First floor															
Second floor															
Third floor															
Fourth floor															
Fifth floor															

Shopper	Department	Floor	Percentage

Dancing Marathon

Five couples entered this year's Dancing Marathon, organised in aid of charity. Each couple consists of a man and woman of the same age and every partnership danced non-stop for a different length of time, starting at noon. Can you match the partners and their ages and say for how long they managed to stay on the floor?

1. Keith didn't dance with Marilyn, who is two years younger than Lola and her partner.

2. Elaine danced with Des. Elaine and Des are younger than Alison and her partner.

3. Alison danced for fifteen minutes longer than Elaine and Des.

4. Shane didn't dance with either Marilyn or Barbara.

5. The man aged 23 had to stop (due to exhaustion) before Morgan left the floor.

6. Barbara and her partner are younger than the couple who danced non-stop for four and a quarter hours, who are one year younger than Keith and his partner.

7. Ritchie and his partner (not Barbara) danced for longer than four hours.

	Alison	Barbara	Elaine	Lola	Marilyn	22	23	24	25	26	3 hrs 15 mins	3 hrs 45 mins	4 hours	4 hrs 15 mins	4 hrs 30 mins
Des															
Keith															
Morgan															
Ritchie															
Shane															
3 hrs 15 mins															
3 hrs 45 mins															
4 hours															
4 hrs 15 mins															
4 hrs 30 mins															
22															
23															
24															
25															
26															

Man	Woman	Age	Time

Playing Card Bingo

Every Thursday night, the local Darby & Joan Club holds prize competitions, one of which is Playing Card Bingo. This week's winning card is shown below. Can you determine the order in which the cards on it were called?

Values of cards are as shown and ace=1, jack=11, queen=12 and king=13.

1. The card called second is of a different suit to the card called eleventh, which has a value half that of the card called eighth. The cards called eighth and eleventh are not in the same horizontal row as one another.
2. The card called thirteenth is directly next to and right of the card called seventh, which is of the same suit as the card called sixth.
3. Card G is called either directly before or directly after card F.
4. The card called tenth is directly next to and right of the card called ninth, which is either directly above or directly below a card with a value half that of the first card to be called. Card H was not called two cards before card L.
5. The card called fourth isn't next to the one called twelfth, which is directly next to and left of that called third, which is either directly above or directly below a card with a value one third that of the card called last.

1st	2nd	3rd	4th	5th
6th	7th	8th	9th	10th
11th	12th	13th	14th	15th

LEFT ← RIGHT →

	A		B	C		D	E	F		G
	6 ♠		2 ♦	4 ♣		A ♠	2 ♥	5 ♥		K ♦
	3 ♣	6 ♦	Q ♣		J ♥	5 ♣		8 ♠	9 ♣	10 ♦
	H	I	J		K	L		M	N	O

127

Scoring Points

Five children sat eating their sandwiches together at lunchtime today, all discussing how well they had done in different tests that morning. Every test had a possible top mark of 75 points, so (as you can see from the grid below) each had indeed excelled. Can you discover not only their respective marks, but the subject of the test in which each took part and the filling each child had in his or her sandwich?

1 The child who scored seventy points isn't Shelley, who had chicken sandwiches for lunch.

2. Shelley scored more points than the child with tuna sandwiches had achieved in the chemistry test.

3. Rose took the history test. The child who took the physics test scored more points than the child who sat the spelling test, who achieved a higher number of points than the child who undertook the maths test.

4. The child with egg and cress sandwiches scored five fewer points than Danny, who didn't have tomato in his sandwiches.

5. The child with salmon sandwiches achieved five fewer points than Bob, who scored five fewer points than Marc.

	55 points	60 points	65 points	68 points	70 points	Chemistry	History	Maths	Physics	Spelling	Chicken	Egg/cress	Salmon	Tomato	Tuna
Bob															
Danny															
Marc															
Rose															
Shelley															
Chicken															
Egg/cress															
Salmon															
Tomato															
Tuna															
Chemistry															
History															
Maths															
Physics															
Spelling															

Child	No of points	Test subject	Sandwich filling

Picture Postcards

The first five customers in the newsagency this morning each bought a postcard with a view of a local scene, together with one other item. Can you discover not only the view on the postcard bought by each person, plus the other item each purchased, but also the order in which each was served by the newsagent?

1. The customer served immediately before Catherine bought a newspaper and the picture postcard of the highest mountain in the region.

2. The person served immediately after Catherine bought a street-map of the city.

3. The beach scene postcard was purchased by a woman. One man bought a comic for his son.

4. Roger was served fourth. He didn't buy the postcard with a picture of the castle.

5. Brian, who bought a notepad, wasn't served last.

6. The person who was served last bought the postcard with a picture of the lake.

	Beach	Castle	Lake	Mountain	Park	Comic	Magazine	Map	Newspaper	Notepad	First	Second	Third	Fourth	Fifth
Brian															
Catherine															
Edna															
Roger															
Stanley															
First															
Second															
Third															
Fourth															
Fifth															
Comic															
Magazine															
Map															
Newspaper															
Notepad															

Customer	Postcard	Other item	Order served

No 128

Figure It Out

Each of the thirty-six squares in the grid is filled with a single digit number from 1 to 9 – each of those numbers being used four times. Use the clues to complete the square, bearing in mind that the same number must not appear in two adjacent (touching) squares in any row across or column down. If the same number is used more than once in any row across or column down it is stated in the relevant clue.

Across:

1. No 5.

2. Two 8s.

3. Total thirty-nine.

4. Total twenty-one.

5. Two 2s. No 1. No 3.

6. Consecutive numbers placed in descending order.

Down:

1. Two 1s. No 2. No 3. No 8.

2. Two 5s. Two 6s. No 3.

3. Two 7s, neither of which is immediately next to and above a 4.

4. Consecutive numbers placed in order.

5. Two 9s. No 4. No 5.

6. Two 1s.

	1	2	3	4	5	6
1						
2						
3						
4						
5						
6						

Apple Hunting

Sam Shade is a New York City Private Investigator. Over the course of five consecutive days he was looking for different men, spending each day in a different part of the Big Apple, where each was known to be living. From the clues, can you work out where Sam went each day, who he was looking for and why he'd been hired to find the man?

1. Ray Schultz is a notorious jewel thief from whom Sam was trying (successfully, as it turned out) to recover a stolen necklace.

2. On Friday, Sam was working in Greenwich Village. Sam tried to trace a missing person on Saturday, but not in Brooklyn.

3. Sam found the bigamist with his so-called wife living at a de luxe apartment in Manhattan.

4. Sam visited Brooklyn the day before he went looking for Harry Knorr. The search for Harry Knorr was either two days before or two days after he tried to trace Arnie Meyer.

5. On Monday he went after Clyde Warner, but not in Harlem.

6. Sam found Dean Bradley in the South Bronx later than he located the forger, who isn't Arnie Meyer.

	Brooklyn	Greenwich	Harlem	Manhattan	South Bronx	Dean Bradley	Harry Knorr	Arnie Meyer	Ray Schultz	Clyde Warner	Bigamy	Blackmail	Forgery	Missing person	Theft
Thursday															
Friday															
Saturday															
Sunday															
Monday															
Bigamy															
Blackmail															
Forgery															
Missing person															
Theft															
Dean Bradley															
Harry Knorr															
Arnie Meyer															
Ray Schultz															
Clyde Warner															

Day	Area	Looking for	Reason

From Service to Service

Many great estates of England suffered the absence of men during World War II and although some did return to their former occupations, a large number did not. The Buckham Estate in Dorset saw five key employees leave, and only one returned to his job when hostilities ceased. What was each man's former occupation, with which branch of the services did he enlist and what was his rank when he left?

1. Len Foster never worked as a gardener on the Buckham estate.

2. The former chauffeur achieved the rank of Corporal just months prior to being demobbed in 1945. Jim Turner's wartime service was with the 17th/21st Lancers.

3. The one-time Royal Navy Petty Officer isn't Alf Daley. After the war, Alf Daley returned to his role of handyman at the Buckham estate, where he worked until he retired at the age of sixty-five. The former footman became a Royal Air Force Flight Sergeant.

4. Percy Abbott, once a Royal Marine Commando, isn't the former butler whose wartime rank was Sergeant.

	Butler	Chauffeur	Footman	Gardener	Handyman	Parachute Regt	RAF	Royal Marines	Royal Navy	17th/21st Lancers	Corporal	Flt Sergeant	Lieutenant	Petty Officer	Sergeant
Percy Abbott															
Alf Daley															
Len Foster															
Cyril Moone															
Jim Turner															
Corporal															
Flt Sergeant															
Lieutenant															
Petty Officer															
Sergeant															
Parachute Regt															
RAF															
Royal Marines															
Royal Navy															
17th/21st Lancers															

Name	Position	Service	Rank

Difficulty Sleeping

Five people staying overnight with Sir George Cross found it hard to sleep (the house is old and everything creaks ominously). After going to bed, each came back down into the library, helped themselves to liberal quantities of Sir George's alcohol and borrowed one of his books. Which guest borrowed each book, what did he or she drink and at what time had he or she originally retired for the night?

1. The person who asked for a large brandy borrowed the science fiction book and had retired to bed later than Raymond, but earlier than the one who thought a tot (or three) of rum would help bring on sleep.

2. Judith who borrowed the romance retired for the night half-an-hour later than the guest who borrowed the history book (who asked for neither the whisky nor the sherry).

3. The guest who drank whisky went to bed one hour before the one who borrowed the biography of George's great-grandfather. The latter guest also went to bed later than both Lou and Lavinia (neither of whom drank whisky).

4. Lavinia wasn't the first to retire for the night.

	Lou	Judith	Kenneth	Lavinia	Raymond	Brandy	Sherry	Port	Rum	Whisky	10.30pm	10.45pm	11.00pm	11.30pm	11.45pm
Biography															
History															
Mystery															
Romance															
Science fiction															
10.30pm										
10.45pm										
11.00pm										
11.30pm										
11.45pm										
Brandy					
Sherry					
Port					
Rum					
Whisky					

Book	Guest	Drink	Bed time

Wannabes

Five friends recently met up after some considerable time, at their former school's reunion party. Each spoke of their time at the school and the aspirations he or she had for life after school, but it's a tough world and none actually ended up in the job he or she had planned to do. What are their full names, what had each hoped to be and what is his or her current occupation?

1. Andrew Donkin's friend (who yearned to be a film star) is now a nurse working at the local hospital.

2. The former pupil surnamed Warburton isn't the one who dreamt of becoming an astronaut or a film star.

3. Leonard (whose surname isn't Fisher) enjoys his job as a window cleaner rather more than he thinks he would have enjoyed the job he originally planned. Neither he nor Cheryl had originally planned to become a lawyer.

4. Neither the person who wanted to be a chemist nor the one who planned to be a lawyer is currently working as a train driver.

5. Leonard had no aspirations to become a chemist. Neither Elizabeth nor Gordon is the person surnamed Unwin, who works as a clerk.

6. Andrew (who never wanted to be an astronaut) isn't a teacher. Elizabeth's surname isn't Fisher.

	Donkin	Fisher	Klein	Unwin	Warburton	Astronaut	Chemist	Film star	Lawyer	Surgeon	Clerk	Nurse	Teacher	Train driver	Window clnr
Andrew															
Cheryl															
Elizabeth															
Gordon															
Leonard															
Clerk															
Nurse															
Teacher															
Train driver															
Window cleaner															
Astronaut															
Chemist															
Film star															
Lawyer															
Surgeon															

Former pupil	Surname	Wanted to be	Became

Sum Code

In this puzzle, every letter of the alphabet represents a different number from 1 to 26. The sums below will help you to crack the code and if any letter does not appear, its value is that remaining once the rest of the puzzle is complete. The only arithmetical signs used in this puzzle are '–' (minus), 'x' (times) and '+' (plus).

?

A	B	C	D	E	F	G	H	I	J	K	L	M

N	O	P	Q	R	S	T	U	V	W	X	Y	Z

?

1	2	3	4	5	6	7	8	9	10	11	12	13

14	15	16	17	18	19	20	21	22	23	24	25	26

?

1. I x Y = T

2. H + P = D

3. R x Y = O

4. G x I = B

5. F x U = N

6. G x Y = C

7. F x J = P

8. Q x Y = K

9. F x Q = M

10. F x G = A

11. F x Y = R

12. U x Y = Z

13. F x W = X

14. E x 3 = (S x U) + 3

15. L has a higher value than V

Sunday Sport

Every Sunday afternoon, five women leave their homes to catch the bus to the sports centre in town, where each participates in a different activity. What is each woman's full name, what is the number of the house at which she lives (see map below) and which sport does she play?

1. Teri lives further south than Odette (who isn't Ms Wild) and further west than the woman who plays softball (who is neither Trina nor Odette).

2. Marianne doesn't live at number 2. Trina's house number is one lower than that of the woman (not Mrs King or Ms Wild) who plays table tennis.

3. Gayle Portman (who doesn't live at number 6) plays hockey. Miss Johnson (who lives at number 5) doesn't play badminton.

	Johnson	King	Lessing	Portman	Wild	No 1	No 2	No 5	No 6	No 9	Badminton	Hockey	Netball	Softball	Table tennis
Gayle															
Marianne															
Odette															
Teri															
Trina															
Badminton															
Hockey															
Netball															
Softball															
Table tennis															
No 1															
No 2															
No 5															
No 6															
No 9															

N
W E
S

1
5
6 2 9

Forename	Surname	House No	Sport

Unwanted Gifts

Isn't it amazing how many free product samples arrive through the letterbox these days? The people who appear in this puzzle were somewhat inundated over the first three days of last week, receiving a record-breaking number of samples of products they never use and never will use… Can you discover precisely how many free samples were posted through each person's letterbox on each of the given days?

1. The person who received one more free sample than Corinne on Monday also received one fewer free sample than Thelma on Tuesday.

2. On Tuesday, Nellie received more samples than Kevin (who didn't get one more than Thelma).

3. Kevin received fewer samples on Wednesday than on either Monday or Tuesday.

4. Whoever received one more free sample than Nellie on Monday also received one more free sample than Jack on Tuesday.

5. The person (not Thelma) who received one more free sample than Corinne on Monday also received one more free sample than Nellie on Wednesday.

6. Jack didn't get exactly thirteen free samples on Monday or fifteen free samples on Wednesday.

7. The person who received one more free sample than Corinne on Wednesday wasn't Thelma.

	Monday 12 13 16 17 19	Tuesday 12 13 14 15 16	Wednesday 13 14 15 17 18
Corinne			
Jack			
Kevin			
Nellie			
Thelma			
Wednesday 13			
Wednesday 14			
Wednesday 15			
Wednesday 17			
Wednesday 18			
Tuesday 12			
Tuesday 13			
Tuesday 14			
Tuesday 15			
Tuesday 16			

Recipient	Monday	Tuesday	Wednesday

Dominological

A standard set of twenty-eight dominoes has been laid out as shown. One is already in position, to give you a start. Can you draw in the edges of the rest? The check-box is provided as an aid to solving.

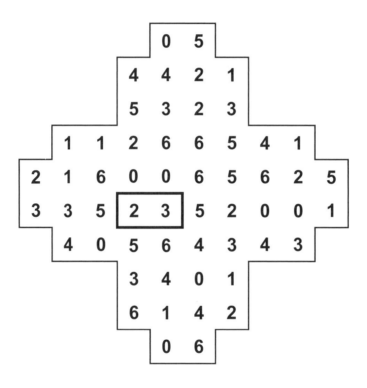

0 - 0		1 - 1		2 - 3	✓	3 - 6	
0 - 1		1 - 2		2 - 4		4 - 4	
0 - 2		1 - 3		2 - 5		4 - 5	
0 - 3		1 - 4		2 - 6		4 - 6	
0 - 4		1 - 5		3 - 3		5 - 5	
0 - 5		1 - 6		3 - 4		5 - 6	
0 - 6		2 - 2		3 - 5		6 - 6	

Happy Anniversary

When five men arrive home from work this evening, they're in for a nice surprise! Not only have their wives bought them presents to celebrate their wedding anniversary, but each woman has arranged a special evening out. Can you discover the name of each woman's husband, together with the gift and surprise she has in store for him?

1. Of the five women: one is Meryl; one is married to Ron; one (not Ruth) has bought her husband a new briefcase; one has bought tickets to a dance; and one is Leslie's wife, who will be taking him to the casino.

2. Of the five women: one is Ruth; one is Bill's wife; one has bought a set of golf clubs for her husband; one is Diane (who will be giving her husband a pair of gold cuff-links); and one is taking her husband to the theatre to see a play starring his favourite actress.

3. Of the five women: one is Florence; one is married to Geoff; one has bought her husband a new jumper; one is taking her husband to the cinema to see a film; one is Ruth (who is taking her husband to his favourite restaurant for dinner).

Grid columns: Bill, Geoff, Leslie, Oliver, Ron, Briefcase, Cuff-links, Golf clubs, Jumper, Watch, Casino, Cinema, Dance, Restaurant, Theatre

Grid rows: Diane, Florence, Meryl, Ruth, Shirley, Casino, Cinema, Dance, Restaurant, Theatre, Briefcase, Cuff-links, Golf clubs, Jumper, Watch

Woman	Husband	Gift	Evening

Minor Accidents

Last Saturday afternoon saw an unusually quiet period in the casualty department at the local hospital, with no sporting injuries arriving at all. In fact, no more than five people arrived for treatment and they were pleasantly surprised to be seen and helped immediately. What was each person's problem, which doctor treated each and at what time?

1. The patient who had occasioned a sprained wrist whilst rolling pastry arrived for treatment fifteen minutes later than Caroline, who wasn't seen by Dr Gedwell.

2. One of Freddy's big toes was gently relieved of a deeply embedded splinter, much to his obvious relief!

3. Dr Stitchett treated the patient who arrived in casualty half-an-hour earlier than the one who had an eye injury.

4. The patient with a broken finger arrived in casualty fifteen minutes later than Rosemary, who had a minor cut on her arm.

5. Dr Makebetter treated the patient who arrived in casualty half-an-hour earlier than Edward.

6. It was so quiet that Dr Plarster went home at three o'clock to catch up on some sleep, so that he'd be alert and ready for the night ahead.

	Broken finger	Eye injury	Cut on arm	Splinter	Sprained wrist	Dr Kurem	Dr Makebetter	Dr Plarster	Dr Stitchett	Dr Gedwell	2.15 pm	2.30 pm	2.45 pm	3.15 pm	3.30 pm
Caroline															
Edward															
Freddy															
Rosemary															
Simon															
2.15 pm															
2.30 pm															
2.45 pm															
3.15 pm															
3.30 pm															
Dr Kurem															
Dr Makebetter															
Dr Plarster															
Dr Stitchett															
Dr Gedwell															

Patient	Problem	Doctor	Time

Card Sharp

What is the face value and suit of each of the cards shown below? All twelve cards used below are of different values and together they total 78. Values of the cards are as per their numbers and ace=1, jack=11, queen=12 and king=13. No card is horizontally or vertically next to another of the same colour and there are four different suits in each horizontal row and three different suits in each vertical column.

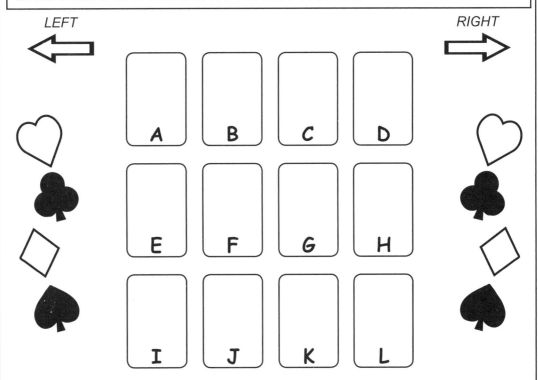

1. Card H is of a different suit to card I, which has a value two lower than that of card K, which has a value two lower than that of card G.

2. Card C has a value two higher than that of card G, but a value two lower than that of card B. Card B has a value two lower than that of card A.

3. Card J is of a different suit to card G, which has a lower value than that of card H.

4. The three of hearts is directly next to and below the seven of clubs, which is next to the nine. The ace isn't directly above the jack.

No 140

Keep on Running

Undeterred by the searing heat of a summer's day, the five women you see in the picture below are out training for the forthcoming Puzzleton Marathon, in which each hopes to take part. Every woman is wearing a differently coloured vest (if we showed the colours in the picture below, it would spoil the puzzle!) and your task is to determine each one's age, position and vest colour.

1. The woman who is fourth is one year younger than the woman in the lead.

2. Victoria is one year younger than the woman in the green vest.

3. Jill isn't the woman wearing the blue vest. Nor is Jill the woman in the pink vest, who is one year older than Rachel, who is one year older than the woman in third place.

4. The youngest runner is Samantha, whose vest isn't yellow.

5. The woman aged nineteen is one place further ahead than Josie, who is one year younger than the woman in the blue vest.

	17 years old	18 years old	19 years old	20 years old	21 years old	1st	2nd	3rd	4th	5th	Blue	Green	Pink	Red	Yellow
Jill															
Josie															
Rachel															
Samantha															
Victoria															
Blue										
Green										
Pink										
Red										
Yellow										
1st					
2nd					
3rd					
4th					
5th					

5th 4th 3rd 2nd 1st

Runner	Age	Position	Vest colour

Park & Read

Five people are sat in the local park at lunchtime, each eating a sandwich and reading something before returning to work in the shopping centre. Can you discover in which different area of the park each sat, together with what he or she was reading and the shop in which he or she works?

1. Alistair (who doesn't work at Tesbury's) sat beside the boating lake during his lunchtime break.

2. The employee who works at the rather unimaginatively-named Dress Shop read the magazine. Stephanie (who didn't read the magazine) chose to sit in the rose garden at lunchtime.

3. Felix almost read his newspaper completely during his lunch break.

4. The employee who read a tour brochure dreamt of foreign travel whilst sitting beside the bowling green.

5. Ginny sat in a deck-chair overlooking the park's main lawn and the Dibleigh's employee sat beside the fish pond.

6. Stephanie wasn't the person reading the trade journal, who works in Tesbury's. Nor does Stephanie work at Falstaff's.

	Boating lake	Bowling green	Fish pond	Main lawn	Rose garden	Magazine	Newspaper	Novel	Tour brochure	Trade journal	Cotter & Co	Dibleigh's	Dress Shop	Falstaff's	Tesbury's
Alistair															
Felix															
Ginny															
Nina															
Stephanie															
Cotter & Co															
Dibleigh's															
Dress Shop															
Falstaff's															
Tesbury's															
Magazine															
Newspaper															
Novel															
Tour brochure															
Trade journal															

Reader	Area	Reading	Shop

Watch Out

Mona's TV has broken down and she can't get it repaired in time to watch her five favourite programmes this evening. However, she does have neighbours, each of whom religiously watches one of the programmes, so has arranged to visit them this evening, going from one house to the next! Can you discover the programme she'll view at each neighbour's house, together with the channel and time of transmission?

1. *News Talk* isn't on Channel 6, nor does Pam ever watch the Channel 1 programme. The one Mona will see at Pam's house is broadcast earlier in the evening than both the programme on Channel 4 and *News Talk*.

2. The programme on Channel 9 starts half-an-hour later than that on Channel 2.

3. *In The Garden* starts earlier than both the programme Mona will watch at John's house and that transmitted on Channel 6.

4. Neither Julia nor Kathy ever watches *Cook with Joe*.

5. *Sportsworld* on Channel 1 starts earlier than either the one Mona will see at Julia's house or the one she'll watch with Kathy.

6. *Nature Today* is broadcast later (but not half-an-hour later) than the programme Mona will see at Julia's house.

	Cook With Joe	In The Garden	News Talk	Nature Today	Sportsworld	Channel 1	Channel 2	Channel 4	Channel 6	Channel 9	7.00pm	8.00pm	8.30pm	9.00pm	10.00pm
John															
Julia															
Kathy															
Owen															
Pam															
7.00pm															
8.00pm															
8.30pm															
9.00pm															
10.00pm															
Channel 1															
Channel 2															
Channel 4															
Channel 6															
Channel 9															

Neighbour	Programme	Channel	Time

Simple as A,B,C?

Each of the small squares in the grid below contains either A, B or C. Every row, every column and each of the two long diagonal lines of six squares contains exactly two of each letter. The information in the clues refers only to the squares in that row or column. To help you solve this problem, we've given as many clues as we think you'll need! Can you tell which letter should be placed into each square?

Across:

1. The Cs are somewhere between the As.

2. The Bs are somewhere between the Cs.

3. Each C is immediately next to and left of an A.

4. The As are further right than the Bs.

5. The As are further right than the Cs.

Down:

1. The Bs are higher than the Cs.

2. The As are higher than the Cs.

5. The As are somewhere between the Bs.

6. The Bs are somewhere between the Cs.

	1	2	3	4	5	6
1						
2						
3						
4						
5						
6						

The Stamp Collectors

Each of these five people collect postage stamps from mainly one country, as well as stamps which cover one particular theme and come from any and all other countries of the world. Can you discover not only their different interests relating to country and theme, but also the total number of stamps each has acquired to date?

1. Harvey has collected neither the fewest nor the most stamps. Neither the person (not Glen) who has the fewest stamps nor the one with 1,090 stamps collects those on the theme of inventions (which aren't in the same album as the stamps from the USA).

2. Neither the person (not Miranda) who collects the fish stamps nor the one who collects those of flowers has a total of either 1,090 or 2,633 stamps. Miranda (who doesn't collect stamps themed on inventions) hasn't 582 or 1,090 stamps in her album.

4. Charlotte doesn't collect Belgian stamps. The person with 2,633 stamps (who doesn't collect inventions or birds themes) has no stamps from Great Britain or the USA.

5. The stamps themed on birds aren't collected by a man. The people who specialise in the stamps from the USA and New Zealand don't also collect stamps on the theme of birds.

6. Glen doesn't collect stamps from Great Britain or New Zealand. The collector (not Charlotte) of British stamps isn't interested in flowers or inventions. Whoever does collect these two themes hasn't a total of 745 stamps.

	Australia	Belgium	Great Britain	New Zealand	USA	Birds	Fish	Flowers	Inventions	Transport	582 stamps	745 stamps	1,090 stamps	2,633 stamps	3,250 stamps
Anthony															
Charlotte															
Glen															
Harvey															
Miranda															
582 stamps											
745 stamps											
1,090 stamps											
2,633 stamps											
3,250 stamps											
Birds						
Fish						
Flowers						
Inventions						
Transport						

Collector	Country	Theme	No of stamps

Roll On

At Roll On Wallpapers, there were five people waiting patiently at the check-out within thirty minutes of the cashier opening the till for trading this morning. Each purchased a quantity of wallpaper in order to decorate his or her lounge. Can you discover the name of each person in the queue, together with the pattern and number of rolls he or she purchased?

1. The customer who bought the wallpaper with random zigzag markings bought one fewer roll than the person (not Patience) who bought the paper with wavy lines.

2. Nicholas bought one more roll than (and was served immediately before) Randolph, who purchased the floral patterned paper for his lounge.

3. The person who bought the striped wallpaper with which to decorate his or her lounge wasn't the last in the queue.

4. The customer who bought three rolls of wallpaper was served earlier than the person who bought the highest number of rolls.

5. Trevor was served immediately before (and bought one fewer roll of wallpaper than) the customer who bought the wallpaper with a polka dot pattern. The latter person wasn't Patience.

	Jocelyn	Nicholas	Patience	Randolph	Trevor	Floral	Polka dots	Stripes	Wavy	Zigzag	3 rolls	4 rolls	5 rolls	6 rolls	8 rolls
First															
Second															
Third															
Fourth															
Fifth															
3 rolls															
4 rolls															
5 rolls															
6 rolls															
8 rolls															
Floral															
Polka dots															
Stripes															
Wavy															
Zigzag															

Order in queue	Customer	Pattern	No of rolls

Patchwork

Each piece in the patchwork square below is decorated with a letter of the alphabet: A, B, C, D, E, F or G. In each horizontal row, vertical column and long diagonal line of seven smaller pieces there are seven different letters: some are already in place. Can you discover which letter fits in every piece? There is only one correct solution to this puzzle – if you take a wrong path along the way, you won't finish the quilt!

1. The letter in piece 2 is the same as the letter in piece 18.

2. The letter in piece 4 is the same as the letter in piece 36.

3. The letter in piece 21 is the same as the letter in piece 25.

4. Piece 6 contains a different letter to the letter in piece 17.

5. Piece 33 contains a different letter to the letter in piece 43.

6. Neither piece 1 nor piece 49 contains the same letter as that in piece 32.

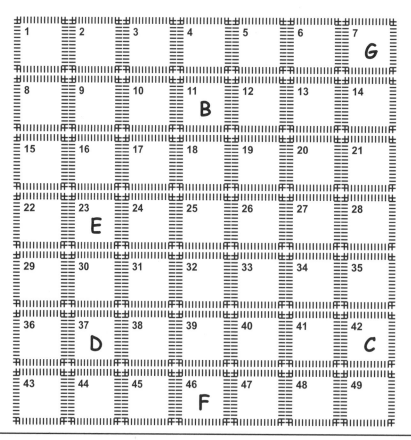

Cross-communications

Various letters crossed in the post last week, as five girls who have been penfriends for a number of years each wrote to one of the other four. Anyone may have written to the girl who wrote to her, or she may have written to one of the others: there's no telling, unless you solve the puzzle! Who wrote to whom, on which day was the letter posted and in which different country does each girl live?

1. The girl who lives in Spain posted her letter to a penfriend two days after Laurel posted a letter.

2. Laurel posted her letter three days earlier than a letter was posted by Caitlin.

3. The letter to Caitlin was posted later in the week than the one from the girl in Gibraltar.

4. Morag didn't post a letter on Saturday.

5. Sheree posted her letter in Hong Kong, doing so earlier in the week than a letter was posted by Morag, who lives in Morocco.

6. The girl who lives in Canada sent her letter the day after the one addressed to Laurel was posted; and the letter to Marie was posted the day after Marie sent a letter.

	Wrote to										Writer's country				
	Caitlin	Laurel	Marie	Morag	Sheree	Tuesday	Wednesday	Thursday	Friday	Saturday	Canada	Gibraltar	H Kong	Morocco	Spain
Caitlin															
Laurel															
Marie															
Morag															
Sheree															
Canada															
Gibraltar															
Hong Kong															
Morocco															
Spain															
Tuesday															
Wednesday															
Thursday															
Friday															
Saturday															

Penfriend	Wrote to	Day posted	Writer's country

Hats Off to Them!

The women who appear in this puzzle have all knitted bobble hats for their sons. Each has used three different colours, from wool left over from previous knitting projects. Can you determine the main colour of the hat every woman has knitted, together with those of its bobble and fold-back, stocking-stitch brim?

1. None of the women who used navy blue wool knitted the hat with a red bobble.

2. The hat with the cream bobble hasn't a yellow brim. The woman who used brown wool made the green bobble, but didn't give her creation a yellow brim.

3. The colours used by Lyndsey are all different to those chosen by Noelle for her son's hat. Noelle didn't knit with yellow wool at all.

4. Beatrix's hat has no colour in common with that knitted by Harriet.

5. Harriet didn't use red wool at all. Harriet used yellow wool, but not to make the bobble of her son's hat.

6. Both Beatrix and Noelle knitted with navy blue wool, although Noelle didn't use navy blue wool to make a bobble.

	Main colour					Bobble					Brim				
	Brown	Green	Navy blue	Orange	Yellow	Cream	Green	Navy blue	Red	Yellow	Cream	Navy blue	Purple	Red	Yellow
Beatrix															
Fenella															
Harriet															
Lyndsey															
Noelle															
Brim Cream															
Navy blue															
Purple															
Red															
Yellow															
Bobble Cream															
Green															
Navy blue															
Red															
Yellow															

Knitter	Main colour	Bobble	Brim

Man & Wife

There were five marriages at the little church at Belweddin last month, thus providing the material for this puzzle! Can you discover each bride's full name (her surname in the grid below is her maiden name) and the full name of the man she married?

1. Mr Crane's wife (formerly either Miss Delaney or Miss Adamson) is either Ella or Debbie.

2. Either Penny or Ella is the former Miss Walters, who married either Richard or Philip.

3. Either Philip or Mike is married to Chris, whose is now either Mrs Jarvis or Mrs Wise.

4. Mike's surname is either Coates or Crane and Mr Jarvis is either Paul or Richard.

5. Either Debbie or Chris married Mr Jarvis and Mr Jarvis's wife is either the former Miss Adamson or the former Miss Walters.

6. Either Miss Adamson or Miss Collins married Gordon, who isn't Mr Anderton.

	Miss					Husband					Mr				
	Adamson	Collins	Delaney	Payne	Walters	Gordon	Mike	Paul	Philip	Richard	Anderton	Coates	Crane	Jarvis	Wise
Chris															
Debbie															
Ella															
Grace															
Penny															
Anderton															
Coates															
Crane															
Jarvis															
Wise															
Gordon															
Mike															
Paul															
Philip															
Richard															

Bride	Miss	Husband	Mr

A Fine Subject

Ivor Novel, the librarian at Puzzleton Library, took a fair amount of money yesterday afternoon, in fines levied on the people in this puzzle, who all returned their books late. Can you discover the time at which each came into the library, the title of the book each returned and the number of days by which it was overdue?

1. Vera came into the library either fifteen minutes earlier or fifteen minutes later than the person who returned *Rook's Lair*, which was two weeks less overdue than the book returned by Vera.

2. Jane came into the library half-an-hour later than Norman.

3. Sally (who returned *Wally's Dream*) came into the library fifteen minutes earlier than the borrower whose book was five weeks overdue.

4. The person who came in last (just as Ivor was about to close the library!) had a book overdue for a greater number of weeks than *Little Aspirations*.

5. Martin arrived at the library fifteen minutes earlier than the person (not Vera) who returned *Jaded Jackdaw*, which was two weeks less overdue than the book returned by Martin.

Borrower	Time	Book title	Overdue

Figure It Out

Each of the thirty-six squares in the grid is filled with a single digit number from 1 to 9 – each of those numbers being used four times. Use the clues to complete the square, bearing in mind that the same number must not appear in two adjacent (touching) squares in any row across or column down. If the same number is used more than once in any row across or column down it is stated in the relevant clue.

Across:

1. Two 4s. The only odd number is 1.

2. Two 5s. No even numbers.

3. Consecutive numbers placed in order.

4. Two 8s. No 3.

5. No 9. Total thirty-three.

6. Two 2s. Two 9s.

Down:

1. Two 7s.

2. Consecutive numbers placed in order.

3. Two 5s.

4. Two 8s. No 2.

5. The highest number is 6.

6. Two 3s are the only odd numbers.

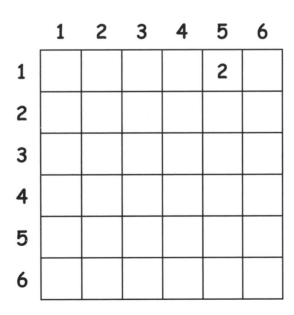

No 152

Eating for Others

Although they'd planned to go out for a slap-up meal together, the people who have kindly agreed to take part in this puzzle decided to forego the pleasure and have just a sandwich and a helping of soup, donating the money they would have spent to charity. Alice prepared the food, according to each person's preferences, but can you work out everyone's full name and what sandwich and soup each decided upon?

1. Jasmine Mayne isn't the person who chose the chicken sandwich.

2. Daniel isn't the person who asked for mulligatawny soup. The person who asked for mulligatawny soup didn't eat the egg sandwich and isn't surnamed Durrell.

3. Alice chose pea soup. Kenny (who had a salad sandwich) isn't the person surnamed Watson, who drank tomato soup.

4. The person (not surnamed Durrell) who had the chicken sandwich isn't Shane.

5. The person surnamed Bates (not Alice or Shane) who tucked into the ham sandwich didn't choose the potato soup.

	Bates	Durrell	Grove	Mayne	Watson	Cheese	Chicken	Egg	Ham	Salad	Mulligatawny	Mushroom	Pea	Potato	Tomato
Alice															
Daniel															
Jasmine															
Kenny															
Shane															
Mulligatawny															
Mushroom															
Pea															
Potato															
Tomato															
Cheese															
Chicken															
Egg															
Ham															
Salad															

Forename	Surname	Sandwich	Soup

No 153

Apples & Pears

It's harvest time in the gardens of Orchard Close and the seven people in this puzzle have just taken different quantities of apples and pears from their trees: their very first pickings this year! Anyone might have picked the same number of apples as pears, so can you pick through the clues below to find out exactly what quantity of apples and pears each harvested?

1. Lynn picked one more pear than whoever picked either one more or one fewer apple than Jerry, who picked one more pear than Dolly. The person who picked three pears picked either seven or eight apples.

2. William picked either one more or one fewer apple than whoever picked one fewer pear than Matthew. Lynn picked either one more or one fewer apple than whoever picked two fewer pears than Jerry.

3. Matthew picked one fewer apple than the person who picked one fewer pear than June. Dermot picked fewer apples than whoever picked two fewer pears than William.

4. June picked more apples than Dermot, who picked either one more or one fewer pear than the person who picked one fewer apple than whoever picked five pears.

	2 apples	3 apples	4 apples	5 apples	6 apples	7 apples	8 apples	3 pears	4 pears	5 pears	6 pears	8 pears	9 pears	10 pears
Dermot														
Dolly														
Jerry														
June														
Lynn														
Matthew														
William														
3 pears														
4 pears														
5 pears														
6 pears														
8 pears														
9 pears														
10 pears														

Name	Apples	Pears

Big Deal

Because he often pulls out more than one at a time, Jamie cannot properly deal playing cards. When he came to his turn to do so at a recent game, each of the other players complained they'd more than the four cards they needed. Jamie tried twice more but, again, no-one was happy, so he gave up and got someone else to deal for him! For each of Jamie's (mis)deals, how many cards were in each player's hand?

1. Leslie had two more cards than Eric on both the first and second deals, but two fewer than Eric on the third deal.

2. Paul wasn't the player to whom Jamie dealt six cards on his second deal and ten on the third. Nor did Paul's third hand contain five cards.

3. After Jamie's third and (thankfully) final attempt at dealing, Fred had more cards than he'd had on the first deal, but fewer than Paul had received on the first deal.

4. After every deal of the cards, each player's hand contained a different number of cards to the quantity in any hand he had been dealt before.

	1st deal					2nd deal					3rd deal				
	5 cards	6 cards	8 cards	9 cards	10 cards	5 cards	6 cards	7 cards	8 cards	9 cards	5 cards	7 cards	9 cards	10 cards	11 cards
Eric															
Fred															
Leslie															
Norman															
Paul															
3rd deal 5 cards															
3rd deal 7 cards															
3rd deal 9 cards															
3rd deal 10 cards															
3rd deal 11 cards															
2nd deal 5 cards															
2nd deal 6 cards															
2nd deal 7 cards															
2nd deal 8 cards															
2nd deal 9 cards															

Player	1st deal	2nd deal	3rd deal

Split Personalities

Fed up with constantly being ticked off for one thing or another at school, little Ivor Badstreak has removed photos of five teachers (each a strict disciplinarian) from the noticeboard in the entrance lobby of the school. He cut each into four pieces (head, body, legs and feet) and then reassembled them so that each new picture contains parts of four different teachers. Can you discover the make-up of the new pictures?

1. Mrs Edgar's smartly-coiffeured head now tops Mr Norton's somewhat overweight and out-of-shape body.

2. Mr Overton's hairy legs (he's the games master, so was photographed wearing a pair of shorts, in case you were wondering!) are in the same photograph as the head of the principal of the school, Miss Plodd.

3. Mr Overton's feet (clad in football boots, see above for reason why) are in the same picture as the body of Miss Nixon.

4. Miss Plodd's skinny legs now end in Mr Norton's rather large feet.

		Body					Legs					Feet				
		Mrs Edgar	Miss Nixon	Mr Norton	Mr Overton	Miss Plodd	Mrs Edgar	Miss Nixon	Mr Norton	Mr Overton	Miss Plodd	Mrs Edgar	Miss Nixon	Mr Norton	Mr Overton	Miss Plodd
Head	Mrs Edgar															
	Miss Nixon															
	Mr Norton															
	Mr Overton															
	Miss Plodd															
Feet	Mrs Edgar															
	Miss Nixon															
	Mr Norton															
	Mr Overton															
	Miss Plodd															
Legs	Mrs Edgar															
	Miss Nixon															
	Mr Norton															
	Mr Overton															
	Miss Plodd															

Head	Body	Legs	Feet

No 156

High Rise

Five friends live in the same block of flats. There are twenty flats per floor (it's a very large block!), so anyone in a flat with a 'higher number than' isn't necessarily on a higher floor: at the request of the postal department, the flats are due to be renumbered because of the confusion this causes! What is the number and floor of the apartment occupied by each friend and for how long has he or she been there?

1. Janine's flat is on the floor below Bridie's.

2. Janine has been a tenant for twice as long as the occupant of flat number 19.

3. Bridie hasn't lived in her apartment for nine years. Her flat has a number eight lower than that occupied by the friend who lives on the seventh floor.

4. Daniel has lived on the fourth floor for three years longer than Louisa has been in flat number 5.

5. The occupant of flat number 13 has lived in the block for fewer than six years.

	Flat 3	Flat 5	Flat 11	Flat 13	Flat 19	Third	Fourth	Fifth	Sixth	Seventh	1 year	2 years	3 years	6 years	9 years
Bridie															
Daniel															
Ian															
Janine															
Louisa															
1 year											
2 years											
3 years											
6 years											
9 years											
Third						
Fourth						
Fifth						
Sixth						
Seventh						

Friend	Flat No	Floor	Period of tenure

Playing Card Bingo

Every Thursday night, the local Darby & Joan Club holds prize competitions, one of which is Playing Card Bingo. This week's winning card is shown below. Can you determine the order in which the cards on it were called?

Values of cards are as shown and ace=1, jack=11, queen=12 and king=13.

1. The card called fourth has a value three lower than that of the card called eighth, which is either directly above or directly below a card (not that called ninth) of the same suit as the card called eighth.
2. The card called tenth has a value three higher than that of the card called next-but-one before card H (which wasn't called immediately before a heart). The card called tenth is directly next to and right of (and is of the same suit as) the card called twelfth.
3. The card called first is directly next to and left of the card called second, which has a value one higher than that of the card called thirteenth. The card called first has a value the same as that of the card called last.
4. Card N wasn't called third. The card called fifth is of the same suit as card M, which was called next-but-one before card L.

1st	2nd	3rd	4th	5th
6th	7th	8th	9th	10th
11th	12th	13th	14th	15th

LEFT ←   RIGHT →

	A	B	C		D	E	F	G
	4 ♦	Q ♥	6 ♠		9 ♣	4 ♣	A ♠	2 ♦
K ♠	7 ♦	9 ♦		K ♥	2 ♣		3 ♠	7 ♥	J ♥
H	I	J		K	L		M	N	O

159

Shopping Study ~ Part I

The five Quinn sisters all work on different floors at the Sparks & Mensa department store in town. In this puzzle you can find out the time at which she arrives for work every morning, together with the distance she has to travel from her home (none lives with any of her sisters) and the method of transport she uses to get to work…

1. May arrives for work at the latest time. Dawn doesn't travel by bus.

2. Leonie arrives five minutes later than the sister who rides her moped to work. The latter lives one mile closer to the store than the woman who arrives earliest each morning.

3. The woman who walks lives furthest from the store and arrives for work ten minutes later than Avril, who lives half a mile closer to the store than Gerda, who drives to work by car each morning, arriving five minutes later than Dawn.

	7.30am	7.35am	7.40am	7.45am	7.50am	1 mile	1½ miles	2 miles	3 miles	3½ miles	Bicycle	Bus	Car	Moped	On foot
Avril															
Dawn															
Gerda															
Leonie															
May															
Bicycle											
Bus											
Car											
Moped											
On foot											
1 mile						
1½ miles						
2 miles						
3 miles						
3½ miles						

Sister	Time at work	Distance	Transport method

Shopping Study ~ Part II

…and in this part of the puzzle, you can find out the department in which each sister works, together with her age and the length of time for which she has been an employee of Sparks & Mensa.

1. Avril works in the toy department. She has been an employee of Sparks & Mensa for one year longer than the sister who works in the stationery department.

2. The woman who works in the stationery department is two years older than the sister who has worked at the store for the shortest time.

3. The woman aged thirty who works in the lighting department has been an employee of Sparks & Mensa for six months longer than Dawn.

4. May is the eldest of the five sisters.

5. The sister who works in haberdashery isn't Gerda, who is two years older than the sister who works in the footwear department.

	Footwear	Haberdashery	Lighting	Stationery	Toys	29 years old	30 years old	31 years old	32 years old	33 years old	6 months	1 year	18 months	2 years	3 years
Avril															
Dawn															
Gerda															
Leonie															
May															
6 months															
1 year															
18 months															
2 years															
3 years															
29 years old															
30 years old															
31 years old															
32 years old															
33 years old															

Sister	Department	Age	Employee for

Eggstra Helpings

Every day last week (Monday to Sunday) Veronica visited one of her seven nieces for lunch. Unfortunately, each produced omelettes, so Veronica's had more than her fair share of eggs just recently. Which niece was visited on each day and what type of omelette did she serve to her aunt?

1. Veronica visited Honor the day after she had lunch with Tammy (who didn't cook the bacon omelette) and both visits were made earlier in the week than the day on which she ate the tomato omelette.

2. Amber cooked the green pepper omelette, which Veronica ate two days before the bacon omelette, but two days after her visit to see Marlene (who served the creamy asparagus omelette).

3. Suzanne (who didn't see her Aunt Veronica on Saturday) was visited later in the week than Polly.

4. Tuesday's omelette was filled with melted cheese, but not by Gail or Honor. Gail produced neither the onion nor the tomato omelette.

	Amber	Gail	Honor	Marlene	Polly	Suzanne	Tammy	Asparagus	Bacon	Cheese	Green pepper	Onion	Pea and ham	Tomato
Monday														
Tuesday														
Wednesday														
Thursday														
Friday														
Saturday														
Sunday														
Asparagus														
Bacon														
Cheese														
Green pepper														
Onion														
Pea and ham														
Tomato														

Day	Niece	Omelette

Laundry Day

Last week, five couples decided to work hard to clear their huge piles of washing and ironing. Any couple may have done washing and ironing on the same day, but no two couples washed or ironed on the same day as each other – and any may have done the ironing before the washing (the ironing being left from a previous washing day!). Who is who's partner and on which day/s did they do the washing and ironing?

1. Jason and his partner (who isn't Candy) did their ironing the day before Candy and her partner did their washing.

2. Jason and his partner (who isn't Pauline) did their washing the day before Pauline and her partner did their ironing.

3. Fern and her partner (not Oliver) did their washing on Tuesday and their ironing on Friday.

4. Morgan and his partner (who isn't Pauline) did the ironing on the same day as the washing.

5. Kurt and his partner did the washing the day before they did the ironing.

6. Amanda and her partner did their washing on Friday.

	Amanda	Candy	Fern	Pauline	Rosa	Washing Monday	Washing Tuesday	Washing Wednesday	Washing Friday	Washing Saturday	Ironing Monday	Ironing Tuesday	Ironing Thursday	Ironing Friday	Ironing Saturday
Jason															
Kurt															
Lance															
Morgan															
Oliver															
Ironing Monday															
Ironing Tuesday															
Ironing Thursday															
Ironing Friday															
Ironing Saturday															
Washing Monday															
Washing Tuesday															
Washing Wednesday															
Washing Friday															
Washing Saturday															

Man	Woman	Washing	Ironing

Sum Code

In this puzzle, every letter of the alphabet represents a different number from 1 to 26. The sums below will help you to crack the code and if any letter does not appear, its value is that remaining once the rest of the puzzle is complete. The only arithmetical signs used in this puzzle are '–' (minus), 'x' (times) and '+' (plus).

?

A	B	C	D	E	F	G	H	I	J	K	L	M

N	O	P	Q	R	S	T	U	V	W	X	Y	Z

?

?

1	2	3	4	5	6	7	8	9	10	11	12	13

14	15	16	17	18	19	20	21	22	23	24	25	26

?

1. D + H = K

2. G = P + S

3. E + N = X

4. Y x Y = R

5. D + U = T

6. D x F = G

7. L = A x Y

8. H x H = S

9. V = Y x Z

10. I x I = B + P

11. M + N = Q

12. Z x I = E + W

13. A + J = B x D

14. R x Y = D + S

15. The value of O is higher than that of T

Family Connections

Five brothers are all married with a child and live in the same street as one another. One of the brothers is Arthur, who lives at No 5 – and he provided the information necessary for this puzzle. To work out the identity of the members of each family (including Arthur's own) according to their house numbers, just follow the clues he has given, remembering that Arthur lives at No 5, of course…

1. Of four of the families: one lives at No 1; one is that of David and his wife Katie; one is that of Lesley and her daughter Emma; and the fourth is that of Grant and his daughter Beatrice.

2. Of four of the families: one is that of Margaret who lives at No 2; one is that of Frank and his son Adam; one is that of Ingrid and her son Derek; and the fourth (of which Carl is not a member) lives at No 3.

	Brother					Wife					Child				
	Arthur	David	Frank	Grant	Harry	Ingrid	Joanne	Katie	Lesley	Margaret	Adam	Beatrice	Carl	Derek	Emma
No 1															
No 2															
No 3															
No 4															
No 5															
Adam															
Beatrice															
Carl															
Derek															
Emma															
Ingrid															
Joanne															
Katie															
Lesley															
Margaret															

House No	Brother	Wife	Child

Washday Blues, Reds, etc

Five people mistakenly put a non-colourfast item into their washing machines with a number of white cotton garments, as a consequence of which the white garments took on the colour of the non-colourfast item. Which non-colourfast item was washed by each person, how many white cotton garments were also in the washing machine and what colour are they now?

1. Of the teeshirt and the item which turned the white garments a dull shade of brown, one was washed by Claire and the other by Donna, who washed fewer articles than Claire.

2. Of Donna and Neil, one washed the blue item and the other washed six white garments.

3. Of Roy and Valerie, one washed a beach-towel and the other washed something which turned the other items pink.

4. Of the person whose white garments are now green and the person who washed five garments, one is Neil and the other washed a pair of trousers.

5. Of the person who washed eleven garments and the one who washed a jumper, one is Roy and the other is Claire.

	Beach-towel	Jumper	Shorts	Teeshirt	Trousers	5 garments	6 garments	8 garments	10 garments	11 garments	Blue	Brown	Green	Grey	Pink
Claire															
Donna															
Neil															
Roy															
Valerie															
Blue															
Brown															
Green															
Grey															
Pink															
5 garments															
6 garments															
8 garments															
10 garments															
11 garments															

Washer	Item	No of garments	Colour

Walking the Dogs

Mrs Jones of the village shop regularly pops out during the day, to deliver an item requested by telephone by one of her less mobile customers. She has five dogs, so takes one out with her every time she delivers something. Can you discover the time at which each dog was taken out yesterday, together with the name of the customer to whom Mrs Jones delivered and the item requested by each?

1. Mrs Jones took Jack for a walk three hours earlier than the time she took the loaf of bread to one customer, but later than she delivered to Mr Argent.

2. Mrs Perry was the person to whom Mrs Jones delivered when she took Bobby for a walk in the morning.

3. Fido was taken out with the delivery of a box of eggs. Jack didn't accompany Mrs Jones when she delivered the sugar.

4. Mrs Jones delivered a pint of milk to Mr Dent in the afternoon.

5. Miss Cooper's delivery was made later in the day than that of a packet of tea, but earlier in the day than Butch was taken for a walk.

	8.30am	11.00am	11.30am	2.00pm	2.30pm	Mr Argent	Miss Cooper	Mr Dent	Mrs Perry	Mr Tring	Bread	Eggs	Milk	Sugar	Tea
Bobby															
Butch															
Fido															
Jack															
Sukie															
Bread											
Eggs											
Milk											
Sugar											
Tea											
Mr Argent						
Miss Cooper						
Mr Dent						
Mrs Perry						
Mr Tring						

Dog	Time	Customer	Item

Dominological

A standard set of twenty-eight dominoes has been laid out as shown. One is already in position, to give you a start. Can you draw in the edges of the rest? The check-box is provided as an aid to solving.

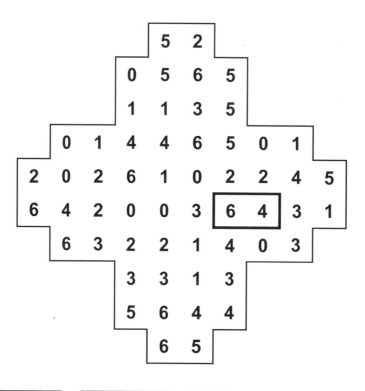

0 - 0		1 - 1		2 - 3		3 - 6	
0 - 1		1 - 2		2 - 4		4 - 4	
0 - 2		1 - 3		2 - 5		4 - 5	
0 - 3		1 - 4		2 - 6		4 - 6	✓
0 - 4		1 - 5		3 - 3		5 - 5	
0 - 5		1 - 6		3 - 4		5 - 6	
0 - 6		2 - 2		3 - 5		6 - 6	

Different Tastes

For this puzzle, six people have lined up their breakfast bowls of porridge oats, as you can see in the picture below. Before the porridge becomes cold, can you discover the name of the owner of each bowl together with the items or substance each prefers to add to his or her porridge each morning.

1. Hal's bowl isn't A and Glenda's bowl isn't C in the picture below.

2. Caroline's bowl is next to and between that belonging to Glenda (who adds chocolate chips to her porridge each morning) and that belonging to Edna (who doesn't add syrup or raisins to her porridge).

3. The person who adds a large dollop of syrup to porridge owns the bowl directly next to and left of Damien's, which is further left than the bowl which belongs to the person who adds a spoonful of treacle.

4. Ferdinand's bowl is next to and right of that belonging to the person (not Edna or Hal) who adds pieces of banana to his or her porridge.

	Caroline	Damien	Edna	Ferdinand	Glenda	Hal	Banana	Chocolate	Raisins	Strawberries	Syrup	Treacle
Bowl A												
Bowl B												
Bowl C												
Bowl D												
Bowl E												
Bowl F												
Banana												
Chocolate												
Raisins												
Strawberries												
Syrup												
Treacle												

LEFT ⟵   RIGHT ⟶

A   B   C   D   E   F

Bowl	Owner	Adds

Pick 'n' Mix

Five women couldn't resist the pick 'n' mix sweet section whilst shopping in their local store the other day. Each chose three different weights of three different types of sweets. Can you discover what every woman bought?

1. The smallest weight of humbugs wasn't bought by Barbara.

2. Eve didn't buy any treacle toffee.

3. Both Barbara and Sara bought mint creams.

4. Barbara didn't buy any treacle toffee.

5. Norma bought some fruit chews.

6. Both Rachel and Sara bought some coffee fudge and bull's-eyes.

	4 ounces					6 ounces					8 ounces				
	Aniseed balls	Bull's-eyes	Humbugs	Mint creams	Treacle toffee	Bull's-eyes	Coffee creams	Coffee fudge	Humbugs	Mint creams	Aniseed balls	Coffee fudge	Fruit chews	Liquorice toffee	Treacle toffee
Barbara															
Eve															
Norma															
Rachel															
Sara															
8 ounces Aniseed balls															
Coffee fudge															
Fruit chews															
Liquorice toffee															
Treacle toffee															
6 ounces Bull's eyes															
Coffee creams															
Coffee fudge															
Humbugs															
Mint creams															

Shopper	4 ounces	6 ounces	8 ounces

The Restauranteurs

The five couples who feature in this puzzle go out to dinner every Saturday night, each couple visiting restaurants which specialise in food from different nations of the world (names of restaurants aren't necessarily indicative of the type of foods served, however). Can you match the couples and say at which restaurant each dined last Saturday night, together with the nationality of the food in which it specialises?

1. Rupert and his girlfriend didn't patronise Alfonso's or the best Chinese restaurant in town, which goes by the unlikely name of La Contessa!

2. Raisa and her boyfriend (who isn't Rupert) visited The Oak Tree, which doesn't serve Thai food.

3. Richard and his fiancée ate a candle-lit dinner for two at Antonio's restaurant.

4. Raymond and his wife Rebecca ate at one of the restaurants last Saturday night.

5. Ruth ate at the restaurant specialising in Mexican food, which isn't The Kitchen.

6. Ryan ate at the restaurant specialising in Italian food, but not with Raisa or Roma.

	Raisa	Rebecca	Roma	Rosie	Ruth	Alfonso's	Antonio's	La Contessa	The Kitchen	The Oak Tree	Chinese	Indian	Italian	Mexican	Thai
Raymond															
Richard															
Robert															
Rupert															
Ryan															
Chinese															
Indian															
Italian															
Mexican															
Thai															
Alfonso's															
Antonio's															
La Contessa															
The Kitchen															
The Oak Tree															

Man	Woman	Restaurant	Type of food

Firm Resolutions

Five people who work at the same firm have decided what they are going to try to give up next year. Actually, each has made the same resolution in a previous year, but none has managed to make the resolution last for more than six months. Use the clues below to resolve the problem of what each person gave up, the year in which he or she last made the attempt and the length of time for which they succeeded.

1. The person who decided to give up swearing managed not to do so for three months longer than the resolution made by Delores lasted.

2. The resolution last made in 2002 was kept for over two months longer than Colin's which, in turn, lasted longer than that of the person who had decided to give up drinking alcohol.

3. The resolution which lasted for two months was last made in 2001.

4. It was in 2004 that someone (not Delores or Colin) first decided to cut out eating sweets. Tony's resolution was last made in 2003.

5. Yolande isn't the person who decided to try to reduce weight by not eating snacks between meals, who managed to keep going for six months, before falling victim to a packet of crisps one afternoon!

Name	Giving up	Last attempt	No of months

Card Sharp

What is the face value and suit of each of the cards shown below? All twelve cards used below are of different values and together they total 81. Values of the cards are as per their numbers and ace=1, jack=11, queen=12 and king=13. No card is horizontally or vertically next to another of the same colour and there are four different suits in each horizontal row and three different suits in each vertical column.

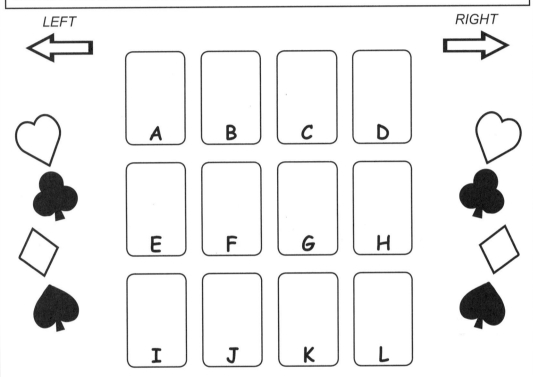

LEFT   RIGHT

1. Card J is neither an ace nor a jack. Card B (which isn't an ace) has a value half that of card C (which is of a different suit to card H).

2. Card H (which is either a diamond or a heart) has a value double that of card L which, in turn, has a value double that of card E (which isn't a club).

3. The two is directly next to and above the eight. The nine is directly next to and above the queen.

4. Card F (which isn't directly next to and below a spade) has a value three higher than that of card K (which isn't a diamond).

5. Card G has a higher value than that of card K, which has a lower value than that of card I (which isn't the king or the jack).

No 172

Stack 'em High

There's a prize of a nice new book ready for the child who can build the highest tower of bricks at school this month and the five children in this puzzle all had a turn. Every child made the effort on a different day, so use the clues below to discover not only the day on which each tried, but also their respective ages and how many bricks he or she used before the tower fell down.

1. Trixie managed to pile up two dozen bricks before her tower collapsed.

2. Jemima made her attempt on Monday.

3. The boy aged eleven who tried on Friday didn't use the highest number of bricks in the construction of his tower.

4. Gerry is one year older than the child who made Thursday's attempt, whose tower used four fewer bricks than were placed on Tuesday.

5. The oldest child used twenty-six bricks and made an attempt later in the week than that made by Stuart, who isn't nine years old.

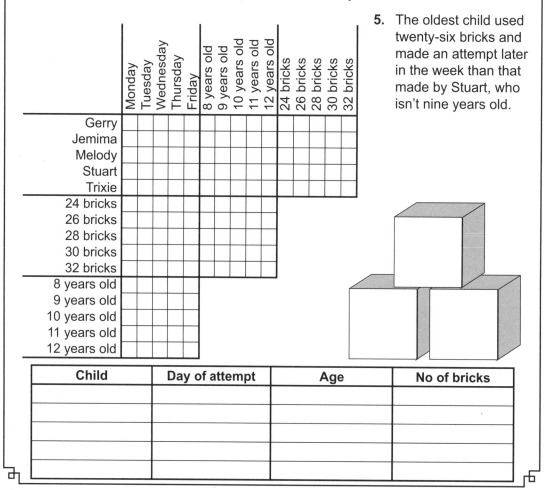

Child	Day of attempt	Age	No of bricks

174

Relationships

Each of the six families in this puzzle is made up of a husband, wife, son and daughter and no member of any one family is related to any member of the other five. Can you decide exactly who is related to whom?

1. Felicity's son is Joe, whose sister isn't Queenie. Queenie's father is Terry, who isn't married to Belinda.
2. Edwina's husband is Unwin. Harry's sister is Naomi.
3. Annie's son isn't Graham or Ian. Ian's father isn't Stan.
4. Vernon's wife isn't Denise. Graham's sister isn't Penny.
5. Penny's mother is Denise, who isn't married to Wally.
6. Liam's father is Wally, who isn't married to Carol.
7. Roberta's mother is Carol, who isn't married to Stan.
8. Olivia's mother isn't Belinda.

	Wife						Son						Daughter					
	Annie	Belinda	Carol	Denise	Edwina	Felicity	Graham	Harry	Ian	Joe	Kevin	Liam	Melanie	Naomi	Olivia	Penny	Queenie	Roberta
Stan																		
Terry																		
Unwin																		
Vernon																		
Wally																		
Xerxes																		
Melanie																		
Naomi																		
Olivia																		
Penny																		
Queenie																		
Roberta																		
Graham																		
Harry																		
Ian																		
Joe																		
Kevin																		
Liam																		

Husband	Wife	Son	Daughter

Patchwork

Each piece in the patchwork square below is decorated with a letter of the alphabet: A, B, C, D, E, F or G. In each horizontal row, vertical column and long diagonal line of seven smaller pieces there are seven different letters: some are already in place. Can you discover which letter fits in every piece? There is only one correct solution to this puzzle – if you take a wrong path along the way, you won't finish the quilt!

1. The letter in piece 1 is the same as that in piece 19.
2. The letter in piece 2 is the same as that in piece 27.
3. The letter in piece 11 is the same as that in piece 41.
4. The letter in piece 15 is the same as that in piece 48.
5. The letter in piece 9 is different to the letter in piece 20.

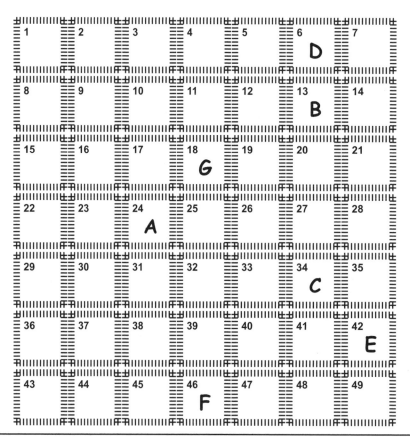

Just in Case

A market researcher stopped twenty men on their way to work this morning, to enquire about the contents of their briefcases and to ask how much of what they regularly take back and forth from work each day is actually needed. One quarter of the men questioned admitted that they don't actually use their briefcases for work papers at all. What is the colour of each man's briefcase and what did it contain?

1. Either Mr Hale or Mr Macleod was the man who admitted that his briefcase contained nothing more than his dirty washing (he is going to the laundry at lunchtime). The gym kit was in either the grey or beige briefcase.

2. James's briefcase contained either a couple of books or his dirty washing.

3. Either David or Walter was carrying the grey briefcase, which contained either a newspaper or the gym kit.

4. Either James or Keith is Mr Stoner, whose briefcase is either black or grey. Mr Cameron's briefcase is either green or tan.

5. David (whose briefcase is either green or grey) was carrying either his lunch or his dirty washing.

6. Tom's surname is either Cameron or Hale.

7. The newspaper (carried by either Mr Hale or Mr Stoner) was in either the beige or the grey briefcase.

	Cameron	Hale	Macleod	Stoner	Woodleigh	Beige	Black	Green	Grey	Tan	Books	Gym kit	Lunch	Newspaper	Washing
David															
James															
Keith															
Tom															
Walter															
Books															
Gym kit															
Lunch															
Newspaper															
Washing															
Beige															
Black															
Green															
Grey															
Tan															

Forename	Surname	Colour	Contents

Simple as A,B,C?

Each of the small squares in the grid below contains either A, B or C. Every row, every column and each of the two long diagonal lines of six squares contains exactly two of each letter. The information in the clues refers only to the squares in that row or column. To help you solve this problem, we've given as many clues as we think you'll need! Can you tell which letter should be placed into each square?

Across:

1. Any three consecutive squares contain three different letters.

2. The As are next to one another.

3. Each B is immediately next to and left of a C.

4. The Bs are somewhere between the Cs.

5. Neither of the squares at either end of the row contains a C.

6. The Cs are somewhere between the As.

Down:

1. No two squares containing the same letter are next to one another.

2. The Bs are lower than the As.

3. The Bs are lower than the Cs.

4. The As are somewhere between the Bs.

5. The Cs are somewhere between the As.

	1	2	3	4	5	6
1						
2						
3						
4						
5						
6						

No 177

Staying In

The five people in this puzzle decided to have a night alone with a take-away meal and a good video to watch on television. Can you discover the title of the film watched by each person, together with the meal each ordered and the drink which he or she had whilst watching the film?

1. Cora watched *Gosford Park*. The person who watched *Doctor Doolittle* didn't drink white wine.

2. The person who watched *Pulp Fiction* enjoyed an Indian curry.

3. Roger drank lager. His choice of film wasn't *Titanic* or *Doctor Doolittle*.

4. Lemonade was the drink chosen by the person who tucked into a generous portion of fish and chips.

5. The person who ordered a pizza isn't Alice, who drank cola with her meal.

6. Whoever watched *Peter Pan* brewed a large pot of tea before settling down for the evening.

7. Edward (who didn't drink tea) enjoyed his Chinese meal.

	Doctor Doolittle	Gosford Park	Peter Pan	Pulp Fiction	Titanic	Chinese	Indian curry	Doner kebab	Fish and chips	Pizza	Cola	Lager	Lemonade	Tea	White wine
Alice															
Cora															
Edward															
Janet															
Roger															
Cola															
Lager															
Lemonade															
Tea															
White wine															
Chinese															
Indian curry															
Doner kebab															
Fish and chips															
Pizza															

Name	Film	Food	Drink

Fixing the Car

Five men who took last week off work as holiday each fixed his car on one of the days, much to the disgust of their families, who had wanted to spend time together and who wholeheartedly wish each man would sell his ancient car in favour of a new one which doesn't need fixing! Can you discover the full name of each man, together with the make of car he owns and the day on which he worked on his vehicle?

1. Mr Chester fixed his ageing Vauxhall on the day (not Thursday) that his wife and children had particularly wanted to go to the zoo.

2. Craig owns the Ford Mustang, which he repaired on Wednesday.

3. Adrian (who isn't Mr Kent) repaired his car two days later in the week than the Fiat was fixed by the man whose wife and family would have preferred to have gone to the beach.

4. Mr Chambers worked on his car on Tuesday.

5. Theo's day for working on his car was earlier in the week than Mr Kent's, but later in the week than that of the man who repaired the Peugeot.

6. The man who repaired the Peugeot is younger than George, but older than Mr Barton.

	Barton	Chambers	Chester	Johnson	Kent	Fiat	Ford	Peugeot	Rover	Vauxhall	Monday	Tuesday	Wednesday	Thursday	Friday
Adrian															
Bill															
Craig															
George															
Theo															
Monday											
Tuesday											
Wednesday											
Thursday											
Friday											
Fiat						
Ford						
Peugeot						
Rover						
Vauxhall						

Man	Surname	Car make	Day of repairs

Caught on the Net

It's easy to be sidetracked on the internet… The five people in this puzzle only intended to spend a few minutes on the internet last night, but spent considerably longer browsing, having been attracted to another site. Can you get at the facts, without being distracted, to work out the reason each originally wanted to use the internet, how long he or she spent online and to what type of site each was drawn?

1. Cathy spent fifteen minutes longer online than the person who ended up on the holiday site, despite having originally intended to use the internet in order to print out a map.

2. Jacqueline didn't visit the chat or healthcare sites. Moira spent longer online than Jerry.

3. The surfer who wanted to read the news spent less time online than Cathy, who didn't end up on the chat site.

4. Jacqueline (who had originally been in search of material for her homework project) spent longer online than Jessica, who spent ten fewer minutes online than the person who'd accessed the internet in order to do the weekly shopping.

5. Jerry had gone online to find out the weather prospects for the next few days. He spent fifteen fewer minutes online than the person who was attracted to the auction site.

	Homework	Map	News	Shopping	Weather	35 minutes	45 minutes	50 minutes	60 minutes	75 minutes	Auction	Chat	Healthcare	Holiday	Puzzles
Cathy															
Jacqueline															
Jerry															
Jessica															
Moira															
Auction															
Chat															
Healthcare															
Holiday															
Puzzles															
35 minutes															
45 minutes															
50 minutes															
60 minutes															
75 minutes															

User	Originally wanted	Time spent	Site attracted to

Robberies

Robin Offen was quite a successful thief, who pulled off a number of crimes over the years, until this year when he was caught red-handed and sentenced to a lengthy jail term. He travelled all over the world and details of his five largest crimes are shown below. Can you discover the year in which Robin stole from each of the listed places, the country in which each robbery took place and the profit he made?

1. The $120,000 haul came from a raid on a bank and the last of Robin's crimes (before he was caught, that is) netted Robin $160,000.

2. The job which earned Robin Offen the most money came as a result of a robbery in Peru.

3. Stealing the night's takings from a casino earned more than the robbery which Robin committed in Wales.

4. The Canadian robbery took place in 2004.

5. Robin's very first earnings as a result of crime came from the sale of a number of exquisite diamond tiaras, snatched after he broke the window of a jewellery shop.

6. The robbery committed in 2002 netted Robin $80,000 more than the profit he received from selling the goods raided from a warehouse in South Africa.

	2001	2002	2003	2004	2005	Austria	Canada	Peru	South Africa	Wales	$40,000	$80,000	$120,000	$160,000	$200,000
Bank															
Casino															
Jewellery shop															
Museum															
Warehouse															
$40,000															
$80,000															
$120,000															
$160,000															
$200,000															
Austria															
Canada															
Peru															
South Africa															
Wales															

Establishment	Year of crime	Country	Profit

Cop Swap

This month, several police officers from different countries are each taking part in a 'cop swap' trading places with one another in order to learn the methods used by their counterparts abroad. Five of the officers taking part are from the USA. Can you detect which state each is from, the squad to which he belongs when working at home and the country in which he is currently living and working?

1. Officer Wyndrake from South Dakota isn't the man from the homicide squad.

2. The police officer visiting New Zealand has a surname containing fewer letters than that of the robbery squad cop.

3. The auto theft cop isn't the man currently in Brazil. The man (not from Texas) currently in Brazil has a longer surname than that of the traffic cop who is currently monitoring the speed of traffic on the motorways of the United Kingdom.

4. Officer O'Leary (who isn't from Alaska or Texas) is studying police methods in Australia.

5. Neither the man from the homicide division nor the auto theft cop is in Pakistan or Australia.

6. Officer Goodman from Missouri isn't a member of the auto theft squad.

	Alaska	Missouri	South Dakota	Texas	Utah	Auto theft	Homicide	Robbery	Traffic	Vice	Australia	Brazil	New Zealand	Pakistan	United Kingdom
Officer Andrews															
Officer Goodman															
Officer O'Leary															
Officer Steinbeck															
Officer Wyndrake															
Australia															
Brazil															
New Zealand															
Pakistan															
United Kingdom															
Auto theft															
Homicide															
Robbery															
Traffic															
Vice															

Officer	State	Squad	Country

Literally Logical

The five people in this puzzle are all studying literature for an examination. Each person's syllabus includes research into one Shakespearean play and the reading of several works by a classic author. Can you discover every student's full name together with the name of the author whose works he or she is reading and the name of the play each is researching?

1. Nancy's syllabus includes the works of Charles Dickens.

2. The works of J R R Tolkien are being studied by the person surnamed Barrie.

3. Martin Scott is one of the five students.

4. Macbeth is being researched by Peter.

5. The person surnamed Stoker isn't researching Romeo & Juliet.

6. The man researching Julius Caesar is surnamed Collins. Another male student is researching King Lear and reading the novels of Thomas Hardy.

7. Lorna isn't the student surnamed Marlowe who is reading the works of Lewis Carroll.

	Barrie	Collins	Marlowe	Scott	Stoker	Jane Austen	Lewis Carroll	Charles Dickens	Thomas Hardy	J R R Tolkien	Julius Caesar	King Lear	Macbeth	Romeo & Juliet	The Tempest
Lorna															
Martin															
Nancy															
Oliver															
Peter															
Julius Caesar															
King Lear															
Macbeth															
Romeo & Juliet															
The Tempest															
Jane Austen															
Lewis Carroll															
Charles Dickens															
Thomas Hardy															
J R R Tolkien															

Student	Surname	Author	Play

Figure It Out

Each of the thirty-six squares in the grid is filled with a single digit number from 1 to 9 – each of those numbers being used four times. Use the clues to complete the square, bearing in mind that the same number must not appear in two adjacent (touching) squares in any row across or column down. If the same number is used more than once in any row across or column down it is stated in the relevant clue.

Across:

1. Two 2s. The only odd number is 1.

2. Consecutive numbers placed in order.

3. Two 1s. No 6. Total twenty-two.

4. Two 9s. No 5. No 8.

5. No 8. Total twenty-seven.

6. Two 9s.

Down:

1. The only even number is 2.

2. No 5. There is a 1 and a 7 with two numbers between them.

3. Consecutive numbers placed in order.

4. The only odd numbers are 1 and 5.

5. Two 7s, with two numbers between them.

6. Two 9s. No 4. No 5.

	1	2	3	4	5	6
1						
2						
3						
4						
5						
6						

Exercise in Mathematics

Five students recently received the results of three of the examinations they had recently taken. Can you discover each individual pupil's results in algebra, geometry and trigonometry?

1. The pupil who achieved a result of 50% in the algebra examination got a result 20% higher for geometry than the student who was given 50% in trigonometry.

2. Edina's trigonometry mark was double that of Barry's algebra mark.

3. The student given a mark of 60% in geometry was given an algebra mark 15% lower than Julie's.

4. Samuel's percentage mark in algebra was the same as his mark in trigonometry.

5. Sheila's mark in geometry was 20% higher than Edina's.

6. Sheila's mark in trigonometry was 20% lower than Edina's.

	Algebra					Geometry					Trig'metry				
	30%	35%	40%	50%	55%	40%	50%	60%	70%	85%	50%	55%	60%	70%	80%
Barry															
Edina															
Julie															
Samuel															
Sheila															
Trig'metry 50%															
55%															
60%															
70%															
80%															
Geometry 40%															
50%															
60%															
70%															
85%															

Pupil	Algebra	Geometry	Trignonometry

A Question of Style

Five women all went to different hairdressers this morning, to get their hair cut and coloured for a special occasion tomorrow. Who visited each of the listed salons, which colour did she choose and which special occasion or event is she attending?

1. Fiona had her hair done because she wanted to look her best for a job interview.

2. Jackie didn't have her hair coloured with Ebony Black and neither she nor Gabrielle (who went to Hair Quality) chose Chestnut Charm.

3. The Snip Shop's customer who had her hair coloured bright pink with (you've guessed it!) Pink Perfection colourant isn't Iona, who is visiting her aunt.

4. The woman who will be attending a retirement party patronised Miranda's Salon.

5. Hannah (who didn't go to Miranda's Salon) chose to have her hair dyed with the Purple Haze colourant.

6. The customer at Top Knotch isn't the one who had her hair done for her wedding this afternoon. Nor did the bride-to-be patronise Hair Quality.

	Fiona	Gabrielle	Hannah	Iona	Jackie	Bouncy Blonde	Chestnut Charm	Ebony Black	Pink Perfection	Purple Haze	Christening	Interview	Retirement	Visit to aunt	Wedding
Hair Quality															
Miranda's Salon															
The Snip Shop															
Top Knotch															
Tracey's Tresses															
Christening															
Interview															
Retirement															
Visit to aunt															
Wedding															
Bouncy Blonde															
Chestnut Charm															
Ebony Black															
Pink Perfection															
Purple Haze															

Salon	Client	Colour	Occasion

Sum Code

In this puzzle, every letter of the alphabet represents a different number from 1 to 26. The sums below will help you to crack the code and if any letter does not appear, its value is that remaining once the rest of the puzzle is complete. The only arithmetical signs used in this puzzle are '−' (minus), 'x' (times) and '+' (plus).

?

A	B	C	D	E	F	G	H	I	J	K	L	M

N	O	P	Q	R	S	T	U	V	W	X	Y	Z

?

?

1	2	3	4	5	6	7	8	9	10	11	12	13

14	15	16	17	18	19	20	21	22	23	24	25	26

?

1. T + X = A
2. J + P = U
3. H + J = W
4. A x T = S
5. E + W = R
6. E + E = V
7. S + X = U
8. E + V = B

9. P x U = Y
10. B + V = N
11. D + G = I
12. N − L = Z
13. H + O = F
14. D + F = Q
15. F + M + P = I + K
16. G + L = N − E

The Passage of Time

Five passengers who shared a carriage on a train each passed the time in a different way. By using the clues below, can you correctly arrive at each person's destination, how long it took to get there and how he or she passed the time en route?

1. The passenger travelling to High Point passed the time by having a quick snooze.

2. The journey to Brentville took exactly one hour.

3. The reading of a magazine helped the shortest journey pass quickly.

4. It took Madeleine fifty-five minutes to reach her destination.

5. Zoë didn't read a novel on her trip to Ayre's Junction. Hers was a longer journey than Dave's, but shorter than that to Middleton.

6. Bob passed the time on his journey (which was longer than that to Middleton) by starting to work his way through a book of crossword puzzles.

	Ayre's Junction	Brentville	High Point	Middleton	Woodbury	30 minutes	45 minutes	55 minutes	60 minutes	80 minutes	Crosswords	Magazine	Newspaper	Novel	Snooze
Alan															
Bob															
Dave															
Madeleine															
Zoë															
Crosswords															
Magazine															
Newspaper															
Novel															
Snooze															
30 minutes															
45 minutes															
55 minutes															
60 minutes															
80 minutes															

Traveller	Destination	Time	Pastime

Baking Days

Everyone is very complimentary of Mrs Baker's cakes; and Mrs Baker certainly makes enough of them! Last week she made five batches of one type of cake per day, each taking a different length of time to cook (some were larger than others and some she had to bake in more than one session). How long did she spend baking each batch, on which day and to whom was the batch presented as a gift?

1. The cherry cakes which Mrs Baker gave to her neighbour were made two days before the seed cakes which Mrs Baker gave to her daughter.

2. Tuesday's baking session took half-an-hour less time to cook than the batch she made (later in the week) for her eldest son.

3. The cakes baked on Thursday took longer to cook than the ginger cakes, which were made the day before the Madeira cakes.

4. The batch baked on Thursday took half-an-hour less time to cook than the batch she presented to her younger son.

5. The batch made on Saturday wasn't given to the vicar's wife.

	1 hour	1½ hours	1¾ hours	2¼ hours	2½ hours	Monday	Tuesday	Thursday	Friday	Saturday	Daughter	Eldest son	Neighbour	Vicar's wife	Youngest son
Cherry cakes															
Chocolate cakes															
Ginger cakes															
Madeira cakes															
Seed cakes															
Daughter															
Eldest son															
Neighbour															
Vicar's wife															
Youngest son															
Monday															
Tuesday															
Thursday															
Friday															
Saturday															

Batch	Time	Day	Presented to

Colourful Calendars

The local Men's Institute has produced its own calendar for next year, with the pictures having been taken by various men whilst on holiday. Every month features a different scene from a country they had visited, so work through the clues below to discover which man took each of the themed photographs, in which country and on which month's page it appears.

1. The picture on October's page was taken in Sweden, but not by Louis.

2. The picture on April's page is of fishermen mending their boats.

3. Louis took the photograph of a busy market in the centre of a town.

4. Mortimer holidays in Holland every year, which is where he took his photograph.

5. The photograph of trees appears on the page for August.

6. The photograph taken in Barbados appears later in the year than that of a sunset, but the month before the picture taken in the United States of America.

7. Johnny's Japanese photo appears two months before that taken by Viv, which isn't of a sunset.

	Johnny	Louis	Mortimer	Reggie	Viv	Barbados	Holland	Japan	Sweden	USA	April	June	July	August	October
Beach scene															
Fishermen															
Market															
Sunset															
Trees															
April															
June															
July															
August															
October															
Barbados															
Holland															
Japan															
Sweden															
USA															

Photograph	Taken by	Country	Month

Playing Card Bingo

Every Thursday night, the local Darby & Joan Club holds prize competitions, one of which is Playing Card Bingo. This week's winning card is shown below. Can you determine the order in which the cards on it were called?

Values of cards are as shown and ace=1, jack=11, queen=12 and king=13.

1. The card called tenth is directly next to and right of that called twelfth, which is either directly above or directly below the card called third, which has a value six higher than that of the card (not M) called sixth.
2. The card called fourth is directly next to and between two cards of the same suit, one of which has a lower value and one of which has a higher value than that of the card called fifth, which is directly next to and left of the card called last.
3. Card D was called next-but-one before card F, which is of the same suit as the card called fourteenth, which has a value three higher than that of the second card to be called. Card L wasn't called ninth.
4. Card M was called earlier than card J, which was called immediately after a card of the same suit as the card (not I or J) called thirteenth.

1st	2nd	3rd	4th	5th
6th	7th	8th	9th	10th
11th	12th	13th	14th	15th

LEFT ⬅   RIGHT ➡

A	B	C			D	E	F	G	H
9 ♦	8 ♠	2 ♦			6 ♥	K ♣	Q ♦	J ♣	8 ♥
	A ♥		3 ♣	4 ♠	7 ♣		5 ♠	10 ♥	5 ♦
	I		J	K	L		M	N	O

Nice work...

...if you can get it! Five of the men who attended a Job-seekers' Day didn't actually want work: they had been attracted by the prospect of free sandwiches! However, a local sandwich bar owner noticed their enthusiasm and has offered each man a job. At what time did each man arrive and leave the room in which the Job-seekers' Day was held and what was the filling in the vast quantity of sandwiches he consumed?

1. Bryn left the room half-an-hour earlier than Joseph.

2. The man who ate the tasty roast beef sandwiches arrived ten minutes earlier than the one who ate ham sandwiches. The man who ate ham sandwiches left ten minutes later than Wesley.

3. The man who arrived first was also the first to leave. He stayed exactly the same amount of time in the room as the man who guzzled his way through many rounds of ham sandwiches.

4. Malcolm left ten minutes earlier than the person who ate the superb cheese sandwiches and who arrived twenty minutes earlier than the one who left at 3.30pm after consuming a large number of chicken sandwiches.

	Arrived at					Left at					Bacon	Beef	Cheese	Chicken	Ham
	10.50am	11.00am	11.20am	11.40am	11.50am	3.00pm	3.30pm	3.50pm	4.00pm	4.10pm					
Bryn															
Joseph															
Malcolm															
Stan															
Wesley															
Bacon											
Beef											
Cheese											
Chicken											
Ham											
3.00pm					
3.30pm					
3.50pm					
4.00pm					
4.10pm					

Name	Arrived	Left	Sandwiches

Dominological

A standard set of twenty-eight dominoes has been laid out as shown. One is already in position, to give you a start. Can you draw in the edges of the rest? The check-box is provided as an aid to solving.

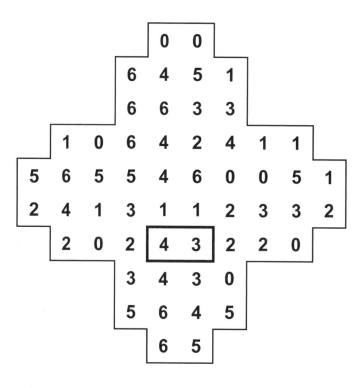

0 - 0		1 - 1		2 - 3		3 - 6	
0 - 1		1 - 2		2 - 4		4 - 4	
0 - 2		1 - 3		2 - 5		4 - 5	
0 - 3		1 - 4		2 - 6		4 - 6	
0 - 4		1 - 5		3 - 3		5 - 5	
0 - 5		1 - 6		3 - 4	✓	5 - 6	
0 - 6		2 - 2		3 - 5		6 - 6	

Look-alikes?

Five women of different ages who turned up for a job interview were somewhat surprised to see that they were all wearing identical skirts and jumpers. However, no girl wore the same colour of skirt or jumper as any other – and each girl wore a jumper in a different colour to that of her skirt. Can you discover not only their ages, but also the colour of the jumper and skirt worn by each interviewee?

1. The woman who wore the green jumper is one year older than the woman who wore the orange jumper.

2. The woman who wore the orange skirt wore a jumper of the same colour as Laura's skirt.

3. Noelle is one year younger than Kath, who wore a jumper of the same colour as that of the skirt worn by the woman aged twenty-five.

4. Laura wore a jumper of the same colour as the skirt worn by the woman in the blue jumper, who is one year older than Mandy.

5. Judith is one year older than the woman who wore the red skirt.

6. The woman aged twenty-four wore a jumper of the same colour as Judith's skirt.

7. The woman in the yellow jumper deliberately avoided a black skirt, as she thought it would make her look waspish!

	21 years old	22 years old	24 years old	25 years old	26 years old	Blue	Green	Orange	Red	Yellow	Black	Blue	Green	Orange	Red
						Jumper					**Skirt**				
Judith															
Kath															
Laura															
Mandy															
Noelle															
Skirt Black															
Blue															
Green															
Orange															
Red															
Jumper Blue															
Green															
Orange															
Red															
Yellow															

Interviewee	Age	Jumper	Skirt

Crazy Critters

Farmer Giles has taken photographs of five of the animals on his smallholding and has cut them each into four pieces (head, body, legs and tail), reassembling them in such a way that each 'new' photo contains pieces of four different animals. We don't know why he did this – but can you say how the photos now look?

1. The lamb's fluffy tail is not in the same picture as the pig's head.

2. The goat's head is now attached to the lamb's body, which isn't in the same picture as the dog's tail.

3. The dog's legs are now attached to the goat's body, which isn't topped by the pig's head.

4. The pig's curly tail is in the same picture as the dog's head.

		Body					Legs					Tail				
		Cow	Dog	Goat	Lamb	Pig	Cow	Dog	Goat	Lamb	Pig	Cow	Dog	Goat	Lamb	Pig
Head	Cow															
	Dog															
	Goat															
	Lamb															
	Pig															
Tail	Cow															
	Dog															
	Goat															
	Lamb															
	Pig															
Legs	Cow															
	Dog															
	Goat															
	Lamb															
	Pig															

Head	Body	Legs	Tail

Simple as A,B,C?

Each of the small squares in the grid below contains either A, B or C. Every row, every column and each of the two long diagonal lines of six squares contains exactly two of each letter. The information in the clues refers only to the squares in that row or column. To help you solve this problem, we've given as many clues as we think you'll need! Can you tell which letter should be placed into each square?

Across:

1. The Cs are somewhere between the Bs.

3. One A is immediately next to and right of a B and the other A is immediately next to and left of a B.

5. The As are further left than the Bs.

6. The As are further left than the Bs.

Down:

1. Each C is immediately next to and below an A.

4. The Cs are lower than the Bs.

6. The As are somewhere between the Bs.

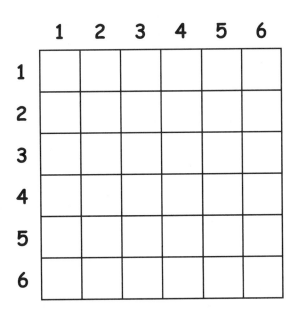

Costume Party

Thirty people lay sunbathing on the beach yesterday morning. See if you can work out the numbers of people lying on the different colours of towels, together with the numbers who wore the different colours of bathing costumes or swimming trunks. All of the information you need is in the clues.
The question is: How many wore purple bathing costumes or trunks?

1. Six were lying on blue towels and one third of those remaining were lying on green towels. Of those remaining, half were lying on white towels and the rest were divided equally between those lying on orange towels and those on red towels.

2. One third of those lying on blue towels, one quarter of those lying on white towels and half of those lying on red towels were men.

3. Of those remaining, half of those lying on blue towels, one quarter of those lying on green towels, one third of those lying on white towels and half of those lying on orange towels were boys.

4. Of those remaining, any lying on blue towels, one third of those lying on green towels, half of those lying on white towels and any lying on red towels were women. Those sunbathers still remaining were all girls.

5. The men lying on either blue towels or white towels wore green swimming trunks, as did any boy lying on either a green or white towel.

6. Any man lying on either a green towel or a red towel wore red swimming trunks. Red was the colour of the costume worn by any girl lying on either a green towel or red towel.

7. Yellow swimming trunks were worn by any boy lying on either a blue towel or an orange towel. Yellow was the colour of the costume worn by any woman lying on either a blue towel or an orange towel.

8. Any remaining sunbathers who were lying on white towels wore navy blue costumes or trunks.

9. Any sunbathers still unaccounted for wore purple bathing costumes or trunks, regardless of the colour of the towel on which they were lying.

The number of people wearing purple bathing costumes or trunks is: _____

Getting Around

These five businesswomen all drove very long distances to meet clients last week. Every businesswoman lives in a different town and each drove to different places on different days. Can you discover where each lives, together with her destination and the day on which she travelled?

1. If the woman who travelled on Thursday is Gina, then she lives in Redport; otherwise the one who travelled on Thursday is Sandra and she lives in Innthorpe.
2. If Fran lives in Innthorpe, then she drove to Pulbury; otherwise she lives in Redport and drove to Bearton.
3. If the woman who lives in Puzzleton drove to Bearton, then she's Fran; otherwise the woman who lives in Puzzleton is Wendy and she drove to Tanbridge.
4. If Ellen lives in Benmoor, then she went to Pulbury; otherwise Ellen lives in Whitbury and went to Southam.
5. If the woman who travelled on Wednesday lives in Benmoor, then the woman who travelled on Friday went to Raymouth; otherwise the woman who travelled on Wednesday lives in Whitbury and the one who travelled on Friday went to Bearton.
6. If the woman who travelled on Tuesday went to Raymouth, then she's Ellen; otherwise the woman who travelled on Tuesday is Fran and she went to Pulbury.

	Home town					Drove to					Monday	Tuesday	Wednesday	Thursday	Friday
	Benmoor	Innthorpe	Redport	Puzzleton	Whitbury	Bearton	Pulbury	Raymouth	Southam	Tanbridge	Monday	Tuesday	Wednesday	Thursday	Friday
Ellen															
Fran															
Gina															
Sandra															
Wendy															
Monday															
Tuesday															
Wednesday															
Thursday															
Friday															
Bearton															
Pulbury															
Raymouth															
Southam															
Tanbridge															

Businesswoman	Home town	Drove to	Day

Patchwork

Each piece in the patchwork square below is decorated with a letter of the alphabet: A, B, C, D, E, F or G. In each horizontal row, vertical column and long diagonal line of seven smaller pieces there are seven different letters: some are already in place. Can you discover which letter fits in every piece? There is only one correct solution to this puzzle – if you take a wrong path along the way, you won't finish the quilt!

1. The letter in piece 1 is the same as that in piece 37.

2. The letter in piece 14 is the same as that in piece 25.

3. The letter in piece 23 is the same as that in piece 42.

4. The letter in piece 28 is the same as that in piece 31.

5. The letter in piece 40 is the same as that in piece 44.

6. The letter in piece 6 is different to the letter in piece 47.

7. The letter in piece 13 is different to the letter in piece 38.

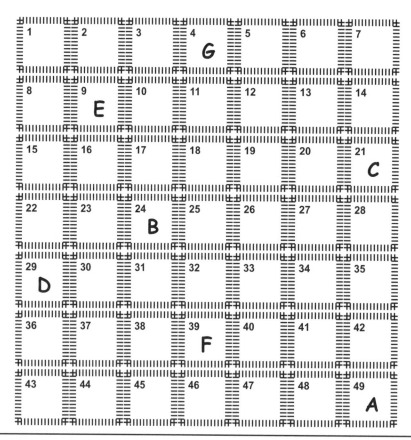

Off Line

> *The five housewives who appear in this puzzle have all needed to call in the police during the course of the past few months, as each has had washing stolen from her line. So far, only pillowcases, sheets and towels have been taken, so it is hoped that the police will find the culprit (who obviously has a large family!) before anything more goes missing. How many items have disappeared from every woman's line?*

1. The woman who has had twelve pillowcases taken has lost two fewer sheets than Lola, who has lost two more pillowcases than the woman who has lost the same number of sheets as the number of towels stolen from Deirdre's washing line.

2. The woman who has had the highest number of towels taken has lost one more sheet (but fewer pillowcases) to the thief than Trudy.

3. The woman who has had six towels stolen has had one more sheet taken than the number unpegged from Sue's line.

4. The woman who has lost the fewest pillowcases has had one fewer sheet taken than the woman who has lost five towels to the thief.

5. The woman who has had six sheets taken has lost more pillowcases and more towels than Trudy.

	6 pillowcases	8 pillowcases	10 pillowcases	12 pillowcases	14 pillowcases	3 sheets	4 sheets	6 sheets	7 sheets	8 sheets	3 towels	4 towels	5 towels	6 towels	7 towels
Deirdre															
Lola															
Mel															
Sue															
Trudy															
3 towels															
4 towels															
5 towels															
6 towels															
7 towels															
3 sheets															
4 sheets															
6 sheets															
7 sheets															
8 sheets															

Housewife	Pillowcases	Sheets	Towels

Young Love

The five teenage girls who work at the department store in Main Street all dashed off after work on Friday evening to meet up with their boyfriends. Each girl met her young man at a prearranged place before they took a bus to a youth club, of which they are both senior members. Can you discover where and when every girl met up with her boyfriend and the number of the bus they then took to the youth club?

1. The couple who took the No 82 to the youth club met outside the bakery at which he works.

2. The couple who took the No 77 bus met later than Estelle and her boyfriend, who had arranged to meet at the bus stop.

3. Marcia (who caught the No 53 bus) didn't meet her boyfriend at the latest of the five times, although she did meet him two minutes later than Amy met her boyfriend (which wasn't at 5.34pm).

4. The girl (not Daphne) who met her boyfriend in the local café took the No 61 bus.

5. Colleen didn't catch the No 61. She met her boyfriend two minutes before one of the couples met up at the entrance to the shopping mall, but later than the meeting time of at least one other couple.

	Bakery	Bus stop	Café	Shopping mall	Street corner	5.34pm	5.36pm	5.38pm	5.40pm	5.42pm	No 53	No 61	No 77	No 82	No 99
Amy															
Colleen															
Daphne															
Estelle															
Marcia															
No 53											
No 61											
No 77											
No 82											
No 99											
5.34pm						
5.36pm						
5.38pm						
5.40pm						
5.42pm						

Girl	Place	Time	Bus No

Well Read

Last year, five sisters joined the Literary Book Circle and each has ordered a different number of books during her time as a member. In what type of books is each sister most interested, in which month did she join the Literary Book Circle and how many books has she purchased to date?

1. Sara didn't join the Literary Book Circle in June.

2. The sister who joined the month before Fara has bought fewer books than the one who is adding to her collection of thrillers.

3. The woman who has bought two dozen books so far joined the month after Cara, but earlier in the year than Fara.

4. Lara (who doesn't like books on gardening) joined the month before the woman (not Sara) who is most interested in books on crime.

5. Tara joined the month before (and has purchased three fewer books than) the sister who loves to read books about wildlife.

	Crime	Gardening	Romance	Thrillers	Wildlife	April	May	June	August	September	12 books	15 books	21 books	24 books	27 books
Cara															
Fara															
Lara															
Sara															
Tara															
12 books										
15 books										
21 books										
24 books										
27 books										
April					
May					
June					
August					
September					

Sister	Type of books	Month joined	No purchased

A Little Behind

The five tenants of Rotten Row Cottages have all fallen a little behind with their rent recently, owing to some unfortunate circumstances that led to heavy calls on their cash. However, they all intend to pay up as quickly as possible, so they won't face eviction! Which Rotten Row Cottage is occupied by each, how much is the weekly rent and how many weeks are they in arrears?

1. Dampe Cottage is rented by Miss Keele, at a higher price per week than the rent charged on Mildew Cottage, which unfortunately lives up to its name!

2. Mr Barber owes the landlord a total of £159.00 and the tenant of the dilapidated Cracky Cottage owes a total of £160.00.

3. Mr Parkinson owes two fewer weeks' rent than the tenant of Sliproof Cottage, who pays less per week than Mrs Napier (who owes more than two weeks' rent).

	Cracky Cottage	Dampe Cottage	Mildew Cottage	Mouldy Cottage	Sliproof Cottage	£40.00	£45.00	£48.00	£50.00	£53.00	2 weeks	3 weeks	4 weeks	6 weeks	8 weeks
Mr Barber															
Mr Davis															
Miss Keele															
Mrs Napier															
Mr Parkinson															
2 weeks															
3 weeks															
4 weeks															
6 weeks															
8 weeks															
£40.00						
£45.00						
£48.00						
£50.00						
£53.00						

Tenant	Cottage	Weekly rent	Weeks in arrears

Vital Statistics

Here are the details of four cousins, each of whom is of a different age, height and weight to the others and has a different occupation. Can you determine the facts relating to every woman?

1. The typist is taller than the oldest cousin.

2. The youngest cousin is one centimetre taller than the clerk, who is two kilogrammes heavier than Bessie.

3. The lightest woman is one year younger than the shortest woman.

4. The nurse is taller than the heaviest woman, who is one year older than the woman (not the nurse) who is 166 centimetres tall.

5. Molly is younger than the person who is 167 centimetres tall and who weighs two kilogrammes less than Rosa, who is one centimetre shorter than the waitress.

	41 years old	42 years old	43 years old	44 years old	164cm	165cm	166cm	167cm	50kg	52kg	54kg	56kg	Clerk	Nurse	Typist	Waitress
Bessie																
Lynne																	
Molly																	
Rosa																	
Clerk																	
Nurse																	
Typist																	
Waitress																	
50kg																	
52kg																	
54kg																	
56kg																	
164cm																	
165cm																	
166cm																	
167cm																	

Cousin	Age	Height	Weight	Occupation

Transport Problem

Seven buses from different places all arrived at the bus station at midday yesterday, leaving again five minutes later on their return journeys. When they arrived, one person alighted from each bus; and each of those seven people then caught one of the other six buses to continue a journey. What were the numbers of the first and second buses on which every person travelled?

1. Claire caught the bus that had been used first by the person who later caught the number 48. Theresa didn't get onto the bus first used by Claire.

2. Quentin alighted from the bus that Stella took for the second part of her journey. This bus has a number one lower than that of the first bus Stella had caught, which was taken by the person who had alighted from the number 47 bus.

3. Jasmine took a second bus with a number two lower than that of the first bus used by Quentin.

4. Norman's first bus (not the No 54) had a number two lower than that of the bus taken second by Pete, whose first bus was the one that Norman later caught.

	First bus							Second bus						
	No 46	No 47	No 48	No 49	No 52	No 54	No 56	No 46	No 47	No 48	No 49	No 52	No 54	No 56
Claire														
Jasmine														
Norman														
Pete														
Quentin														
Stella														
Theresa														
No 46														
No 47														
No 48														
No 49														
No 52														
No 54														
No 56														

Second bus

Passenger	First bus	Second bus

Coats of Many Colours

Each of the women in this puzzle decided to replace her old, drab winter coat with a new one in a brighter colour. At the same time, each also bought another accessory. Can you discover not only the colours of every woman's old and new coats, but also which accessory she purchased?

1. The woman who bought a pair of leather boots owned either the black or rusty red coat and bought either the lilac or bright yellow coat.

2. Angelina bought either a pair of gloves or a handbag. The woman who bought the royal blue coat used to own either the brown or grey coat.

3. Myrna's old coat was either beige or brown. Either Myrna or Evelyn is the woman who bought the lime green coat (together with either a pair of gloves or a handbag). The woman who bought the handbag has never owned a beige coat.

4. The woman who bought the lilac coat used to own either the beige or brown coat.

5. The woman who bought a new silk scarf has switched the colour of her coat from either brown or rust to either lime green or royal blue.

6. Tina switched from either black or brown to either lilac or yellow.

7. Lydia bought either a pair of shoes or a handbag. She switched from either beige or rust to either royal blue or scarlet.

	Old coat					New coat									
	Beige	Black	Brown	Grey	Rust	Lilac	Lime green	Royal blue	Scarlet	Yellow	Boots	Gloves	Handbag	Scarf	Shoes
Angelina															
Evelyn															
Lydia															
Myrna															
Tina															
Boots															
Gloves															
Handbag															
Scarf															
Shoes															
Lilac															
Lime green															
Royal blue															
Scarlet															
Yellow															

Woman	Old coat	New coat	Accessory

Purchasing Power

When Dan and Michelle decided to buy five new electrical appliances, they didn't just visit one shop – they went to five different shops to make their purchases. Can you discover the order in which they visited every shop, together with the name of the assistant who served them and the item they bought there?

1. Dan and Michelle bought a new fridge from the female assistant in Metson's earlier than they bought the microwave oven, but later than they had been served by Philip in Walter & Co.

2. Dan and Michelle were served by the two women in two consecutively visited shops.

3. The assistant who sold the freezer to Dan and Michelle isn't Johnnie.

4. Either Luke sold the dishwasher and Melanie serves in Electrique; or Luke sold the microwave oven and Clarice serves in Electrique.

5. Fletcher's was visited immediately before the shop in which Melanie serves, which was visited immediately before the shop in which Dan and Michelle bought a new washing machine.

	First	Second	Third	Fourth	Fifth	Clarice	Johnnie	Luke	Melanie	Philip	Dishwasher	Fridge	Freezer	Microwave	W machine
Brand & Son															
Electrique															
Fletcher's															
Metson's															
Walter & Co															
Dishwasher											
Fridge											
Freezer											
Microwave											
W machine											
Clarice						
Johnnie						
Luke						
Melanie						
Philip						

Shop	Order	Assistant	Item

Plumb Jobs

Five householders telephoned Piper & Floode Same Day Plumbing Services on different days last week, seeking an emergency repair to something which was broken and leaking badly. Piper & Floode immediately sent different plumbers to each client, so can you discover which plumber called at each person's home, what he repaired and on which day?

1. Kevin fixed a leaking tap in one householder's kitchen.

2. The plumber who fixed the bathroom pipe did so earlier in the week than the man who called on Mr Shaw, but two days later in the week than the kitchen pipe was fixed.

3. Mr Timson's call was later in the week than that made by Mrs Yale.

4. Arnold covered the first call of the week: Stephen didn't cover the last.

5. The bathroom tap was fixed on Thursday, but not by Roger.

6. Mrs Walsh had her leaking boiler repaired, but not on Tuesday.

7. Bill (who didn't call on Mr Timson) visited someone the day after the call made by the plumber who dealt with Mr Richards' problem.

	Arnold	Bill	Kevin	Roger	Stephen	Bathroom pipe	Bathroom tap	Boiler	Kitchen pipe	Kitchen tap	Monday	Tuesday	Wednesday	Thursday	Friday
Mr Richards															
Mr Shaw															
Mr Timson															
Mrs Walsh															
Mrs Yale															
Monday															
Tuesday															
Wednesday															
Thursday															
Friday															
Bathroom pipe															
Bathroom tap															
Boiler															
Kitchen pipe															
Kitchen tap															

Householder	Plumber	Repaired	Day

Card Sharp

What is the face value and suit of each of the cards shown below? All twelve cards used below are of different values and together they total 88. Values of the cards are as per their numbers and ace=1, jack=11, queen=12 and king=13. No card is horizontally or vertically next to another of the same colour and there are four different suits in each horizontal row and three different suits in each vertical column.

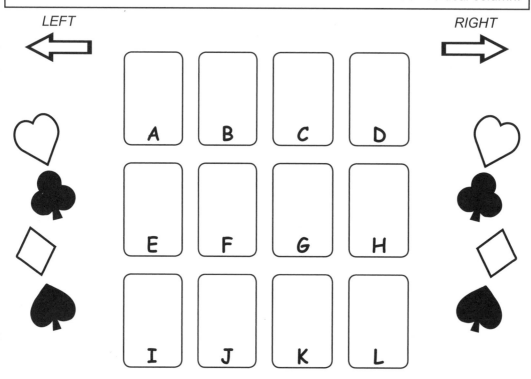

LEFT

RIGHT

1. Cards I, J, K and L have values totalling forty-two. Card L has a higher value than that of card K, which has a higher value than that of card J, which has a higher value than that of card I.

2. The four of hearts is directly next to and left of a club, but not directly next to and above a club.

3. The king (which is not a spade) is directly next to and above the ten.

4. The value of card C is half that of card B (which is not a heart).

5. The jack is neither a heart nor a diamond. Card D is of a higher value than that of card A, which has a value two higher than that of card G.

Visits to Granny

Granny Arbuckle's five granddaughters each paid her a surprise visit yesterday afternoon. They all live some way from Granny, but called in whilst returning from a journey somewhere else. Granny was delighted to see them, of course, but thought the neighbours would be surprised by the number of cars outside! In what order did each arrive, what is the colour of her car and which gift did she bring Granny?

1. Mattie (who doesn't drive the white car) bought a box of chocolates for Granny.

2. The granddaughter whose car is grey bought Granny a bunch of flowers.

3. The granddaughter whose car is silver bought granny a nice new scarf and arrived earlier than Katie.

4. Patsy didn't arrive fourth, although she did arrive later than the granddaughter who gave Granny the book.

5. The last granddaughter to arrive doesn't drive the black car.

6. Dawn (whose car is red) isn't the granddaughter who arrived first, bearing the gift of Granny's favourite brand of scented soap.

	First	Second	Third	Fourth	Fifth	Black	Grey	Red	Silver	White	Book	Chocolates	Flowers	Scarf	Scented soap
Dawn															
Fran															
Katie															
Mattie															
Patsy															
Book															
Chocolates															
Flowers															
Scarf															
Scented soap															
Black															
Grey															
Red															
Silver															
White															

Granddaughter	Order	Car colour	Gift

Christmas Post

> The five women in this puzzle all received different numbers of cards, party invitations and parcels by post last Christmas. Any woman may have received two or more of the same quantity of any of the three items, but no woman received exactly the same number of cards, invitations or parcels as any other. Exactly how many cards, invitations and parcels did each woman receive?

1. Marian received fewer cards than either invitations or parcels.

2. Wilma received fewer parcels than Stephanie, who received one fewer card than Wilma, who received one fewer invitation than the tallest woman (who isn't Valerie or Marian).

3. The woman who received one more invitation than Stephanie also received one more parcel than Jane (who didn't get exactly thirteen party invitations).

4. The woman who received one more card than Wilma also received one more parcel than Valerie.

5. The woman who got seventeen invitations didn't also get seventeen cards.

	13 cards	14 cards	15 cards	17 cards	18 cards	12 invitations	13 invitations	16 invitations	17 invitations	19 invitations	12 parcels	13 parcels	14 parcels	15 parcels	16 parcels
Jane															
Marian															
Stephanie															
Valerie															
Wilma															
12 parcels															
13 parcels															
14 parcels															
15 parcels															
16 parcels															
12 invitations															
13 invitations															
16 invitations															
17 invitations															
19 invitations															

Woman	Cards	Invitations	Parcels

Charity Begins...

...in the Charity Shop! Each of these five women spent different amounts of money on various days last week, in their local charity shop. Can you discover the day on which she visited, what she bought and how much she spent?

1. Sandra visited the charity shop two days before Patricia bought something there.

2. Moira spent £2.25 in the shop the day before the table-lamp was purchased.

3. Caroline paid £1.75 for a book the day after the visit made by the woman who spent £2.00.

4. The woman who visited the shop on Wednesday bought a knitted tea-cosy.

5. Someone bought an umbrella for £1.50 on Monday.

	Monday	Tuesday	Wednesday	Thursday	Friday	Book	Jacket	Table-lamp	Tea-cosy	Umbrella	£1.25	£1.50	£1.75	£2.00	£2.25
Caroline															
Moira															
Patricia															
Sandra															
Thelma															
£1.25															
£1.50															
£1.75															
£2.00															
£2.25															
Book															
Jacket															
Table-lamp															
Tea-cosy															
Umbrella															

Shopper	Day	Item	Spent

213

Grandmas

Five women all became great-grandmothers for the first time yesterday, when their eldest granddaughters all gave birth to bouncing babies. Coincidentally, the five women were all born on 1 July, as were their eldest granddaughters. Can you discover not only the year in which each woman was born, but the name of her granddaughter and the year in which SHE was born?

1. Bryony's grandmother was forty-four years of age when Bryony was born.

2. Tracey's granddaughter (not Penny) is one year younger than Trish, whose grandmother was born in 1943.

3. The oldest woman's first granddaughter is the youngest woman.

4. Melissa's grandmother isn't one year younger than Eloise.

5. Sharon's granddaughter was born in 1978.

6. Lucy's grandmother is Alison, who isn't the youngest of the five new great-grandmothers, although she is younger than Penny's grandmother.

	Grandmother's year of birth					Granddaughter					Granddaughter's year of birth				
	1932	1933	1942	1943	1944	Bryony	Lucy	Melissa	Penny	Trish	1976	1977	1978	1981	1982
Alison															
Eloise															
Margaret															
Sharon															
Tracey															
1976															
1977															
1978															
1981															
1982															
Bryony															
Lucy															
Melissa															
Penny															
Trish															

Grandmother	Year of birth	Granddaughter	Year of birth

It's a Hold-up!

Five commuters sat in their cars in the middle of traffic jams this morning, listening to the local radio's report of the problems. Each report came through at a different time and what you need to do is decide the time at which each motorist heard the announcement relating to his or her route, as well as the problem causing the traffic jam and the length of time for which every journey was delayed.

1. Jasper's journey was delayed due to a truck having broken down. He listened to an announcement of the hold-up half an hour earlier than that concerning black ice (which didn't affect Angela's journey at all).

2. Errol's drive to work was made longer by a minor landslide. This problem was announced earlier than 8.15am, but later than the one reporting the problem which delayed one commuter for fourteen minutes.

3. The earliest announcement didn't report a car accident.

4. The problem of cattle in the road caused a delay of one fewer minute than Angela's, an announcement for which was made earlier than that involving the cattle.

5. The latest announcement wasn't heard by Hazel, whose trip to work took sixteen minutes longer than usual.

6. The commuter who suffered the longest delay didn't hear the 7.55am announcement.

	7.30am	7.45am	7.55am	8.00am	8.15am	Black ice	Car accident	Cattle	Landslide	Truck b'down	11 minutes	12 minutes	14 minutes	16 minutes	17 minutes
Angela															
Dermot															
Errol															
Hazel															
Jasper															
11 minutes															
12 minutes															
14 minutes															
16 minutes															
17 minutes															
Black ice															
Car accident															
Cattle															
Landslide															
Truck breakdown															

Commuter	Announcement at	Problem	Delay time

Simple as A,B,C?

Each of the small squares in the grid below contains either A, B or C. Every row, every column and each of the two long diagonal lines of six squares contains exactly two of each letter. The information in the clues refers only to the squares in that row or column. To help you solve this problem, we've given as many clues as we think you'll need! Can you tell which letter should be placed into each square?

Across:

1. The Cs are somewhere between the As.

3. The Cs are somewhere between the Bs.

5. The Cs are somewhere between the Bs.

6. The As are not next to one another.

Down:

1. The Bs are lower than the As.

2. The Bs are somewhere between the Cs.

4. The Bs are somewhere between the Cs.

6. The Bs are lower than the As.

	1	2	3	4	5	6
1						
2						
3						
4						
5						
6						

Habitual Readers

Every afternoon, the same five people come into Puzzleton Library's reading room, to read their favourite newspapers. Can you discover the time (it's always the same!) that each arrives and leaves, together with the newspaper each prefers?

1. Marc always arrives half an hour earlier than the person who always reads the *Puzzleton Telegraph* and Marc always leaves earlier than the person who always reads the *Puzzleton Independent*.

2. Benny always arrives three quarters of an hour earlier than the person who always reads *Puzzleton Times* and Benny always leaves five minutes earlier than Samantha.

3. Rachel always leaves twenty minutes later than Harold, who always arrives half an hour later than Rachel.

4. The person who reads the *Puzzleton Mirror* always arrives fifteen minutes earlier than the one who always reads the *Puzzleton Guardian*.

Grid columns — Arrives at: 1.30pm, 1.45pm, 2.15pm, 2.30pm, 3.00pm; Leaves at: 3.15pm, 3.20pm, 3.25pm, 3.35pm, 3.45pm; Newspapers: P'ton Guardian, P'ton Independent, P'ton Mirror, P'ton Telegraph, P'ton Times.

Rows: Benny, Harold, Marc, Rachel, Samantha, P'ton Guardian, P'ton Independent, P'ton Mirror, P'ton Telegraph, P'ton Times, 3.15pm, 3.20pm, 3.25pm, 3.35pm, 3.45pm.

Reader	Arrives at	Leaves at	Newspaper

Sum Code

In this puzzle, every letter of the alphabet represents a different number from 1 to 26. The sums below will help you to crack the code and if any letter does not appear, its value is that remaining once the rest of the puzzle is complete. The only arithmetical signs used in this puzzle are '−' (minus), 'x' (times) and '+' (plus).

?

A	B	C	D	E	F	G	H	I	J	K	L	M

N	O	P	Q	R	S	T	U	V	W	X	Y	Z

?

?

1	2	3	4	5	6	7	8	9	10	11	12	13

14	15	16	17	18	19	20	21	22	23	24	25	26

?

1. A = B x C
2. D = E x F
3. G = B x P
4. X = C x K
5. W = C x C
6. O = F x F
7. Y = B x Q
8. H = C x F

9. I = E x K
10. J = E x Q
11. K = B x E
12. M = B x N
13. T = C x E
14. V = B x F
15. M = U + Z
16. Z + R = L − R

Post-holiday Blues

Five men who stood talking in a bar recently discovered that they had all lost something abroad, whilst on holiday earlier this year. Can you discover what each man drank, where he holidayed and what he'd lost?

1. Either the man who drank cola or the one who drank lager lost his camera at some point during his holiday, which was either in Egypt or Japan. His name is either Cliff or Vincent.

2. Either Emile or Vincent is the man who thinks he may have thrown away his house keys at the same time as he disposed of some unwanted brochures handed to him by a tour guide. He drank either cola or wine whilst telling his tale.

3. Cliff lost either his binoculars or his camera whilst in either India or Majorca.

4. The man who drank pale ale isn't the one who holidayed in Thailand and lost either his binoculars or his sunglasses.

5. Either Emile or Jess is the man who drank lager and who had holidayed in either Japan or Majorca.

6. The man who holidayed in Egypt lost either a brand new book or his house keys.

	Cola	Lager	Pale ale	Whisky	Wine	Egypt	India	Japan	Majorca	Thailand	Binoculars	Book	Camera	House keys	Sunglasses
Cliff															
Emile															
Jess															
Sean															
Vincent															
Binoculars															
Book															
Camera															
House keys															
Sunglasses															
Egypt															
India															
Japan															
Majorca															
Thailand															

Man	Drink	Holidayed in	Lost

Every One a Winner

The five couples in this puzzle are all celebrating a major lottery win of $15,000,000. Their syndicated entry finally (after so many years) paid off and, until now, their lives had been very routine, so they are looking forward to 'living a little'. Can you discover the full name of the husband and wife who make up each couple (wives share their husbands' surnames) and the number of the neighbouring house at which they live?

1. Mr & Mrs Donaldson live in a house with a number either one higher or one lower than that owned by Gordon and his wife and either one higher or one lower than that owned by Vera and her husband.

2. Tessa and her husband live in a house with a number two lower than that owned by Arthur and his wife.

3. Colin (not Mr Paige) lives in a house with a number two higher than that owned by Rhoda and her husband (not Mr Paige or Mr Vine).

4. Cecily lives in a house with a higher number than Arthur's.

5. Janet O'Connor isn't married to Edward, who lives at No 5.

6. Edward isn't married to Rhoda or Tessa.

	Cecily	Janet	Rhoda	Tessa	Vera	Donaldson	King	O'Connor	Paige	Vine	No 5	No 6	No 7	No 8	No 9
Arthur															
Colin															
Edward															
Gordon															
Ivan															
No 5															
No 6															
No 7															
No 8															
No 9															
Donaldson															
King															
O'Connor															
Paige															
Vine															

Husband	Wife	Surname	House No

Playing Card Bingo

Every Thursday night, the local Darby & Joan Club holds prize competitions, one of which is Playing Card Bingo. This week's winning card is shown below. Can you determine the order in which the cards on it were called?

Values of cards are as shown and ace=1, jack=11, queen=12 and king=13.

1. The card called ninth has a value half that of the card called tenth, which is either directly above or directly below the card called first (which is of the same suit as the card called second).
2. The card called fourth (which isn't a club) is directly next to and left of the card called sixth, which has a value five higher than that of the card called fourteenth.
3. The card called last (which isn't a club) has a higher value than that of card D, which has a higher value than that of the card called seventh. Card D was called next-but-one after card E.
4. The card called eleventh isn't directly next to the card called thirteenth, which has a lower value than that of the card called eighth, which is directly above the card called twelfth.

1st	2nd	3rd	4th	5th
6th	7th	8th	9th	10th
11th	12th	13th	14th	15th

LEFT ⟵

RIGHT ⟶

A	B	C		D	E	F	G		H
J ♠	2 ♣	10 ♣		9 ♡	7 ♢	4 ♡	8 ♡		7 ♠
10 ♢	4 ♢		A ♠	6 ♢		K ♣	A ♢		5 ♡
I	J		K	L		M	N		O

221

No 220

Frequent Flyer

On each of five days last week, Fred took a domestic flight from his local airport to the capital, to visit clients. For each of the listed days, can you discover the flight number of the plane on which Fred had booked a seat, the time at which it took off and the gate number from which it departed?

1. Flight NE33 left at a time one hour later in the day than the flight which departed from gate 14.

2. The flight from gate 16 at 0900 hours was taken on an earlier day than the one which departed from gate 9.

3. Flight BB63 from gate 6 left ninety minutes later in the day than the last flight taken by Fred.

4. The flight with the latest departure time left from gate 4 and was taken the day before flight KB19, which left thirty minutes later in the day than flight DF46.

5. Flight DF46 departed from a gate with a higher number than the flight which Fred took on Wednesday.

Day of flight	Flight No	Take-off time	Gate No

222

No 221

Figure It Out

Each of the thirty-six squares in the grid is filled with a single digit number from 1 to 9 – each of those numbers being used four times. Use the clues to complete the square, bearing in mind that the same number must not appear in two adjacent (touching) squares in any row across or column down. If the same number is used more than once in any row across or column down it is stated in the relevant clue.

Across:

1. Total twenty-one.

2. Two 1s. Total twenty-three.

3. Two 3s. No 8.

4. Consecutive numbers placed in order.

5. Total thirty-nine.

6. Two 9s. Total thirty-four.

Down:

1. Two 4s. Two 8s.

2. Two 9s. No even numbers.

3. Three 2s. No odd numbers.

4. Two 5s. The only even number is 6.

5. Two 6s. No 1.

6. The only even number is 2.

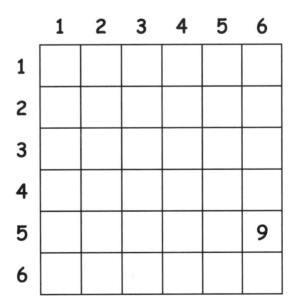

One of Each

Each of these five women has one daughter, one nephew and one niece, all of three different ages. Can you determine the ages of each woman's daughter, nephew and niece?

1. Selina's nephew is older than Nell's niece, but younger than Veronique's daughter.

2. Nell's niece is one year older than Selina's daughter, but younger than Veronique's nephew.

3. Brenda's daughter is older than Veronique's nephew, but younger than Katrina's nephew.

4. Brenda's nephew is older than Veronique's niece.

5. Brenda's niece is older than Katrina's daughter, but younger than Katrina's niece.

	Daughter					Nephew					Niece				
	16 years old	19 years old	20 years old	21 years old	23 years old	15 years old	17 years old	20 years old	22 years old	23 years old	15 years old	17 years old	18 years old	20 years old	22 years old
Brenda															
Katrina															
Nell															
Selina															
Veronique															
Niece 15 years old															
Niece 17 years old															
Niece 18 years old															
Niece 20 years old															
Niece 22 years old															
Nephew 15 years old															
Nephew 17 years old															
Nephew 20 years old															
Nephew 22 years old															
Nephew 23 years old															

Woman	Daughter	Nephew	Niece

Dominological

A standard set of twenty-eight dominoes has been laid out as shown. One is already in position, to give you a start. Can you draw in the edges of the rest? The check-box is provided as an aid to solving.

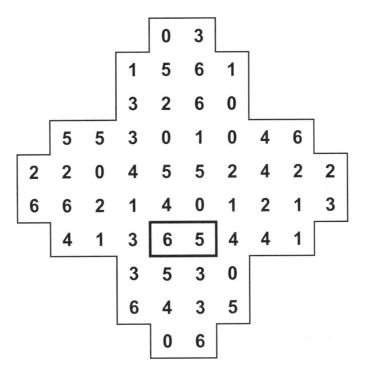

0 - 0		1 - 1		2 - 3		3 - 6	
0 - 1		1 - 2		2 - 4		4 - 4	
0 - 2		1 - 3		2 - 5		4 - 5	
0 - 3		1 - 4		2 - 6		4 - 6	
0 - 4		1 - 5		3 - 3		5 - 5	
0 - 5		1 - 6		3 - 4		5 - 6	✓
0 - 6		2 - 2		3 - 5		6 - 6	

No 224

Ssshhh!

Five fans of films from the era of silent movies were delighted when local cinemas showed a series of films featuring their favourite stars. Each cinema devoted one evening per month. In this puzzle, you can discover not only the name of the favourite star of each of the fans, but also the name of the cinema which screened the film he or she saw last month and the date on which it was shown.

1. Virginia saw the film screened on the 12th and Don saw the one shown at the ABC Cinema.

2. Giles booked his seat at the Palace cinema in advance, so keen was he to see his favourite star. The Palace's 'Silent Night' was two evenings later than the showing attended by Ted, who went to see *Pearl's Mistake*, starring his favourite silent movie star, Pearl White.

3. The audience for *Easy Street*, starring Charlie Chaplin, didn't include Don.

4. The Roxy cinema's screening of the film *The Plastic Age* featuring Clara Bow took place earlier in the month than the Plaza's showing of *The Wind*, starring Lillian Gish.

5. The film seen on the 18th of the month was at the Gaeity cinema.

6. The Buster Keaton film wasn't shown on the 14th of the month.

	Clara Bow	Charlie Chaplin	Lillian Gish	Buster Keaton	Pearl White	ABC cinema	Gaeity cinema	Palace cinema	Plaza cinema	Roxy cinema	12th	14th	16th	18th	20th
Don															
Giles															
Lynne															
Ted															
Virginia															
12th											
14th											
16th											
18th											
20th											
ABC cinema						
Gaeity cinema						
Palace cinema						
Plaza cinema						
Roxy cinema						

Fan	Favourite star	Cinema	Date

Check Out the Facts

The first five women through the checkout at the local mini-market this morning each spent different amounts. Can you discover the full name of the woman in every position in the queue, together with the amount she spent?

1. The first woman in the queue didn't spend the most money. The woman who spent €22.12 isn't Mrs Hobart.

2. The customer who spent the least was served immediately before the woman (not Mrs Flinders) who spent €22.22.

3. Anthea George spent ten cents more than Mrs Flinders, who was served immediately after Anthea.

4. Coral spent ten cents less than Venetia (who isn't Mrs Flinders).

5. Mrs Connolly was served either immediately before or immediately after Lucinda, who spent ten cents less than Mrs Connolly.

	Anthea	Coral	Imogen	Lucinda	Venetia	Connolly	Feighan	Flinders	George	Hobart	€21.92	€22.02	€22.12	€22.22	€22.32
First															
Second															
Third															
Fourth															
Fifth															
€21.92															
€22.02															
€22.12															
€22.22															
€22.32															
Connolly															
Feighan															
Flinders															
George															
Hobart															

Order in queue	Forename	Surname	Spent

No 226

Patchwork

Each piece in the patchwork square below is decorated with a letter of the alphabet: A, B, C, D, E, F or G. In each horizontal row, vertical column and long diagonal line of seven smaller pieces there are seven different letters: some are already in place. Can you discover which letter fits in every piece? There is only one correct solution to this puzzle – if you take a wrong path along the way, you won't finish the quilt!

1. The letter in piece 1 is the same as that in piece 19.

2. The letter in piece 3 is the same as that in piece 43.

3. The letter in piece 4 is the same as that in piece 47.

4. The letter in piece 11 is the same as that in piece 35.

5. The letter in piece 24 is the same as that in piece 40.

6. The letter in piece 5 is different to the letter in piece 31.

7. The letter in piece 32 is different to the letter in piece 41.

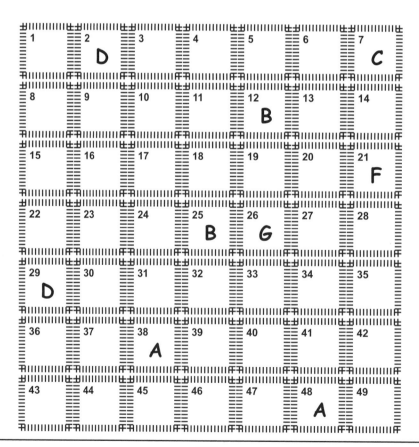

Trading Up

Car dealer, Les Scrappett had a good afternoon, with five customers part-exchanging their cars for newer, more expensive models. As is often the way with logic puzzles, no customer exchanged his or her car for one of the same make. At what time did each arrive, which model was part-exchanged and for which new car?

1. Mrs Taylor was the last customer of the afternoon.

2. Mr Malone bought a new Vauxwoo and arrived later than Mr Hudson, who didn't part-exchange the old Daevo.

3. The customer who arrived at three o'clock bought a new Dathall, but didn't part-exchange the old Daevo.

4. One customer part-exchanged a Volgeot for a brand new Daevo.

5. The man who bought a new Peutsun didn't part-exchange the Dathall.

6. Miss Jarvis hates Dathalls, so has never owned one and would never own one!

7. The customer who came at two o'clock part-exchanged the ancient Peutsun.

	1.00pm	2.00pm	3.00pm	4.00pm	5.00pm	Old car Daevo	Dathall	Peutsun	Vauxwoo	Volgeot	New car Daevo	Dathall	Peutsun	Vauxwoo	Volgeot
Mr Bailey															
Mr Hudson															
Miss Jarvis															
Mr Malone															
Mrs Taylor															
New car Daevo															
Dathall															
Peutsun															
Vauxwoo															
Volgeot															
Old car Daevo															
Dathall															
Peutsun															
Vauxwoo															
Volgeot															

Customer	Time	Old car	New car

Wake Up Calls

Between half past five and six o'clock, five people checked into the Paradiso Hotel yesterday afternoon and each requested a wake-up call at a different time this morning. Can you discover the name of the person booked into each room and the time at which he or she arrived, as well as the time of their respective wake-up calls?

1. Miss Jones asked for a wake-up call fifteen minutes earlier than that requested by Mr Headley. Mr Headley didn't arrive fifteen minutes earlier than whoever asked for the earliest wake-up call.

2. Mr Loxley arrived earlier than the resident of Room 109, but five minutes later than the person who asked for the latest wake up call and who occupied a room with a number four lower than that taken by Mr Kane.

3. The resident of Room 107 requested a wake-up call forty-five minutes earlier than that asked for by Mrs Ivy, who wasn't the first of the five people to check in.

4. Mr Kane asked for a wake-up call at 6.15am and arrived five minutes later than the resident who was given the keys to Room 101.

	Mr Headley	Mrs Ivy	Miss Jones	Mr Kane	Mr Loxley	5.30pm	5.40pm	5.45pm	5.50pm	5.55pm	6.00am	6.15am	6.30am	6.45am	7.00am
Room 101															
Room 103															
Room 107															
Room 109															
Room 111															
6.00am															
6.15am															
6.30am															
6.45am															
7.00am															
5.30pm															
5.40pm															
5.45pm															
5.50pm															
5.55pm															

Room	Resident	Arrived at	Wake-up call time

A Good Match

Five women who all work in the same office turned up one cold day each wearing a hat, gloves and scarf in three different colours. They decided that they'd swap their hats and scarves, so that each now possesses a hat, gloves and scarf in just the one colour. Can you find out the colour of the gloves owned (and kept) by each woman, as well as the (two different) colours of the hat and scarf she gave away?

1. Helga used to own a white scarf but not a turquoise hat.

2. Helga gave her hat to Brenda, who never had a pink scarf.

3. Diane didn't give her hat to Jenny.

4. The woman whose gloves are yellow used to own the pink hat.

5. The woman whose gloves are pink used to own a yellow hat, but not a turquoise scarf.

6. Josephine is now wearing Diane's scarf and Jenny's hat.

	Gloves					Hat					Scarf				
	Cream	Pink	Turquoise	White	Yellow	Cream	Pink	Turquoise	White	Yellow	Cream	Pink	Turquoise	White	Yellow
Diane															
Brenda															
Helga															
Jenny															
Josephine															
Scarf Cream															
Pink															
Turquoise															
White															
Yellow															
Hat Cream															
Pink															
Turquoise															
White															
Yellow															

Woman	Gloves	Hat	Scarf

Presidential Elections

There are two main candidates (T Baines and M Hobbs) for the post of President of the Students' Society at Puzzleton College and the election is drawing near. Last week, there were five different opinion polls, with different sample sizes of students, giving ten different percentages (excluding the "don't knows") in support of the two candidates. What was the sample size and what percentage did each poll reveal?

1. The first poll surveyed five fewer students than the fourth poll, which showed a larger percentage lead (in other words, the difference between the candidates' percentages was wider) for one candidate over the other than any other poll.

2. The third poll was conducted with a larger sample size than the fifth poll.

3. Baines was leading by two per cent in the first poll and Hobbs was leading by three per cent in the second poll.

4. The third poll gave Baines forty-five per cent and questioned five more students than the poll that showed Hobbs as being in the lead, with forty-four per cent.

5. Baines polled forty-six per cent in the poll in which Hobbs's percentage was two higher than that of Baines's result in the fifth poll.

	110 students	120 students	125 students	130 students	140 students	Baines 40%	43%	45%	46%	47%	Hobbs 41%	42%	44%	48%	49%
First poll															
Second poll															
Third poll															
Fourth poll															
Fifth poll															
Hobbs 41%															
42%															
44%															
48%															
49%															
Baines 40%															
43%															
45%															
46%															
47%															

Poll order	Sample size	Baines	Hobbs

A Moving Story

The five couples in this puzzle have just moved house and now live in a town thirty miles from their old home. Can you discover who is married to whom, which town each has moved from and the town in which each couple now lives?

1. Gus and his wife have moved to Baywood, which is where Jeremy and his wife used to live.

2. Heidi and her husband didn't move from Crowville.

3. Daisy and her husband moved from the town where Crispin and his wife (not Shirley) now live.

4. Benjamin and his wife didn't move from Edgeburgh.

5. Camilla and her husband used to live in Fishbrook, which is where Heidi and her husband (not Jeremy) have made their new home.

6. Although they haven't seen them recently, Sid and his wife Hilary are great friends of the couple who moved from Crowville.

	Camilla	Daisy	Heidi	Hilary	Shirley	Moved from Baywood	Moved from Crowville	Moved from Dawston	Moved from Edgeburgh	Moved from Fishbrook	Moved to Baywood	Moved to Crowville	Moved to Dawston	Moved to Edgeburgh	Moved to Fishbrook
Benjamin															
Crispin															
Gus															
Jeremy															
Sid															
Moved to Baywood															
Moved to Crowville															
Moved to Dawston															
Moved to Edgeburgh															
Moved to Fishbrook															
Moved from Baywood															
Moved from Crowville															
Moved from Dawston															
Moved from Edgeburgh															
Moved from Fishbrook															

Husband	Wife	Moved from	Moved to

Red, White & Blue

These women are dressed in various red, white and blue items. Any may be dressed in more than one item in these colours, so use the clues below to find out exactly what each is wearing from the waist up, from the waist down and on her feet.

1. Joanne is wearing a blue jumper but not a white skirt.

2. Isabel isn't wearing a white jumper.

3. Pauline isn't wearing a pair of shoes, nor is she wearing blue trousers.

4. Olive is wearing red shorts but not red boots.

5. The women wearing jackets are also wearing trousers.

6. The women wearing white in the 'waist up' category are wearing shoes.

7. The women with white footwear are also wearing skirts.

	Waist up					Waist down					Footwear				
	Blue cardigan	Blue jumper	Red jacket	White jacket	White jumper	Blue skirt	Blue trousers	Red shorts	White skirt	White trousers	Blue trainers	Red boots	Red shoes	White shoes	White trainers
Isabel															
Olive															
Joanne															
Pauline															
Sylvia															
Blue trainers															
Red boots															
Red shoes															
White shoes															
White trainers															
Blue skirt															
Blue trousers															
Red shorts															
White skirt															
White trousers															

Name	Waist up	Waist down	Footwear

Increasing Service

Five rectors from neighbouring parishes are trying to encourage people to attend church more frequently. Can you discover who is the rector of each church, together with the new group each has planned to introduce and the average number of people who attend Sunday service every week?

1. The Reverend King is introducing a Sunday school for children.

2. Neither St Anthony's nor All Saints' church have rectors with plans to introduce a crèche.

3. The highest weekly attendance is at St Luke's.

4. An average of sixty-four people attend the services conducted by the Reverend Ogden. He isn't the rector of St Paul's, who is planning to introduce bible classes.

5. The rector of All Saints' church isn't planning to introduce a mothers' group.

6. The Reverend Linton isn't the rector at the church with the smallest weekly attendance, where a youth club is planned.

7. The rector of St Stephen's is the Reverend Marsh, whose weekly congregation numbers more than that at the church where the Reverend Linton preaches.

	Revd King	Revd Linton	Revd Marsh	Revd Nairn	Revd Ogden	Bible classes	Crèche	Mothers' group	Sunday school	Youth club	42 people	53 people	64 people	75 people	86 people
All Saints'															
St Anthony's															
St Luke's															
St Paul's															
St Stephen's															
42 people															
53 people															
64 people															
75 people															
86 people															
Bible classes															
Crèche															
Mothers' group															
Sunday school															
Youth club															

Church	Rector	Activity	Attendance

Celebrity Auction

As part of an effort to raise money for charity, an auction is being held and various large industries and well-known people have been approached for donations. Five television celebrities responded immediately to the call and have donated personal items for which the public can bid. Can you discover their full names, the name of the programme of which he or she is the star and the item he or she has pledged?

1. Judy (who is the hostess in the popular game show *Bet You Can't!*) isn't the celebrity surnamed Westwood, who donated a pair of boots to the charity auction.

2. The celebrity surnamed Rushmore has donated a pair of jeans to the event and TV's 'it' girl Kate has donated a pair of silk stockings, previously worn by herself!

3. The star of the TV sitcom *The Love Match* who has donated the shirt isn't Tom Adamson.

4. The celebrity surnamed Stein appears in the comedy series *Joking Apart*.

5. Sindy (whose surname isn't Jackson) doesn't appear in the fortnightly nature programme *Wild Wanders*.

	Adamson	Jackson	Rushmore	Stein	Westwood	Bet You Can't!	House Huntin'	Joking Apart	The Love Match	Wild Wanders	Boots	Jeans	Shirt	Stockings	Teddy bear
Adam															
Judy															
Kate															
Sindy															
Tom															
Boots															
Jeans															
Shirt															
Stockings															
Teddy bear															
Bet You Can't!															
House Huntin'															
Joking Apart															
The Love Match															
Wild Wanders															

Forename	Surname	Programme	Donation

Coming Home

Mr & Mrs McDonagh's five sons have all been working abroad on temporary contracts and each is returning home next week, flying into a different airport – luckily they're arriving on different days, so Mr & Mrs McDonagh's offer to meet each man at the airport won't involve too much of a dash! Can you discover where each has been working, the airport at which his plane will land and the day of his return?

1. The first man to return home will be landing at Stanwick airport.

2. George has been working as part of an engineering team in Dubai.

3. Patrick will arrive home two days earlier than his younger brother, who has been working in Austria and who will land at Luchester airport.

4. The man whom the McDonaghs will meet at Gatrow airport will arrive the day before the one flying home from Ecuador.

5. Joe will arrive on Tuesday, but not at Mansted airport. Neither Patrick nor Joe will be landing at Heathton airport.

6. Both Dave and Joe are looking forward to the reunion with the brother who has been working in Canada.

7. The man flying into Mansted airport will arrive home later than Simon.

	Austria	Barbados	Canada	Dubai	Ecuador	Gatrow	Heathton	Luchester	Mansted	Stanwick	Monday	Tuesday	Wednesday	Thursday	Friday
Dave															
George															
Joe															
Patrick															
Simon															
Monday															
Tuesday															
Wednesday															
Thursday															
Friday															
Gatrow															
Heathton															
Luchester															
Mansted															
Stanwick															

Son	Country	Airport	Arrival day

Working Women

The women in this puzzle are all neighbours and each absolutely detests one household chore which is the favourite of one of the other women. Can you discover who lives at each of the given house numbers and the job she loves and hates?

1. Mrs Frost (who works all day in a restaurant and who hates cooking when she gets home) lives in a house with a number one lower than that occupied by the woman who hates cleaning windows.

2. Ironing is the job most preferred by the woman who hates doing the dusting. She lives in a house with a number two higher than that of Mrs White's house.

3. Mrs Browne loves the chore that Mrs Davis hates; and hates the chore that Mrs Frost loves.

4. Mrs Dean's house has a number two higher than that of the woman who hates doing the ironing.

5. The woman who loves cooking lives at a house with a number four higher than that of the house occupied by Mrs White.

6. The woman who hates vacuuming doesn't live at No 14.

	Mrs Browne	Mrs Davis	Mrs Dean	Mrs Frost	Mrs White	Loves Cooking	Loves Dusting	Loves Ironing	Loves Vacuuming	Loves Windows	Hates Cooking	Hates Dusting	Hates Ironing	Hates Vacuuming	Hates Windows
No 14															
No 16															
No 17															
No 18															
No 20															
Hates Cooking															
Hates Dusting															
Hates Ironing															
Hates Vacuuming															
Hates Windows															
Loves Cooking															
Loves Dusting															
Loves Ironing															
Loves Vacuuming															
Loves Windows															

House No	Occupant	Loves	Hates

Shopaholics

The five women in this puzzle all exceeded their budgets last week, having been attracted by goods on offer in the sales. Every woman spent between $300 and $400 on impulse purchases and each went out shopping on a different day (Monday to Sunday). Can you discover the day on which she shopped, together with the amount she spent?

1. Geraldine spent less than Susan, but more than Lois.

2. Whoever went on Saturday's shopping spree spent twenty dollars less than Kirsty, but more than was spent by the woman who shopped on Sunday.

3. The bill for Tuesday's shopping trip amounted to twenty dollars less than Cassie's, but more than was spent by Susan.

4. The woman who spent the most shopped the day before the one who spent $330, but the day after the woman who spent $320.

5. The woman who shopped the day before Bernadette spent forty dollars more than Bernadette.

	Monday	Tuesday	Wednesday	Thursday	Friday	Saturday	Sunday	$320	$330	$340	$350	$360	$370	$380
Bernadette														
Cassie														
Geraldine														
Joyce														
Kirsty														
Lois														
Susan														
$320							
$330							
$340							
$350							
$360							
$370							
$380							

Shopper	Day	Spent

Simple as A,B,C?

Each of the small squares in the grid below contains either A, B or C. Every row, every column and each of the two long diagonal lines of six squares contains exactly two of each letter. The information in the clues refers only to the squares in that row or column. To help you solve this problem, we've given as many clues as we think you'll need! Can you tell which letter should be placed into each square?

Across:

1. The Bs are somewhere between the As.

2. The Bs are not in adjacent squares.

3. The Bs are further left than the As.

6. The Cs are further left than the Bs.

Down:

1. Neither B is next to and above a C.

2. The Bs are higher than the As.

4. The As are higher than the Cs.

5. The As are lower than the Cs.

6. The Cs are somewhere between the As.

	1	2	3	4	5	6
1						
2						
3						
4						
5						
6						

Such a Sweet Woman

Magda is such a kind neighbour. She's always helping people, doing good turns, without asking or even anticipating any reward; so she was delighted when, last week, five of her neighbours called on different days bearing a bunch of flowers and another gift in return for her help. Can you discover the name of the person who called each day, together with the type of flowers and other gift he or she brought?

1. Quentin called the day before the person (not Tina) who gave Magda a pair of theatre tickets and a large bunch of carnations.

2. Penelope presented Magda with a bouquet of lilies, but she wasn't the neighbour who called round on Tuesday.

3. The neighbour who presented Magda with an armful of asters and a bottle of wine isn't Tina, who thanked her for babysitting.

4. Rob gave her a bunch of roses on Monday, as his way of saying "thank you" to Magda for her help in typing his coursework notes.

5. Magda received a large tin of biscuits the day before someone gave her a bracelet.

6. The person who called on Saturday didn't give the chocolates.

	Penelope	Quentin	Rob	Sean	Tina	Asters	Carnations	Freesias	Lilies	Roses	Biscuits	Bracelet	Chocolates	Theatre tickets	Wine
Monday															
Tuesday															
Thursday															
Friday															
Saturday															
Biscuits											
Bracelet											
Chocolates											
Theatre tickets											
Wine											
Asters						
Carnations						
Freesias						
Lilies						
Roses						

Day	Caller	Flowers	Other

Wedding Belles

Five of Letitia's closest friends attended her wedding at eleven o'clock last Saturday morning, each leaving home and arriving at the church at a different time. From the clues below, can you discover each woman's departure and arrival times and the colour of the outfit she wore?

1. The woman who arrived at the church at 10.25am took the shortest time to travel and left home five minutes earlier than Audrey, whose dress wasn't pink.

2. Constance wore a floaty cream-coloured outfit and Joan (who took more than half an hour to get from home to the church) wore a turquoise suit. One of these two women arrived first and the other arrived last at the church.

3. Gail wasn't the woman dressed in blue.

4. The woman in the pale blue dress (who left home earliest) didn't arrive at 10.40am, although she did take the longest time to get to the church.

	Left home					Got to church					Outfit colour				
	9.50am	9.55am	10.05am	10.15am	10.20am	10.10am	10.25am	10.35am	10.40am	10.45am	Blue	Cream	Lemon	Pink	Turquoise
Audrey															
Constance															
Gail															
Joan															
Melanie															
Blue															
Cream															
Lemon															
Pink															
Turquoise															
10.10am															
10.25am															
10.35am															
10.40am															
10.45am															

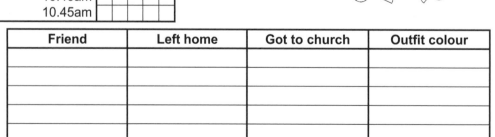

Friend	Left home	Got to church	Outfit colour

Across America

The five business executives in this puzzle each made trips to client companies situated in two different American states last week: one on the east and one on the west side. Can you discover who's who and where they went?

1. The woman surnamed Jenkins travelled to Idaho.

2. Olivia Marchant didn't travel to New Hampshire. Nor was she the person who visited clients in both Florida and Washington.

3. Carla went to Maine and Ellen (whose surname isn't Richards or Thomkins) visited a client in Oregon.

4. The man who travelled to Virginia isn't surnamed Richards.

5. Joseph's surname isn't Thomkins.

6. The executive who travelled to Georgia is younger than the one who went to Nevada.

	Jenkins	Marchant	Richards	Thomkins	Underwood	Florida	Georgia	Maine	New Hampshire	Virginia	California	Idaho	Nevada	Oregon	Washington
Ellen															
Joseph															
Carla															
Martin															
Olivia															
California															
Idaho															
Nevada															
Oregon															
Washington															
Florida															
Georgia															
Maine															
New Hampshire															
Virginia															

Executive	Surname	Eastern state	Western state

Storage Problem

The six people in this puzzle have decided to de-clutter their kitchen cupboards and throw out anything out of date or unwanted. Whilst they were at this task they counted the numbers of bottles, cans and packets in just one cupboard: why they did this, we don't know, but it makes for a great puzzle! Can you determine the exact quantity of bottles, cans and packets each person possessed?

1. Fran counted twice as many packets as the number of bottles counted by Gina (who counted two more bottles than whoever found ten cans in the cupboard).

2. The number of cans found by Seamus was one higher than the number of bottles found by Fran, who counted two more cans than Moira.

3. Kenny found three more cans than Nigel, who counted two more bottles than Moira, who counted four more packets than Kenny, who found more bottles than Seamus.

4. Nigel found more packets than Seamus.

5. Gina counted two more cans than packets.

	2 bottles	3 bottles	4 bottles	6 bottles	7 bottles	8 bottles	7 cans	8 cans	9 cans	10 cans	12 cans	13 cans	6 packets	8 packets	10 packets	14 packets	16 packets	18 packets
Fran																		
Gina																		
Kenny																		
Moira																		
Nigel																		
Seamus																		
6 packets																		
8 packets																		
10 packets																		
14 packets																		
16 packets																		
18 packets																		
7 cans																		
8 cans																		
9 cans																		
10 cans																		
12 cans																		
13 cans																		

Name	Bottles	Cans	Packets

Card Sharp

What is the face value and suit of each of the cards shown below? All twelve cards used below are of different values and together they total 82. Values of the cards are as per their numbers and ace=1, jack=11, queen=12 and king=13. No card is horizontally or vertically next to another of the same colour and there are four different suits in each horizontal row and three different suits in each vertical column.

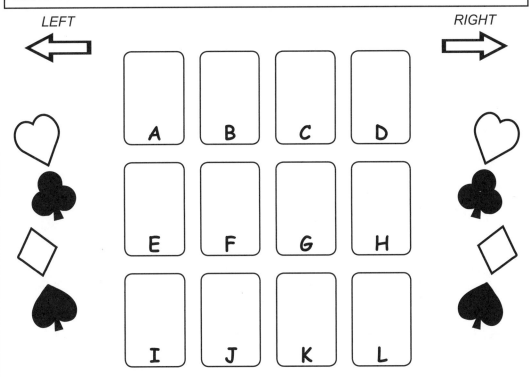

LEFT

RIGHT

1. Card C (which isn't a diamond) has a value one higher than that of card H. Card D is a spade.

2. The king is of a different suit to the ace. The four of hearts appears somewhere in this puzzle.

3. The queen of diamonds is directly next to and left of the five.

4. The two of hearts is directly next to and below the ten, which is directly next to and below the three.

5. The jack of clubs is directly next to and below the eight, which is directly next to and left of the king.

Early Morning Deliveries

Jack is a milkman who delivers to most of the residents of Walton Street. This morning he had five extra items to deliver along with the milk, as requested by the householders. Can you discover who lives at each address, how many pints of milk each has per day and what extra item he or she asked Jack to deliver today.

1. Mr Nutton takes two pints of milk every day.

2. Jack delivered five pints of milk and half a pint of double cream to one address this morning.

3. Mrs Weller didn't order any cheese.

4. Miss Barton (who asked for a loaf of bread) isn't the householder at No 18, who has one pint of milk per day.

5. Mr Franks who lives at No 15 takes one more pint of milk per day than the customer who asked Jack to deliver a small sack of potatoes.

6. The resident of No 23 has twice as much milk every morning as the householder at No 29, who had asked Jack to deliver the eggs.

	Mrs Anderson	Miss Barton	Mr Franks	Mr Nutton	Mrs Weller	1 pint	2 pints	3 pints	4 pints	5 pints	Bread	Cheese	Cream	Eggs	Potatoes
No 15															
No 17															
No 18															
No 23															
No 29															
Bread															
Cheese															
Cream															
Eggs															
Potatoes															
1 pint															
2 pints															
3 pints															
4 pints															
5 pints															

House No	Householder	Milk order	Other item

A Haunting Story

The Puzzleton Society for Psychical Research sent an investigator to various locations across the county last year, to investigate new reports of hauntings. Can you work out which investigator was sent to the listed places, the apparition he or she was researching and the month in which the investigation took place?

1. The investigation into the reported sighting of a Roman soldier was undertaken next after that into the reports of a mysterious black dog.

2. Mr Tyler's investigation was undertaken next after that of Dr Morton.

3. There had been approximately twenty sightings of the grey lady reputed to haunt Loxbury Manor before the Puzzleton Society for Psychical Research sent an investigator to check out the stories.

4. The sightings at Dixter Hall were investigated before Mrs Naseby's case, but later in the year than that relating to the ghost of a child.

5. Dr Collins investigated the haunting at the Ace Supermarket, which had nothing to do with the ghost of the child.

6. The earliest investigation of the year (not into the sighting of a ghost of a witch or a child) took place at Hanbury Heights, a newly-erected block of flats.

	Dr Collins	Dr Morton	Mrs Naseby	Miss Parkinson	Mr Tyler	April	May	August	September	November	Black dog	Child	Grey lady	Roman soldier	Witch
Ace Supermarket															
Dixter Hall															
Hanbury Heights															
Loxbury Manor															
Oldcastle Abbey															
Black dog															
Child															
Grey lady															
Roman soldier															
Witch															
April															
May															
August															
September															
November															

Location	Investigator	Month	Apparition

Meet the Chefs

Fletcher's is one of the most renowned restaurants in the country and maintains its reputation for superlative food by employing five of the world's leading chefs. Can you discover their names, together with the year in which they joined the staff of Fletcher's and the country in which each originally made his name?

1. No man's surname has exactly the same number of letters as that of his forename.

2. The man surnamed Grosliche has never been to Japan.

3. The man who had formerly been the top chef at one of France's most prestigious hotels started work at Fletcher's the year before Will, but the year after Mr Marks.

4. Roger from Russia started at Fletcher's one year earlier than the man from Japan.

5. Francesco joined the staff of Fletcher's the year after Anton took up his employment there.

6. Axel Danbury started at Fletcher's the year after the man who had originally made his name in the restaurants of London, England.

	Danbury	Grosliche	Marks	Wang	Zarné	2001	2002	2003	2004	2005	England	France	Germany	Japan	Russia
Anton															
Axel															
Francesco															
Roger															
Will															
England																
France																
Germany																
Japan																
Russia																
2001																
2002																
2003																
2004																
2005																

Forename	Surname	Year of joining	Country

Walking the Dog

These chaps have a nightly routine of taking their dogs for a walk, then returning past the Pig & Whistle pub – except that, naturally, each man does not walk straight past the pub: he calls in for a drink on his way home! Where does each man walk his dog, at what time does he leave the house and for how long is he usually out?

1. The man (not Tim) who goes out at the latest time only stays out for half an hour. He walks to the local shop to get a paper each night.

2. Adam exercises his dog by taking him down to the harbour and back and is usually out for fifteen minutes longer than the man who leaves at 8.45pm each evening.

3. The man who walks his dog around the streets is usually out for fifteen minutes longer (and returns home half an hour later) than Colin.

4. The man who walks his dog around the lake is usually out for half an hour longer than Robert, who leaves his house later than Adam goes out.

	Harbour	Lake	Local shop	Park	Streets	8.00pm	8.15pm	8.30pm	8.45pm	9.00pm	30 minutes	45 minutes	1 hour	1 hour 30 mins	1 hour 45 mins
Adam															
Colin															
Robert															
Steven															
Tim															
30 minutes															
45 minutes															
1 hour															
1 hour 30 mins															
1 hour 45 mins															
8.00pm															
8.15pm															
8.30pm															
8.45pm															
9.00pm															

Name	Walk	Goes out at	Usually out for

Essay Exercise

Publishers Bills & Moon organised a short-story writing competition last year which attracted so many entries that they have repeated their sucess again this year – if you want to enter, the stories need to be in by the end of the month, by the way! Can you discover the full name of the five authors who were awarded prizes (and also contracts!) last year and the places given to them by the panel of judges?

1. *Time After Time* was the title of John's entry and third prize was awarded to the essay entitled *I Can't Recall*.

2. Robert (whose surname isn't Garner) was awarded second prize. His cousin is George Player, who also won a prize in the competition (but not for *Starstruck*).

3. The first prize (a gold pen and a substantial sum of money) wasn't awarded to Miss Elwood. Nor was Miss Elwood awarded fourth place in the competition.

4. Fifth place was given to the story written by the entrant surnamed Norton.

5. Harriet's entry achieved a higher position than *The Rose Tree*, written by the entrant surnamed Purvis.

Author	Surname	Short-story	Place

Contivision Song Contest

Every year the Contivision Song Contest is broadcast to all four corners of the globe and features five singers who have won the right to perform. This year's Contivision Song Contest will be televised tomorrow night, but because we know you can't wait that long to find out who will be appearing, we've listed the entrants, their songs and the order in which they will sing – so just follow the clues to find out!

1. This year's Contivision Song Contest is being held in London (the Europeans won last year's event, so must hold the Contest this year, rather than compete) and Honor is very much looking forward to performing her song, *A Lonely Love*, on the stage of the Royal Albert Hall.

2. Jasmine's song is *My Gift* and she will be performing two places later in the programme than the singer of *Yours Forever*.

3. The first song to be sung won't be the Asian entry, *Peace to You*.

4. Andreas will be singing earlier than the performer from South America, but later than the singer of *Worldly Love*.

5. The last song of the evening will be the African entry.

6. Petunia will perform second. She isn't singing *Yours Forever* and *Yours Forever* isn't the North American entry.

	Africa	North America	South America	Asia	Australasia	A Lonely Love	My Gift	Peace to You	Worldly Love	Yours Forever	First	Second	Third	Fourth	Fifth
Andreas															
Honor															
Jasmine															
Marcus															
Petunia															
First											
Second											
Third											
Fourth											
Fifth											
A Lonely Love						
My Gift						
Peace to You						
Worldly Love						
Yours Forever						

Entrant	Continent	Song	Order

Baby Boom

No fewer than five babies were born on New Year's Day this year, in the maternity ward of Puzzleton hospital. The proud mothers were duly interviewed and photographed by the local newspaper but, since you probably haven't seen a copy, the clues below will help you to discover the time at which each mother gave birth, together with her surname and the name of her child.

1. Carolyn Hawkins occupied the bed next to that taken by Julia Walton's mother, who wasn't the last of the five women to give birth.

2. Rose produced her offspring directly before Amanda was born, although later than Mrs Fiske become a mother.

3. Larry's mother is Camille, whose surname isn't Reeves.

4. Donna was the fourth woman to give birth on New Year's Day.

5. Harmony was the second baby to be born.

6. Mrs Levine was the third mother to give birth to a child at Puzzleton hospital on 1 January.

	Camille	Carolyn	Donna	Marnie	Rose	Fiske	Hawkins	Levine	Reeves	Walton	Amanda	Harmony	Julia	Larry	Michael
1.03am															
1.59am															
3.32am															
9.30am															
11.15am															
Amanda											
Harmony											
Julia											
Larry											
Michael											
Fiske						
Hawkins						
Levine						
Reeves						
Walton						

Order	Mother	Surname	Baby

Split Personalities

Bored with continually having to watch films rented from the local video shop by various members of her family, Mrs Yapton has taken a mild form of revenge by cutting photos of their five all-time favourite stars into four pieces (head, body, legs and feet) and then reassembling them in such a way that each new picture contains pieces of four old ones. How has Mrs Yapton reassembled the photographs?

1. Marilyn Monroe's body is in the same picture as John Wayne's legs, which don't end in Frank Sinatra's feet.

2. Frank Sinatra's feet aren't in the same picture as the head of Marilyn Monroe.

3. John Wayne's body isn't attached to Oliver Hardy's head, which is in the same photo as Doris Day's legs.

4. Doris Day's body is in the same picture as Oliver Hardy's feet, which aren't attached to Frank Sinatra's legs.

		Body					Legs					Feet				
		Doris Day	Oliver Hardy	Marilyn Monroe	Frank Sinatra	John Wayne	Doris Day	Oliver Hardy	Marilyn Monroe	Frank Sinatra	John Wayne	Doris Day	Oliver Hardy	Marilyn Monroe	Frank Sinatra	John Wayne
Head	Doris Day															
	Oliver Hardy															
	Marilyn Monroe															
	Frank Sinatra															
	John Wayne															
Feet	Doris Day															
	Oliver Hardy															
	Marilyn Monroe															
	Frank Sinatra															
	John Wayne															
Legs	Doris Day															
	Oliver Hardy															
	Marilyn Monroe															
	Frank Sinatra															
	John Wayne															

Head	Body	Legs	Feet

Figure It Out

Each of the thirty-six squares in the grid is filled with a single digit number from 1 to 9 – each of those numbers being used four times. Use the clues to complete the square, bearing in mind that the same number must not appear in two adjacent (touching) squares in any row across or column down. If the same number is used more than once in any row across or column down it is stated in the relevant clue.

Across:

1. Two 1s.

2. Consecutive numbers placed in order.

3. Two 3s. Two 9s. No 6.

4. Consecutive numbers placed in order.

5. Two 7s.

6. Two 4s. No 2.

Down:

1. No 4.

2. Total thirty-nine.

3. Two 1s. No 6.

4. Consecutive numbers placed in order.

5. Two 8s. No 2.

6. Two 2s.

```
        1   2   3   4   5   6
     ┌───┬───┬───┬───┬───┬───┐
   1 │   │   │   │   │   │   │
     ├───┼───┼───┼───┼───┼───┤
   2 │   │   │   │   │   │   │
     ├───┼───┼───┼───┼───┼───┤
   3 │   │   │   │   │   │   │
     ├───┼───┼───┼───┼───┼───┤
   4 │   │   │   │   │   │   │
     ├───┼───┼───┼───┼───┼───┤
   5 │   │   │   │   │   │   │
     ├───┼───┼───┼───┼───┼───┤
   6 │   │   │   │   │   │   │
     └───┴───┴───┴───┴───┴───┘
```

Fun Run

Six friends are currently taking part in a marathon, trying to raise cash in donations and sponsorship pledges, for the local hospice. Can you name the runner in each of the numbered vests, as shown in the picture below, as well as determine the colour of his vest (not shown in the picture below, as that would spoil the puzzle!)?
NB – 'Left' and 'right' are from your point of view as you look at the picture.

1. Joel is wearing an even number on his vest, which isn't green.

2. The runner in the blue vest is wearing an even number on his vest and is pictured directly next to and right of Keith. Keith is pictured directly next to and right of the man (not Oliver) in the black vest.

3. The man in the green vest is pictured directly between Oliver on the left and Lenny on the right. Lenny is further right than the runner in the yellow vest.

4. Neil is wearing the number ten on his vest.

5. The man wearing a red vest is further right than the one in the white vest.

Number	Runner	Vest colour

Relative Choices

In this puzzle there are six families consisting of a mother, a father and a daughter. In every family the forenames of each mother, father and daughter begin with three different letters. For instance, Alan's wife isn't Amelia and neither Alan nor Amelia have a daughter named Augusta. Can you work out who is related to whom?

1. Amelia and her husband have a daughter whose name begins with the same letter as the initial of both Bob's wife and Clara's husband.

2. Daphne and her husband have a daughter whose name begins with the same letter as the initial of both Christina's father and Bella's mother.

3. Edmund's wife has a name which begins with the same letter as the initial of Daphne's husband.

4. Elaine's husband (who isn't Fred) has a name which begins with the same letter as the initial of Christina's mother.

5. Edmund's daughter has a name which begins with a different letter to the initial of Bella's father.

	Father						Daughter					
	Alan	Bob	Craig	Daniel	Edmund	Fred	Augusta	Bella	Christina	Diane	Emma	Florence
Amelia												
Brenda												
Clara												
Daphne												
Elaine												
Felicity												
Augusta												
Bella												
Christina												
Diane												
Emma												
Florence												

Mother	Father	Daughter

Georgie's Dates

According to the nursery rhyme: "Georgie Porgie, pudding and pie, kissed the girls and made them cry". However, it was the other way around last week, when Georgie met five women introduced from a dating agency! Poor Georgie was not at all impressed by any of the women… Can you discover on which night he dated each, together with her age and the reason why Georgie didn't want to date her again?

1. Anita was Georgie's date two evenings after he met with the woman who is eleven years older than Nadine. Nadine's problem (in Georgie's opinion) is that she is extremely stuck-up (snobbish) and patronising.

2. The woman who had doused herself with cheap perfume and, consequently, smelled awful, is six years older than the one Georgie met on Thursday evening.

3. Maureen is five years older than the woman (not Monday's date) who was, to use Georgie's own words, "as ugly as sin".

4. The youngest woman (who bored Georgie witless with her non-stop, inane chatter) was dated the evening before Delores.

5. The oldest woman didn't meet with Georgie on Monday evening.

6. Georgie's date with Nadine wasn't the evening before he met with Maureen.

	Monday	Tuesday	Wednesday	Thursday	Friday	22 years old	28 years old	33 years old	39 years old	44 years old	Boring	Self-centred	Smelled awful	Stuck-up	Very ugly
Anita															
Delores															
Kristel															
Maureen															
Nadine															
Boring											
Self-centred											
Smelled awful											
Stuck-up											
Very ugly											
22 years old					
28 years old					
33 years old					
39 years old					
44 years old					

Date	Evening	Age	Problem

Bring & Buy

The eight people in this puzzle all brought along something for the church's annual Bring & Buy Sale: then they all purchased an item donated by one of the others! From the clues below, can you work out what each gave and bought?

1. Emily donated an ornamental vase and bought whatever Tilly had donated.
2. Howard bought the box of home-grown vegetables and donated something which Patricia purchased. Patricia donated the printer.
3. The person who donated an old barometer and bought a book isn't Laurence.
4. Albert (who didn't buy the vase) either gave or bought the wooden footstool.
5. The cake was either baked by Ray and bought by Dean or it was baked by Dean and bought by Ray.
6. Neither the item bought by Albert nor that bought by Tilly had been donated by Laurence.
7. Whoever donated the vegetables bought a footstool.
8. Tilly was pleased with her purchase, which hadn't been donated by Dean.

	GAVE								BOUGHT							
	Barometer	Book	Cake	Clock	Footstool	Printer	Vase	Vegetables	Barometer	Book	Cake	Clock	Footstool	Printer	Vase	Vegetables
Albert																
Dean																
Emily																
Howard																
Laurence																
Patricia																
Ray																
Tilly																
Barometer																
Book																
Cake																
Clock																
Footstool																
Printer																
Vase																
Vegetables																

Name	Gave	Bought

Buy & Buy

Each of these women managed to get a real bargain in the sales. What are their full names, what was each one's bargain and from which shop was it purchased?

1. Either Gloria or Sandra is the woman who shopped at Town Girl and bought either a jacket or a suit. The woman who shopped at Fashion House bought either a coat or a jacket.

2. Lesley (whose surname is either Gordon or Wishman) shopped at either Ella's Boutique or Fashion House.

3. Either Harriet or Gloria is the woman who bought the coat (and whose surname is either Mitchell or Wishman).

4. Either Lesley or Sandra is the woman who shopped at Fashion House (and whose surname is either Holford or Mitchell).

5. Mrs Abbott (who shopped at either Ella's Boutique or Kent & Moore) bought either a jacket or a skirt.

6. Miss Gordon shopped at either Jayne's or Town Girl.

	Abbott	Gordon	Holford	Mitchell	Wishman	Coat	Dress	Jacket	Skirt	Suit	Ella's Boutique	Fashion House	Jayne's	Kent & Moore	Town Girl
Bonita															
Gloria															
Harriet															
Lesley															
Sandra															
Ella's Boutique															
Fashion House															
Jayne's															
Kent & Moore															
Town Girl															
Coat															
Dress															
Jacket															
Skirt															
Suit															

Shopper	Surname	Bought	Shop

Visitors

Six women travelled by car to visit one another. Every woman both made one visit and received one visit. Can you discover the name of the town in which each lives, together with the name and home town of the woman she visited?

1. The woman who lives in Holbury drove to Winford.

2. Judy (who lives in Marsham) was visited by Linda.

3. Judy drove to see the woman in Arkbourne, who isn't Linda.

4. Magdalene drove to see the woman (not Charlene) who visited Deanna.

5. Deanna (who lives in Tunfield) visited the woman in Cosbrook.

	Lives in						Visited						Drove to					
	Arkbourne	Cosbrook	Holbury	Marsham	Tunfield	Winford	Charlene	Deanna	Judy	Linda	Magdalene	Phoebe	Arkbourne	Cosbrook	Holbury	Marsham	Tunfield	Winford
Charlene																		
Deanna																		
Judy																		
Linda																		
Magdalene																		
Phoebe																		
Drove to Arkbourne																		
Cosbrook																		
Holbury																		
Marsham																		
Tunfield																		
Winford																		
Visited Charlene																		
Deanna																		
Judy																		
Linda																		
Magdalene																		
Phoebe																		

Name	Lives in	Visited	Drove to

Pullover Problem

Convinced that her five great-nieces are suffering as a result of being far from home at university, Mrs Purl knitted each a pullover, to keep her warm. Unfortunately, her eyesight isn't what it was and she hadn't followed the pattern correctly, with the result that none of the pullovers is wearable. Never mind, it's the thought that counts! How old is each great-niece, what colour is her pullover and what's wrong with it?

1. Ava (who is younger than Tamara) has a pullover which is far too small and would perhaps fit a nine-year-old girl.

2. The 19-year-old great-niece was given the cream pullover.

3. The 20-year-old great-niece has a pullover with a neck so tight that she can't get it over her head.

4. The 21-year-old great-niece is Shelagh.

5. The green pullover which has exceedingly long sleeves was knitted for a younger great-niece than Dora, who didn't receive the white pullover from Mrs Purl.

6. Jenny (whose pullover is pink) is older than the great-niece whose pullover has sleeves of odd design.

	18 years old	19 years old	20 years old	21 years old	22 years old	Brown	Cream	Green	Pink	White	Long sleeves	Neck tight	Odd sleeves	Sleeves tight	Too small
Ava															
Dora															
Jenny															
Shelagh															
Tamara															
Long sleeves																
Neck tight											
Odd sleeves											
Sleeves tight											
Too small											
Brown					
Cream					
Green					
Pink					
White					

Great-niece	Age	Pullover colour	Problem

Colourful Kids

Iris' five children are all out playing in the garden, wearing a jacket, sweater and trousers in various colours. Can you discover exactly what each child is wearing?

1. Neither Jilly nor Milly is wearing the maroon jacket. The child in the maroon jacket isn't wearing a pink or white jumper. Nor is the child in the maroon jacket wearing crimson or purple trousers.
2. The child in purple trousers isn't wearing a beige jacket and the one in black trousers isn't wearing a yellow jumper.
3. Willy's trousers aren't green or grey and the child in grey trousers isn't wearing a brown or maroon jacket. The child in grey trousers is neither Billy nor Jilly.
4. Milly's jacket isn't brown and her trousers aren't grey. Jilly's jumper isn't white.
5. The child in the maroon jacket isn't wearing green trousers. The child in the scarlet jacket isn't wearing crimson or purple trousers.
6. Neither Jilly nor Milly is wearing a scarlet jacket or a yellow jumper.
7. The child in the blue jacket isn't wearing an orange or white jumper.
8. Dilly's jacket is neither beige nor scarlet and her jumper is neither pink nor yellow.

	Jacket					Jumper					Trousers				
	Beige	Blue	Brown	Maroon	Scarlet	Cream	Orange	Pink	White	Yellow	Black	Crimson	Green	Grey	Purple
Billy															
Dilly															
Jilly															
Milly															
Willy															
Black															
Crimson															
Green															
Grey															
Purple															
Cream															
Orange															
Pink															
White															
Yellow															

Child	Jacket	Jumper	Trousers

No 261

Mmmm...

The five women in this puzzle spent more than they'd bargained for in the bakery this morning, enticed into making 'impulse purchases' by the display of cakes and the glorious smell of warm, freshly-baked bread (try to stay with the puzzle please and ignore your rumbling tummy!). In what order did each queue in line, which item had she originally gone in to buy and how much did she spend?

1. Of the five women: one was second in the queue, one was Dora, one spent $3.80, one originally just wanted a crusty bread roll and one spent twenty cents more than the woman who had only meant to purchase the crusty bread roll.

2. Of the five women: one was third in the line, one originally wanted a doughnut, one spent $4.00, one was Dinah and one spent ten cents less than Dinah.

3. Of the five women: one had only gone in for a sausage roll, one was last in the line, one spent $3.70, one was Debbie and one spent ten cents more than Debbie.

4. Of the five women: one spent $3.60, one originally just wanted a chocolate eclair, one was fourth in the queue, one was Delia and one was Denise (who wasn't third in the queue).

5. Of the five women: one spent $3.90, one originally just wanted a strawberry jam Swiss roll, one was first in line, one was Denise and one stood immediately in front of Denise in the queue.

	First	Second	Third	Fourth	Fifth	Bread roll	Chocolate eclair	Doughnut	Sausage roll	Swiss roll	$3.60	$3.70	$3.80	$3.90	$4.00
Debbie															
Delia															
Denise															
Dinah															
Dora															
$3.60											
$3.70											
$3.80											
$3.90											
$4.00											
Bread roll						
Chocolate eclair						
Doughnut						
Sausage roll						
Swiss roll						

Shopper	Position	Wanted	Spent

No 262

Commuting Times

The five commuters who have kindly agreed that their details can be used for this puzzle each catch a differently numbered bus to work every morning. Can you discover not only the number of the bus each takes, but also its time and the length of time it takes for each commuter to get to his or her place of employment?

1. The person who takes fifteen minutes to get to work catches the bus which arrives at 7.55am each morning.

2. The commuter (not Claudine) who has a journey time of thirty minutes catches the bus fifteen minutes later than the arrival time of the No 28 (taken by Rosie).

3. The one who catches a bus five minutes later than Dirk has a journey time one quarter of an hour longer than Dirk's and catches a bus with a number five higher than that taken by Dirk.

4. Nigel's bus arrives ten minutes before that taken by the commuter whose journey time is ten minutes longer than Andy's (and who catches a bus with a number five higher than that taken by Andy).

5. The commuter who takes the No 33 to work each morning doesn't have the shortest journey time.

Commuter	Bus No	Time caught	Journey time

264

Five Little Pigs

The five children in the family featured in this puzzle are all diligently saving their pocket money. Every child owns a piggybank of a different colour and each has saved a different amount of money. From the clues below, can you discover the owner of each piggybank, together with its colour and contents?

1. Veronica's piggybank contains one fewer dollar (and is further left) than the orange piggybank.

2. Jodie's piggybank isn't the one which contains sixteen dollars, which is directly next to and left of the piggybank which contains fourteen dollars.

3. The white piggybank is directly next to and right of Donny's, which contains fifty cents less than the white piggybank.

4. The blue piggybank (which isn't A in the picture below) doesn't belong to Jodie.

5. Peter's piggybank is directly next to and left of the red one, which contains fifty cents less than Peter's.

	Donny	Jodie	Peter	Ronald	Veronica	Blue	Green	Orange	Red	White	$13.50	$14.00	$15.00	$15.50	$16.00
Piggybank A															
Piggybank B															
Piggybank C															
Piggybank D															
Piggybank E															
$13.50										
$14.00										
$15.00										
$15.50										
$16.00										
Blue					
Green					
Orange					
Red					
White					

LEFT ⇐   RIGHT ⇒

A B C D E

Piggybank	Owner	Colour	Amount saved

Simple as A,B,C?

Each of the small squares in the grid below contains either A, B or C. Every row, every column and each of the two long diagonal lines of six squares contains exactly two of each letter. The information in the clues refers only to the squares in that row or column. To help you solve this problem, we've given as many clues as we think you'll need! Can you tell which letter should be placed into each square?

Across:

1. The Cs are somewhere between the Bs.

5. The Bs are further right than the Cs.

6. The As are further left than the Cs.

Down:

1. The As are somewhere between the Bs.

2. The Bs are somewhere between the Cs.

3. The As are higher than the Bs.

5. Each A is directly next to and above a B.

6. The Bs are somewhere between the As.

On the Record

Lucy Lang regularly reviews up and coming bands for the magazine Pop-Hits, but although she is accurate in her descriptions of bands and their music, she isn't usually correct in her predictions of the success of their first records in the music charts. With which recording company has each band signed and what was the position predicted by Lucy and actual position reached by their first hit record?

1. Lucy Lang didn't have very high expectations for the boy-band (she considered them far too old!), but they reached No 3 in the charts, despite only being predicted to climb to No 12.

2. The band which reached No 2 in the charts has a name four letters longer than that of the band which signed a five-year contract with GCO.

3. The Cliffhangers signed with Virgo Records and reached No 15, which was better than Lucy Lang had predicted.

4. The band predicted to reach No 17 signed with Cemtella.

5. The band which reached No 18 in the charts isn't Musiqua.

6. Lucy Lang didn't think that The Moonmen (who signed with Folydor) would do as well as the band contracted to Plum Music. In the event, The Moonmen achieved a position more than two higher than that of the band with Plum Music.

	Cemtella	Folydor	GCO	Plum Music	Virgo Records	No 2	No 12	No 15	No 17	No 22	No 2	No 3	No 15	No 18	No 20
	Label					Predicted chart position					Actual chart position				
The Cliffhangers															
The Hagglers															
Jay and the Rooks															
The Moonmen															
Musiqua															
Actual No 2															
No 3															
No 15															
No 18															
No 20															
Predicted No 2															
No 12															
No 15															
No 17															
No 22															

Band	Label	Predicted position	Actual position

No 266

Take a Chance

Joel has six dozen raffle tickets in his wallet, for five raffles to be drawn on the listed dates. Can you discover the first prize associated with each raffle, the number of tickets Joel has for it and the price he paid per ticket?

1. The tickets priced at fifty cents each offer a top prize of a week's holiday in Holland and Joel has two more of these than of the ones at the highest price, which are for a raffle to be drawn on 19 July.

2. The tickets priced at $1.10 each (of which Joel holds fourteen) are for the raffle to be drawn one month later than those for which the top prize is a sports car.

3. The draw for the hamper of food will be held three months earlier than that for which the top prize is a computer.

4. The tickets for the raffle to be drawn first cost more than those for which he has the highest number of tickets.

GRAND RAFFLE
Draw Date
19 July
(See overleaf for prizes)

	Car	Computer	Food hamper	Holiday	Television	10 tickets	12 tickets	14 tickets	16 tickets	20 tickets	$0.50	$0.70	$0.90	$1.10	$1.30
16 March															
12 May															
9 June															
19 July															
28 September															
$0.50															
$0.70															
$0.90															
$1.10															
$1.30															
10 tickets															
12 tickets															
14 tickets															
16 tickets															
20 tickets															

Draw date	First prize	No of tickets	Price each

No 267

Walking in the Rain

These five people take exercise by going out for a walk every afternoon. Yesterday, despite the heavy rain, was no exception and each took an umbrella to avoid getting too wet. Can you discover the time at which each takes his or her daily stroll, together with the number of minutes he or she was out of the house and the colour of every person's umbrella?

1. Barbara walked for two fewer minutes than the person with the black umbrella, who didn't leave the house two hours later than the person with the grey umbrella.

2. The person with the black umbrella left his or her house exactly one hour later than the one who walked for twenty minutes.

3. Charles walked for six fewer minutes than the person with the green umbrella, who left home half an hour later than David, whose umbrella isn't grey.

4. David was out for a shorter period of time than both the tallest person and Barbara, but for longer than Gwen, whose umbrella is red.

	1.30pm	2.00pm	3.00pm	3.30pm	4.00pm	14 minutes	16 minutes	20 minutes	22 minutes	24 minutes	Black	Blue	Green	Grey	Red
Barbara															
Charles															
David															
Gwen															
Trevor															
Black															
Blue															
Green															
Grey															
Red															
14 minutes															
16 minutes															
20 minutes															
22 minutes															
24 minutes															

Walker	Time	Minutes walking	Umbrella colour

No 268

Having a Lovely Time!

Cora received five postcards last week, from different friends on holiday in various countries. She stuck them on her wall, as shown in the picture below. Can you work out who sent each card, the country in which each is holidaying and the day on which Cora received the card? NB – 'Left' and 'right' are from your point of view as you look at the picture below.

1. The card sent by Mel was received earlier than both the one from Tony and that sent from Norway.

2. The card from Jeff is next to and between Tony's and the one which arrived last.

3. The card from Vivienne is further right than that from Thailand.

4. Mel's card arrived the day after the one (not sent by Jeff) which Cora placed next to and left of Tony's.

5. The card from Cyprus arrived later than the one from Scotland, which arrived later in the week than Jeff's card.

6. The first card to arrive wasn't sent by Craig.

	Craig	Jeff	Mel	Vivienne	Tony	Cyprus	Hawaii	Norway	Scotland	Thailand	Monday	Tuesday	Thursday	Friday	Saturday
Postcard A															
Postcard B															
Postcard C															
Postcard D															
Postcard E															
Monday										
Tuesday										
Thursday										
Friday										
Saturday										
Cyprus					
Hawaii					
Norway					
Scotland					
Thailand					

LEFT ⬅   **RIGHT** ➡

A	B	C	D	E

Postcard	Sender	Holiday country	Arrival day

No 269

Patchwork

Each piece in the patchwork square below is decorated with a letter of the alphabet: A, B, C, D, E, F or G. In each horizontal row, vertical column and long diagonal line of seven smaller pieces there are seven different letters: some are already in place. Can you discover which letter fits in every piece? There is only one correct solution to this puzzle – if you take a wrong path along the way, you won't finish the quilt!

1. The letter in piece 1 is the same as the letter in piece 32.

2. The letter in piece 11 is the same as the letter in piece 20 and both are the same as the letter in piece 36.

3. The letter in piece 38 is the same as the letter in piece 23.

4. The letter in piece 31 is the same as the letter in piece 40.

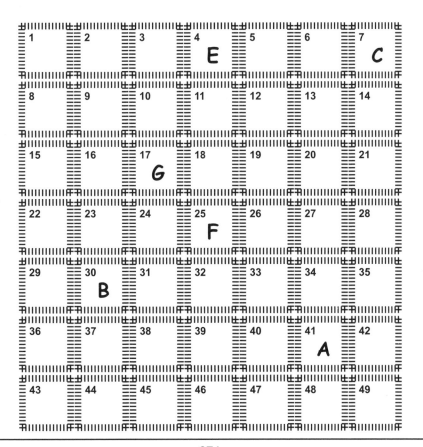

Solutions

No 1

Whisky goes to the park 4 times per week (clue 2) and Rusty 5 times (clue 5). The dog taken once per week isn't Bonzo (1) or Pip (4), so Bobby. The dog taken twice isn't Pip (4), so Bonzo and Pip is taken 3 times. Pip belongs to Mrs Beale (4) and lives at No 2 (6). The dog at No 1 isn't Bobby (4), so Bonzo, who (3) belongs to Miss French. Mr Carter's dog is Bobby (1). Mr Taylor lives at No 3 (2) and his dog isn't Rusty (5), so Whisky. By elimination, Mrs Morris owns Rusty. She doesn't live at No 5 (7), so No 4 and Mr Carter lives at No 5.

Thus:

Bobby, No 5, Mr Carter, once;
Bonzo, No 1, Miss French, twice;
Pip, No 2, Mrs Beale, 3 times;
Rusty, No 4, Mrs Morris, 5 times;
Whisky, No 3, Mr Taylor, 4 times.

No 2 *The Necklace*

John returned the briefcase left in a taxi (clue 3) and Kenny returned the house keys (clue 4). The item Pete found on the train (1) wasn't a wallet or watch (2), so car keys. Tuesday's item was left in the waiting room (5), so not by Lynda (4), thus Kenny's find wasn't on Monday. Monday's find wasn't of the wallet or watch (2), or car keys (3), so the briefcase. Tuesday's wasn't the wallet or watch (2), so house keys and (4) Lynda's find in the car park was on Wednesday. This wasn't the watch (2), so the wallet. By elimination, Sandra found the watch on a bus. Sandra's find was on Thursday (2), so Pete's was on Friday.

Thus:

Monday, briefcase, taxi, John;
Tuesday, house keys, waiting room, Kenny;
Wednesday, wallet, car park, Lynda;
Thursday, watch, bus, Sandra;
Friday, car keys, train, Pete.

No 3 *R & J (Act 2)*

The two women (Ingrid and Mandy, grid) are surnamed Holford (MISS, clue 2) and Clayton (MRS, clue 4). Mark wrote *Mark of Cain* (2) and George wrote *Capital Charisma* (3). So Robert is Willis who wrote *Final Frontiers* (3). The author of *Gentle Lady* isn't Mandy (1), so Ingrid. Mandy wrote *Garden of Desire*. Thus she isn't Miss Holford (2), so she's Mrs Clayton and Ingrid is Miss Holford. Mandy's piece didn't take 11 hours (4), so (1) Mandy's took 10 hours, Ingrid 8 hours and the poet surnamed Chester took 7 hours. The one surnamed Jork took 11 hours (4), so Robert (Willis, above) took 9 hours. Mark's surname is thus Chester (2), so George's is Jork.

Thus:

George, Jork, *Capital Charisma*, 11 hours;
Ingrid, Holford, *Gentle Lady*, 8 hours;
Mandy, Clayton, *Garden of Desire*, 10 hours;
Mark, Chester, *Mark of Cain*, 7 hours;
Robert, Willis, *Final Frontiers*, 9 hours.

No 4

The linebacker wore No 43 (clue 4). The cousin in the No 13 shirt wasn't the running back (clue 3) or offensive linesman (5), so the quarterback's shirt had No 23 and the wide receiver's blue shirt had No 13. The quarterback supports the Blue Sox (4). The running back supports the Jetstars (3). The man in green who supports the Dolphins isn't the offensive linesman (5), so the line backer and the offensive linesman's shirt had No 53. The running back thus wore No 33, thus his shirt isn't white (1) or orange (3), so yellow. The quarterback's shirt was orange (3). The offensive linesman thus wore white. He doesn't support the Eagles (1), so the Harlequins. The wide receiver supports the Eagles.

Thus:

Linebacker, No 43, green, Dolphins;
Offensive linesman, No 53, white, Harlequins;
Quarterback, No 23, orange, Blue Sox;
Running back, No 33, yellow, Jetstars;
Wide receiver, No 13, blue, Eagles.

No 5 *The Necklace*

Each woman lent and borrowed two completely different articles of clothing (intro). Helen borrowed a skirt (clue 3), so not from Claire who (clue 2) lent a jumper. Nor did Claire lend to herself or Simone or Georgina (2). So Claire lent a jumper to Stephanie (who thus borrowed a jumper). The woman who borrowed a hat isn't Claire or Simone (1), so Georgina. Since Claire lent to Stephanie (above), Stephanie lent the hat to Georgina (2), who (3) lent a skirt to Helen. Simone didn't lend to herself, so to Claire and (by elimination) Helen lent to Simone. The woman who lent a coat didn't borrow a coat (intro) or a dress (4), so a skirt. Thus (above) Helen lent the coat. By elimination, Simone lent the dress (to Claire, above) and borrowed the coat.

Thus:

Claire, jumper, Stephanie, dress;
Georgina, skirt, Helen, hat;
Helen, coat, Simone, skirt;
Simone, dress, Claire, coat;
Stephanie, hat, Georgina, jumper.

No 6 *1st Cycle*

The Larkin child had a cold (clue 2) and Veronica Roberts had a tummy ache (clue 4). The Crooke child didn't have a fever or a headache (1), so earache and is the girl taken home by Mr O'Connor. The feverish child was taken home by Mr Ball (3), so Veronica was taken by Mrs Warne (4), thus the Larkin child by Miss Morton. By elimination, Mrs Hale took the child with a headache. Leon didn't have a fever or headache (1), so a cold. Petunia didn't have an earache (1) or fever (3), so a headache. Thus Hannah is the Crooke girl and Norman had a fever. Norman's surname isn't Price (5) so Dillinger. Petunia's surname is Price.

Solutions

Thus:
Hannah, Crooke, earache, Mr O'Connor;
Leon, Larkin, cold, Miss Morton;
Norman, Dillinger, fever, Mr Ball;
Petunia, Price, headache, Mrs Hale;
Veronica, Roberts, tummy ache, Mrs Warne.

No 7 *Open Window*

Herb walked 45 miles to Tipton (clue 1) and someone walked 66 miles (furthest) to Pip's Point (clue 2), so the distance from Northwood to Mole End was 49 miles (3), that to Daw Creek was 59 miles and (by elimination) that to Highwater was 40 miles. Keith walked 45 miles (3). Mel started from Gradbury (1) and Graham from Awlford (2). Keith didn't start from Bunston (3), so Southam. Thus Wayne walked from Northwood (to Mole End) and Herb from Bunston. The man who walked 66 miles wasn't Graham (2) or Keith (3), so Mel. Keith didn't go to Daw Creek (3), so Highwater. Graham walked to Daw Creek.

Thus:
Graham, Awlford, Daw Creek, 59 miles;
Herb, Bunston, Tipton, 45 miles;
Keith, Southam, Highwater, 40 miles;
Mel, Gradbury, Pip's Point, 66 miles;
Wayne, Northwood, Mole End, 49 miles.

No 8

Lance Lingfield was 4th (clue 4) and Aardvark was 1st (clue 9), so Mr Fisher ridden by Mucklow (8) was 3rd and (1) Mucklow wore purple. Freshman's jockey wore green (7). Bouncer wore red (3) and Armstrong didn't wear yellow (6), so either orange or green: thus he didn't ride Aardvark (9). So he wasn't 1st or 5th (6), so 2nd. He didn't ride Parmesan (2) or Risky Business (5), so Freshman (green, 7). The jockey in orange didn't ride Parmesan (2). By elimination, Potterton was 1st and wore yellow and Risky Business was 4th and ridden by Lingfield.

Thus:
Aardvark, Potterton, yellow, 1st;
Freshman, Armstrong, green, 2nd;
Mr Fisher, Mucklow, purple, 3rd;
Parmesan, Bouncer, red, 5th;
Risky Business, Lingfield, orange, 4th

No 9

Remember throughout that twins have names starting with four different letters (intro). Girls' names are Darlene Mary (clue 1) and Helen Lynne (clue 4). The boy whose 2nd name is Stephen has a sister whose 2nd is Dinah (3). The boy whose 2nd is Hubert is the brother of Margaret (5) whose 2nd name isn't thus Holly, nor is it Amelia (2), so she's Margaret Susan. Andrew Damian's sister isn't Helen Lynne (4) or (initial) Darlene Mary. His sister's 2nd name isn't Amelia (intro), so Holly and (by elimination) her 1st name is either Louisa or Sharon. Anna's 2nd name isn't Amelia, so Dinah. Simon's 2nd name is Alan (1). Mark's 2nd isn't

Michael (intro) or Stephen (2) and he isn't the brother of Margaret (initial), so his 2nd isn't Herbert. Thus he's Mark Lance and (by elimination) his sister's 2nd name is Amelia and her 1st is Sharon. Louisa's 2nd name is thus Holly. Darlene Mary's brother's 2nd isn't Michael (initial), so Alan. Helen Lynne's brother isn't Hector or Liam, so David, whose 2nd name isn't thus Herbert, so Michael. Hector's 2nd name isn't Hubert, so Stephen. Liam's 2nd name is Hubert.

Thus:
Andrew, Damian, Louisa, Holly;
David, Michael, Helen, Lynne;
Hector, Stephen, Anna, Dinah;
Liam, Hubert, Margaret, Susan;
Mark, Lance, Sharon, Amelia;
Simon, Alan, Darlene, Mary.

No 10 *Short Story*

Writers have assumed forenames relating to their sex. Gwyneth's is Lizzie (clue 2), so (clue 1) Gertie Ginsucker's is Denise and Griselda writes as Jane Reid. Male surnames are Grotwit (3) and Gadwhistle (5). Gerard writes as Mr Soul (4), so Godfrey is Mr Gadwhistle who writes as Mr Lovelace (5) and Gerard is Mr Grotwit, who (3) writes as Stanley: thus Godfrey writes as Arthur. Ms Gungho who writes as Ms Harmony (6) is (by elimination) Gwyneth, so Griselda's surname is Gloop and Gertie writes as Ms Gentle.

Thus:
Griselda, Gloop, Jane, Reid;
Gertie, Ginsucker, Denise, Gentle;
Godfrey, Gadwhistle, Arthur, Lovelace;
Gwyneth, Gungho, Lizzie, Harmony;
Gerard, Grotwit, Stanley, Soul.

No 11 *The Necklace*

The racing bet brought in 180 Euros (clue 5), so the shares dividend netted 280 Euros (clue 2) and the gas bill amount was 300 Euros. Thus the gas bill was (1) paid for from the 310 Euros received. The works bonus was 260 Euros (4) and the lottery win netted 190 Euros. By elimination, the sale of the computer raised 310 Euros. The received amounts of 180 and 190 Euros paid for the 150 and/or 175 Euros bills (1), so the received amounts of 260 and 280 Euros paid for the 200 and/or 250 Euros bills. The shares dividend was thus used to pay the 200 Euros bill (5) and the racing bet paid the 175 Euros bill. By elimination, the lottery win paid the 150 Euros bill and the works bonus paid the 250 Euros bill. The garage bill was 150 Euros (3) and the phone bill was 250 Euros. The electricity bill was 200 Euros (6) and the tax bill was 175 Euros.

Thus:
Electricity, 200 Euros, shares dividend, 280 Euros;
Garage, 150 Euros, lottery win, 190 Euros;
Gas, 300 Euros, sale of computer, 310 Euros;
Phone, 250 Euros, works bonus, 260 Euros;
Tax, 175 Euros, racing bet, 180 Euros.

Solutions

No 12

Hugh's surname is Boyd (clue 4), so David is the MAN surnamed Jones (clue 2) who is studying chemistry. The music student is going to Australia (4), so (2) David is going to India. Megan is going to Denmark (1). The person going to Australia isn't Janet (1) or Hugh (4), so Gwynneth. The WOMAN going to Italy is studying computing (5), so Hugh is going to Spain and Janet to Italy. Janet's surname isn't Hann (3), so Griffith. Megan is Hann. Her subject isn't mathematics (3), so literature and the mathematics student is Hugh.

Thus:

David, Jones, chemistry, India;
Hugh, Boyd, mathematics, Spain;
Gwynneth, Williams, music, Australia;
Janet, Griffith, computing, Italy;
Megan, Hann, literature, Denmark.

No 13

Quantities not on the grid are 10 cakes, 8 pies and 8 tarts. The 7 and 11 pies weren't bought on the 2nd Saturday (clue 1), the 5th Saturday (clue 4) or the 1st Saturday (5), so either the 3rd or 4th Saturdays. Thus 11 pies were bought on the 3rd Saturday (2) and 7 on the 4th; so 10 pies were bought on the 1st (5). On the 5th she bought 6 pies (4), so 9 were bought on the 2nd. She bought 9 cakes on the 1st (1). She bought 8 or 12 cakes on the 3rd (2). The number of cakes bought on the 5th wasn't 11 (3), so (2) 7 and she bought 8 on the 3rd. The 9 pies weren't bought with 11 cakes (3), so 12 and she bought 11 on the 4th. Thus (one more pie on the 4th than the 5th) she bought one more tart on the 4th than the 5th (3). On the 3rd, she bought two fewer tarts than on the 5th (2), thus she bought 9 tarts on the 5th, 10 on the 4th and 7 on the 3rd. She didn't buy 5 tarts on the 1st (1), so 6 and bought 5 tarts on the 2nd.

Thus:

1st Saturday, 9 cakes, 10 pies, 6 tarts;
2nd Saturday, 12 cakes, 9 pies, 5 tarts;
3rd Saturday, 8 cakes, 11 pies, 7 tarts;
4th Saturday, 11 cakes, 7 pies, 10 tarts;
5th Saturday, 7 cakes, 6 pies, 9 tarts.

No 14

Cards total 81 (intro), so the jack is missing. Card H is a spade (clue 5), so F is a club (intro) and E or G are either hearts or diamonds. J isn't a heart (clue 4), so a diamond and (intro) B is a heart, as is L, so D is a diamond. F has a value three times that of H (5) and A isn't the ace (6), so F isn't the 3. Thus F is either the 6, 9 or queen, H is either the 2, 3 or 4 (5) and A is either the 4, 7 or 10. The 5 of spades isn't I or K (1), A or H (above), so it's C. A is a club, I is a spade and K is a club (intro). L is either a 3 or a 4 (3) and B is either a 2 or a 3. So the 2, 3 and/or 4 are B, H and/or L. Card A is thus the 10 (6) and F is the queen. H is the 4 (1) and the J the 7. Thus D is the 6 (6). L is the 3 (3) and B is the 2. K is the 8 (2). The king of diamonds isn't E (4), so G and E is a heart. The three hearts (B, E and

L) total either six or fourteen and cards I and J have a total of either eight or sixteen (card I being either the ace or 9, as is card E). Thus (4) cards I and J total eight and cards B, E and L total fourteen. So card I is the ace and E is the 9.

Thus:

10C 2H 5S 6D
9H QC KD 4S
AS 7D 8C 3H

No 15 *Gift of Magi*

Jimmy's gift is in blue paper (clue 1) and Stuart's for his Aunt Judith (clue 5) is in pink paper. The silver paper wraps the vase for Aunt Bessie (2), so (3) Paul's gift for his Aunt Madge is in red paper. Aunt Caroline's gift isn't in purple paper (4), so blue and the purple paper wraps the candle (4) which is thus for Auntie Lesley. Stuart didn't buy the mug or teapot (5), so a book. Aunt Caroline's gift isn't the teapot (4), so mug and the teapot is for Aunt Madge. Keith didn't buy the vase (2), so the candle. Richard bought the vase.

Thus:

Book, Stuart, Aunt Judith, pink;
Candle, Keith, Auntie Lesley, purple;
Mug, Jimmy, Aunt Caroline, blue;
Teapot, Paul, Aunt Madge, red;
Vase, Richard, Auntie Bessie, silver.

No 16

The children with blue/white, green/white and red/white scarves got either the football, transfers and/or pencils (clue 1), so the one with a blue/red scarf who didn't get a colouring book (clue 3) got wax crayons, thus the one with the blue/green scarf got a colouring book. Jolly didn't get the crayons (2), so has the red/white scarf and Frost's scarf is blue/red (3). The child with the blue/green scarf wasn't 9th or 10th (3), so either 4th or 5th (4), as was the child with the green/white scarf. Thus the child with the blue/red scarf (crayons, above) was 10th (2) and Krimble was 5th. The 4th child wasn't Frost or Jolly (3) or Meek (5), so Bliss. By elimination, Meek's scarf is blue/white and Frost was 10th. Meek didn't get the football or transfers (5), so pencils. Bliss didn't get the football (1) or transfers (5), so a colouring book. By elimination, Krimble's scarf is green/white. Krimble didn't get transfers (1), so a football. Jolly got transfers. Thus Jolly was 7th (5) and Meek 9th.

Thus:

Bliss, 4th, blue/green, colouring book;
Frost, 10th, blue/red, wax crayons;
Jolly, 7th, red/white, transfers;
Krimble, 5th, green/white, football;
Meek, 9th, blue/white, pencils.

No 17

Remember throughout that there were three different quantities each day. On Monday and Friday, she counted 7 items (clue 2), so not one button (clue 1). She didn't count one button on Wednesday or

Solutions

Thursday (3), so on Tuesday. She didn't count one stamp on Tuesday (intro), Monday or Friday (1 and 2) or Thursday (3), so Wednesday. Thus she didn't count 7 of anything on Tuesday or Wednesday (1). The 7 buttons weren't counted on Monday or Friday (2), so Thursday. On Monday she didn't find 2 of anything (4), so found 6 buttons and either 7 or 8 stamps. There were 2 coins on Wednesday (3), so not 2 buttons (intro). Thus there were 8 buttons on Wednesday and 2 buttons on Friday. The 2 stamps weren't found on Friday (intro) or Thursday (3), so Tuesday. The day when she counted 3 coins plus 5 stamps (5) wasn't Monday (7 or 8 stamps, above) or Friday (2 buttons), so Thursday. The 8 stamps weren't counted on Friday (5), so Monday. On Friday she thus had 7 stamps, so the day on which 7 coins were counted was Monday. She found 4 coins on Tuesday (2) and 5 on Friday.

Thus:

Monday, 6 buttons, 7 coins, 8 stamps;
Tuesday, 1 button, 4 coins, 2 stamps;
Wednesday, 8 buttons, 2 coins, 1 stamp;
Thursday, 7 buttons, 3 coins, 5 stamps;
Friday, 2 buttons, 5 coins, 7 stamps.

No 18

```
C  A  B  A  B  C
B  C  A  B  A  C
C  B  A  C  A  B
A  C  B  B  C  A
A  A  C  C  B  B
B  B  C  A  C  A
```

No 19

Joanne wore Iain's jumper (clue 2). Philip didn't wear Malcolm's (clue 1) or Joanne's (2), so Suzanne's. Malcolm wore Joanne's (1). Suzanne's right sock wasn't blue (4), so the child in Philip's jumper plus a blue right/grey left sock was Iain. Suzanne wore Malcolm's jumper. Her left sock was the same colour as Malcolm's right (1), Malcolm's left was the same as Joanne's right (2) and Philip's left was the same as Suzanne's right (4). Thus the child with the blue left sock was Joanne and the one with the grey right sock was Philip. Philip's left wasn't beige (4), nor was he the child with (3) a white right/red left sock, so his left was white, as was Suzanne's right. Suzanne's left was red (3). Malcolm's left was beige and his right was red. Joanne's right sock was beige.

Thus:

Iain, Philip's jumper, blue right, grey left;
Joanne, Iain's jumper, beige right, blue left;
Malcolm, Joanne's jumper, red right, beige left;
Philip, Suzanne's jumper, grey right, white left;
Suzanne, Malcolm's jumper, white right, red left.

No 20 *R & J*

No-one is 64 (grid). The woman aged 58 (youngest) isn't married to Frank (clue 2), Terry (clue 3), Adam (5) or Gordon (6), so to John. The men aged 58 and

66 aren't John (2), Terry (3) or Gordon (6). Adam's wife isn't 68 (5), so Adam is 58 and his wife is 60. Thus Frank is 66, so (2) John is 68. He isn't married to Yolande (3), Lucille or Kathy (4) or Annette (6), so Geri and (1) Lucille is 60 (thus is Adam's wife, above). Kathy's husband is 62 (4). Annette's husband isn't Gordon or Frank (6), so Terry. Thus Gordon is 62 (6) and Terry is 60. By elimination, Yolande is Frank's wife. Annette is 68 (3) and Yolande is 66, so Kathy is 62.

Thus (his age, her age):

Adam, Lucille, 58, 60;
Frank, Yolande, 66, 66;
Gordon, Kathy, 62, 62;
John, Geri, 68, 58;
Terry, Annette, 60, 68.

No 21 *R & J / Eliz Eng*

No play lasts 100 minutes (grid). The 105-minute play hasn't 4 women (clue 1) 3 women (clue 2), 1 woman (3) or 5 women (4), so 2 women. The 90-minute play hasn't 4 (1), 3 (2) or 5 (4), so one woman. Thus it isn't *Devil's Task* (3). *Devil's Task* doesn't run for 105 minutes (3), so 110 (4) and 5 women are in the 115-minute play. The 90-minute play isn't *Eglantine* (1), *Lucinda's Diary* or *Time Matters* (5), so *The First Post*. *Eglantine* thus runs for 105 minutes (1) and 4 women are in Devil's Task, so 3 are in the 95-minute play. *Time Matters* runs for 115 minutes (5). *Lucinda's Diary* thus runs for 95 minutes. *The First Post* has 3 men (2), so *Time Matters* has 5 men (5) and *Eglantine* has 6. The play with 7 men isn't *Devil's Task* (4), so *Lucinda's Diary*. *Devil's Task* has 4 men.

Thus:

Devil's Task, 110 minutes, 4 men, 4 women;
Eglantine, 105 minutes, 6 men, 2 women;
The First Post, 90 minutes, 3 men, 1 woman;
Lucinda's Diary, 95 minutes, 7 men, 3 women;
Time Matters, 115 minutes, 5 men, 5 women.

No 22

E isn't 7 but is at least 6 (clue 1), so (clue 2) E=6 and G and/or Z are 2 and/or 3 (1). C=4 and U=24 (14). O=26 and B=5 (11). N=10 (2). P=7 and A=25 (9). If Z=2 and G=3 (above), then J=14 (12) and V would be 5 (13) – but (above) B=5. So Z=3 and G=2. J=21 (12). V=11 (13). H=1 and S=22 (5). Q=T+1 (3) so (3 and 7) Q=9, T=8 and W=17. R is either 12 or 14 (6), so (4) R=12 and L=15. X=14 (6). D=13 (10). I=16 and K=20 (15). M=19 and F=18 (8). By elimination (intro), Y=23.

Thus:

A=25; B=5; C=4; D=13; E=6; F=18; G=2; H=1; I=16; J=21; K=20; L=15; M=19; N=10; O=26; P=7; Q=9; R=12; S=22; T=8; U=24; V=11; W=17; X=14; Y=23; Z=3.

No 23 *R & J / Eliz Eng*

There is at least 15 minutes between the end of one performance and the start of the next (intro). The evening performance of *Sunlight Express* ends at

Solutions

8.45 (clue 3), so (times and lengths shown) starts at 6.30 and runs for 2 hours 15 minutes, so doesn't start at 4.10. *Dogs* runs for 2 hours 45 minutes and has a matinée at 4.15 (3), which thus ends at 7.00, so (intro) the evening performance of *Dogs* is at 7.15. The play which runs for 2 hours 30 minutes isn't *Wall Street Crush* (1) or *Hello Molly* (4), so *High Tune*. No matinée ends at 6.20 (5), so the play of 2 hours 10 minutes doesn't start at 4.10. Thus *Hello Molly* isn't 1 hour 50 minutes long (4), so it's 2 hours 10 minutes long and the play which starts at 4.10 runs for 1 hour and 50 minutes and (by elimination) is *Wall Street Crush*. The play starting at 3.45 and 6.45 isn't *High Tune* (2), so *Hello Molly*. *Wall Street Crush* doesn't begin at 7.10 (1), so 7.00 and *High Tune* at 7.10. *High Tune* runs for 2 hours 30 minutes (above) and doesn't end at 6.20 (5), so doesn't start at 3.50. Thus *High Tune* starts at 3.55 and *Sunlight Express* at 3.50.

Thus:
Dogs, 4.15pm, 7.15pm, 2 hours 45 mins;
Hello Molly, 3.45pm, 6.45pm, 2 hours 10 mins;
High Tune, 3.55pm, 7.10pm, 2 hours 30 mins;
Sunlight Express, 3.50pm, 6.30pm, 2 hours 15 mins;
Wall Street Crush, 4.10pm, 7.00pm, 1 hour 50 mins.

No 24

The woman who types at 70 hasn't a data entry speed of 90 (clue 2), 70 or 80 (clue 4) or 120 (6), so 100. Karen's data entry speed is 80 (4). Hannah's shorthand speed is either 70 or 80 (1), so her data entry speed isn't 120 and her typing speed isn't 60 or 70 (6), thus her data entry speed isn't 100 (above). So Hannah's data entry speed is 90 (1) and Lynda's is 70. The woman who writes shorthand at 70 doesn't type at 70 (6), so Julia types and writes shorthand at 75. Thus in clue 6, Julia is the woman whose data entry speed is 120, so Mary's is 100. Thus Mary types at 70 (above), so Hannah at 55 (2). Mary's shorthand speed isn't 80 (6), so 90 (5) and Hannah's is 80. Lynda's shorthand speed is 100 (1), so Karen's is 70. Karen doesn't type at 60 (6), so 50 and Lynda types at 60.

Thus:
Hannah, 90spm, 80wpm, 55wpm;
Julia, 120spm, 75wpm, 75wpm;
Karen, 80spm, 70wpm, 50wpm;
Lynda, 70spm, 100wpm, 60wpm;
Mary, 100spm, 90wpm, 70wpm.

No 25

You will need the solution to the previous puzzle in order to solve this one. The only woman with a minimum of 80 shorthand and 65wpm typing (clue 2) is Mary (previous puzzle), thus Mary was placed in work by James on Thursday. The agent who placed someone on Friday wasn't Terry (clue 1) or Pauline (4). Julia is the fastest at data entry (previous puzzle), so since Mary was placed on Thursday (above), Clarice didn't place on Friday (3), so Friday's placement was Simon's. The slowest typist is Karen (previous puzzle)

who was placed at Ink-Mart by Clarice (3) and Julia went to P J Willis. Pauline placed someone at Cooper's (4). Julia's placement wasn't on Friday (3), so her agent was Terry. Lynda has the fastest shorthand speed (previous puzzle) and was placed two days after Julia (1) who was placed the day before Karen (3), so Julia on Monday, Karen Tuesday and Lynda Wednesday. Thus Hannah was placed on Friday and Lynda was placed by Pauline. Mary went to Smith & Brown (4) and Hannah to Tringle & Co.

Thus:
Hannah, Tringle & Co, Simon, Friday;
Julia, P J Willis, Terry, Monday;
Karen, Ink-Mart, Clarice, Tuesday;
Lynda, Cooper's, Pauline, Wednesday;
Mary, Smith & Brown, James, Thursday.

No 26

In the diagonal line 7-43, the only place for the E is in piece 7. Piece 29 doesn't contain D, so (clue 1) D isn't in piece 49. Thus in the diagonal 1-49, the D is in 41. So (clue 5) 15=D. The letter in 14 and 45 (3) isn't D, so in column 7-49, the D is in 28. Pieces 29 and 49 (1) are either B or F, so in 1-43, the E is in 22. Thus in 3-45, 38=E. The E in 6-48 isn't in 34 (2), so 20. Thus in 4-46, 32=E. Pieces 33 and 42 (4) contain either B or F, so in 1-49, 17=A and 25=C. In 1-43, the C isn't in 29 (1), so 8. In 7-43, 13=A. Pieces 14 and 45 (3) contain either G or A, so in 3-45, the C is in 3. In 5-47, 40=C. In 7-49, 14=G, 35=A and 45=G (3). In 8-14, the D isn't in 12 (5), so 11. Piece 43 is B or F, as is 49 (above), thus 48=C, 46=A and 44=D. So 4=B, 2=A and 5=D. By elimination, 12 and 33 contain B and/or F, so 19=G and 26=A. Thus 18=F, 16=B, 34=G, 30=C, 27=B, 24=F, 10=B, 12=F, 23=G, 37=F, 42=B, 49=F, 43=B, 29=F, 33=B and 39=G.

Thus:

G	A	C	B	D	F	E
C	E	B	D	F	A	G
D	B	A	F	G	E	C
E	G	F	C	A	B	D
F	C	D	E	B	G	A
A	F	E	G	C	D	B
B	D	G	A	E	C	F

No 27

The £1.20 tip followed spilt coffee (clue 1) and Daniel dropped cutlery (clue 5). Angela didn't serve cold vegetables, spill coffee or muddle the order (2), so put her thumb in the soup, thus (6) got £1.80. The £1.20 tip wasn't for Martin (1) or Cora (3), so Elizabeth. Table 14 left £1.50 (4), so Martin at table 2 (3) got £1.30. Daniel didn't get £2.00 (5), so £1.50 and Cora got £2.00. She didn't muddle an order (2), so served cold vegetables and Martin muddled an order. Table 7's waitress wasn't Cora or Elizabeth (5), so Angela. Elizabeth didn't serve at table 20 (7), so table 24 and Cora served at table 20.

Solutions

Thus:
Angela, table No 7, thumb in soup, £1.80;
Cora, table No 20, cold vegetables, £2.00;
Elizabeth, table No 24, spilt coffee, £1.20;
Daniel, table No 14, dropped cutlery, £1.50;
Martin, table No 2, muddled order, £1.30.

No 28 *The open window*

The New Zealand group went on Friday (clue 1) and the historians on Wednesday (clue 2). Saturday's trip was to the Tower of London and wasn't taken by the teachers from Sweden (3) or the police officers (6). The journalists went to Canterbury (5), so the birdwatchers went on Saturday. The Americans went the day before the journalists (5), so neither party went on Tuesday. Tuesday's group wasn't of police officers (6), so teachers. The police officers went out the day after the trip to Hampton Court (6), so the trip to Hampton Court was made by the historians, the police officers went on Thursday and the journalists on Friday. Tuesday's trip wasn't to Wisley (4), so Windsor. Thursday's was to Wisley. The police officers were from America (5). The historians weren't from Russia (2), so Australia. The birdwatchers were from Russia.

Thus:
Birdwatchers, Sat, Russian, Tower of London;
Historians, Wed, Australian, Hampton Court;
Journalists, Fri, N Zealanders, Canterbury Cathedral;
Police officers, Thurs, American, Wisley Gardens;
Teachers, Tues, Swedish, Windsor Castle.

No 29 *Gift of magi*

The girl who got 99% isn't Opal (clue 1), Naomi (clue 2) or Lorinda (3), so Pamela (4) and Marilyn got 97%. No-one got 95% (grid). The girl with 93% isn't Naomi (2) or Lorinda (3), so Opal and Lorinda got 91%. Naomi got 89%. Lorinda has ginger hair (2). Either Marilyn or Pamela has dark blonde hair (1). Naomi's isn't light blonde or light brown (2), so dark brown. Opal's hair isn't light blonde (3), so light brown. Opal has long hair (3), so Lorinda and Naomi have medium length hair. The girl with wavy/medium hair isn't Naomi (2), so Lorinda and Naomi's is straight/medium. Marilyn's is thus straight/long (4), so Opal's is wavy/long and Pamela's is curly/short. It isn't dark blonde (1), so light blonde. Marilyn's is dark blonde.

Thus:
Lorinda, wavy/medium, ginger, 91%;
Marilyn, straight/long, dark blonde, 97%;
Naomi, straight/medium, dark brown, 89%;
Opal, wavy/long, light brown, 93%;
Pamela, curly/short, light blonde, 99%.

No 30

2	4	6	4	8	9
5	1	3	8	2	8
2	3	4	5	6	7
1	5	3	9	7	6
3	2	9	6	9	5
1	7	1	7	8	4

No 31

The mug was made after 3 attempts (clue 1). Those who had 2 and/or 5 attempts made the bowl and/or gift for a cousin (clue 4), so aren't the people who gave the plate to a niece (1) or the jug to a father-in-law (2), so these items were made after either 4 and/or 6 attempts. Mr Turner made something for his mother (3) and a woman gave to a niece (1) and cousin (4). Mr Gordon didn't give to his son (5), so father-in-law. Thus he had 4 attempts (5) and the person who gave to a son had 5. The one who gave to a niece thus had 6 attempts, the one who gave to a cousin had 2 and the mother's gift was made after 3 attempts. By elimination, the vase was given to a cousin and the bowl to a son. Miss Adams didn't make the vase (2) or bowl (5), so plate. Mrs Vole had 5 attempts (3), so Mrs Bright had 2.

Thus:
Miss Adams, plate, 6 attempts, niece;
Mrs Bright, vase, 2 attempts, cousin;
Mr Gordon, jug, 4 attempts, father-in-law;
Mr Turner, mug, 3 attempts, mother;
Mrs Vole, bowl, 5 attempts, son.

No 32

The man who spoke in 2005 doesn't specialise in lexicology (clue 2), climatology or anthropology (clue 3) or sociology (4), so psychology. The man from St Ann's spoke in 2004 (4) and (2) isn't the lexicologist. Nor is his subject anthropology (3) or sociology (4), so climatology. Dr Barker spoke in 2005 (3) and the anthropologist from Wale spoke in 2003. The lexicologist spoke in 2002 (2) and Professor Toft in 2001. By elimination, Professor Toft's subject is sociology. He isn't from Camford (1) or Newchester (2), so Hervard. The lexicologist isn't from Newchester (2), so Camford. The Newchester man spoke in 2005. The man from Camford (2002, above) isn't Dr Allwood or Dr Myers (1), so Professor Ling. Dr Allwood thus spoke in 2004 (1) and Dr Myers in 2003.

Thus:
2001, Professor Toft, sociology, Hervard;
2002, Professor Ling, lexicology, Camford;
2003, Dr Myers, anthropology, Wale;
2004, Dr Allwood, climatology, St Ann's;
2005, Dr Barker, psychology, Newchester.

No 33 *Odyssey*

The person who went to Richford on Monday wasn't Ann (clue 2), Norman (clue 4) or David (5). Norman's trip to Marwell wasn't on Monday (1), so (3) Lynette didn't go to Richford on Monday (3). Thus Gordon went to Richford on Monday, so (6) David went to Abbeyville on Monday. The person who went to Abbeyville on Friday wasn't Norman (1), Gordon (2) or Ann (5), so Lynette. Lynette went to Richford on Thursday (7). Norman went to Richford the day before David (5), so Norman on Tuesday and David on Wednesday. Ann went to Richford on Friday. Lynette went to Marwell on Monday (4) and Ann went to Abbeyville on Tuesday

277

Solutions

(5). Norman went to Marwell on Thursday (3), so Abbeyville on Wednesday. Gordon went to Abbeyville on Thursday. By elimination, Ann went to Marwell on Wednesday. David didn't go to Marwell on Friday (2), so Tuesday and Gordon went there on Friday.

Thus (Abbeyville, Marwell, Richford):

Ann, Tuesday, Wednesday, Friday;
David, Monday, Tuesday, Wednesday;
Gordon, Thursday, Friday, Monday;
Lynette, Friday, Monday, Thursday;
Norman, Wednesday, Thursday, Tuesday.

No 34

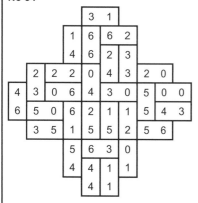

			3	1				
		1	6	6	2			
		4	6	2	3			
	2	2	2	0	4	3	2	0
4	3	0	6	4	3	0	5	0	0
6	5	0	6	2	1	1	5	4	3
	3	5	1	5	5	2	5	6
			5	6	3	0		
			4	4	1	1		
				4	1			

No 35

Remember throughout that each sowed seeds beginning with 3 different letters, none the same as the initial of his/her forename (intro). Parsley wasn't sown with carrots or spinach (clue 2) or cabbages (clue 6), so beetroot. Chives weren't sown with cabbages or carrots (intro) or parsnips (3), so spinach; thus not with carnations (intro). Carnations weren't sown with beetroot (5), so parsnips, thus not with mint (5). Chris didn't sow chives (plus spinach) or carnations (plus parsnips), so his vegetable seeds are the beetroot. Mint wasn't sewn with cabbages (4), so carrots, thus not with marigolds. Marigolds weren't sown with parsley (plus beetroot) or cabbages (6), so spinach. Heliotrope wasn't sewn with mint (plus carrots) or cabbages (4), so beetroot. Martin didn't sow mint or marigolds (intro) or parsnips (1), so his vegetable seeds are cabbages. Laura didn't sow carrots (plus mint) or chives (1), so sage; thus not with spinach, so parsnips. Sandy didn't sow spinach (intro), so carrots, not with sunflowers (intro), so violets. Olivia thus sowed marigolds and Martin sowed sunflowers plus lovage.

Thus:

Chris, heliotrope, parsley, beetroot;
Laura, carnations, sage, parsnips;
Martin, sunflowers, lovage, cabbages;
Olivia, marigolds, chives, spinach;
Sandy, violets, mint, carrots.

No 36

Steve Dodge's villain is either Captain Prior or Major Klink (clue 3). Bob Varmint is in the same book as a hero whose surname begins with a later letter of the alphabet than that of its author (clue 2) who thus isn't Wayne, Shyan or Rogers, so Carson. Robbie Gomez appeared in the same book as Matt Kirby (1). Tim Carson's hero isn't Luke Rock (5), thus he's Glen Derrick. Major Klink isn't in the same book as Bob Bailey or Joe Appleton (4), so Luke Rock. The hero in *Texas Tightspot* isn't Matt Kirby (1), Bob Bailey, Joe Appleton or Luke Rock (4), so Glen Derrick. The hero in *Frontier Town* isn't Bob Bailey, Joe Appleton or Luke Rock (4), so Matt Kirby. Ray Rogers' hero isn't Matt Kirby and he didn't write *Gunfighter* or *Showdown* (1), so he wrote *The Last Stand* and (6) his hero isn't Bob Bailey. Thus Ray Rogers' hero with a three-letter forename (1) is Joe Appleton. *Showdown* wasn't written by Steve Dodge or Dave Shyan (3), so Alan Wayne. The villain in *Showdown* isn't Captain Prior or Major Klink (3), so Eddie Walker. Luke Rock is thus in *Gunfighter* and Bob Bailey is in *Showdown*. By elimination, Captain Prior is in *The Last Stand*. *Gunfighter* wasn't written by Dave Shyan (3), so Steve Dodge. Dave Shyan wrote *Frontier Town*.

Thus:

Alan Wayne, *Showdown*, Bob Bailey, Eddie Walker;
Dave Shyan, *Frontier Town*, Matt Kirby, Robbie Gomez;
Ray Rogers, *The Last Stand*, Joe Appleton, Captain Prior;
Steve Dodge, *Gunfighter*, Luke Rock, Major Klink;
Tim Carson, *Texas Tightspot*, Glen Derrick, Ben Varmint.

No 37

Megan married in June (clue 2). The wedding in Portugal wasn't in January (clue 4), so Joanna's was in August (3) and Brenda's was in Portugal in March. January's wedding was in Albania (4). Sally married Philip in January (5), so Tina married in October, (6) in France. Joanna was married to John in Spain (1) and Megan married in Greece. Jenny's youngest friend was married in March, but not to Vernon, so Brenda's husband isn't Vernon. Vernon isn't married to Tina (6), so Megan. Tina didn't marry Peter (2), so Richard. Peter married Brenda.

Thus:

Brenda, Peter, Portugal, March;
Joanna, John, Spain, August;
Megan, Vernon, Greece, June;
Sally, Philip, Albania, January;
Tina, Richard, France, October.

No 38

Card E was called 5th (clue 1), K 11th, J 12th and C 7th. The card called 14th is N (4) and O was 9th, so F was 3rd. Card A was called 1st (2) and H 2nd. D was called 10th (2), M 15th (last) and L 6th. Card G was called 8th and B 13th (3), so I was called 4th.

Solutions

Thus:
1st A, 2nd H, 3rd F, 4th I, 5th E, 6th L, 7th C, 8th G, 9th O, 10th D, 11th K, 12th J, 13th B, 14th N, 15th M.

No 39 *The Necklace / Gifts of Magi*
Victoria's surname is Pounde (clue 5). Miss Doller shopped in Purse-busters (clue 2) and Mrs Sheckle in Money-mall (3). Verna who shopped in Bymoor & Sons (1) isn't Mrs Yenn (2), so Mrs Franks. Vera shopped in Supa-Bargain (1), so (by elimination) her surname is Yenn. Mrs Sheckle isn't Venetia (3), so Valerie. Venetia is Miss Doller and Victoria shopped at Wall et Cie. The woman who spent $60 isn't Venetia (2), Valerie (3), Verna (4) or Victoria (5), so Vera. The one who spent $20 isn't Venetia (3), Verna or Victoria (4), so Valerie. The one who spent $50 isn't Venetia (2) or Verna (4), so Victoria. Verna spent $40 (2) and Venetia $30.
Thus:
Valerie, Sheckle, $20, Money-mall;
Venetia, Doller, $30, Purse-busters;
Vera, Yenn, $60, Supa-Bargain;
Verna, Franks, $40, Bymoor & Sons;
Victoria, Pounde, $50, Wall et Cie.

No 40 *Odyssey (Sirens)*
Julia didn't buy at 9.05 (clue 6), so at either 9.35 or 10.05 (clue 5) and Sheena at either 10.35 or 11.05. Thus Sheena didn't pay $2.00 (4), so Julia paid $2.00 (5) and (6) Louise $2.20. Magda paid $2.40 (1) for the magazine with face mask. Julia bought at 9.35 (4), so Sheena at 10.35 (5). Patsy bought at 11.05 (3). She didn't pay $1.80 (3), so $1.90 and Sheena paid $1.80. Julia's magazine didn't have the bath oil (2), eye-shadow (3) or lip liner (4), so shampoo. The lip liner wasn't Patsy's or Sheena's (4), so Louise's. Louise thus bought at 9.05 (4), so Magda at 10.05. Patsy's magazine didn't have bath oil (2), so eye-shadow. Sheena's had bath oil.
Thus:
Julia, 9.35am, $2.00, shampoo;
Louise, 9.05am, $2.20, lip liner;
Magda, 10.05am, $2.40, face mask;
Patsy, 11.05am, $1.90, eye-shadow;
Sheena, 10.35am, $1.80, bath oil.

No 41 *R & J (Stars)*
Lou's star-sign isn't Aries (clue 1), Taurus or Cancer (clue 2) or Aquarius (3), so Gemini. Tricia's isn't Aquarius or Taurus (4) or Cancer (5), so Aries. Beth's isn't Taurus or Cancer (2), so Aquarius. Rowena's isn't Cancer (5), so Taurus; thus Delia's is Cancer. Mrs Wise isn't the chemist or nurse (2), the teacher or the cook (4), so the hairdresser. Mrs Wise isn't Tricia (4). Tricia (Aries, above) isn't a chemist or cook (1) or a teacher (4), so a nurse. Her surname isn't Thomson, Roberts or Gold (1), so Poitier. The teacher and hairdresser aren't Rowena (5) or Delia (Cancer, above), so they're Beth and/or Lou. Beth (Aquarius, above) isn't the teacher (3), so she's the hairdresser and Lou is the

teacher. Miss Thomson isn't Rowena (1) or Delia (3), so Lou. Miss Gold isn't Delia (3), so Rowena; thus Delia's surname is Roberts. Delia isn't a cook (4), so a chemist. Rowena is the cook.
Thus:
Beth, Wise, hairdresser, Aquarius;
Delia, Roberts, chemist, Cancer;
Lou, Thomson, teacher, Gemini;
Rowena, Gold, cook, Taurus;
Tricia, Poitier, nurse, Aries.

No 42
Samantha ordered carrot cake and got ginger cake (clue 1). Dave ordered the cake given to Kylie (clue 4) and the cake ordered with Assam tea was given to Wayne (5), so the person who ordered Assam wasn't Dave or Wayne. Nor was Assam ordered by Kylie (4) or Judy (5), so by Samantha. Thus Wayne got the carrot cake, so (2) drank Lapsang Souchong. Since Kylie got whatever Dave ordered (4), she didn't drink Darjeeling tea (6) or Ceylon (4), so Earl Grey tea. Kylie ordered Swiss roll (2). The Darjeeling-drinker got the cake Wayne ordered (6), so Wayne didn't order ginger cake (Samantha got ginger/drank Assam, above). Dave's order went to Kylie (4), so wasn't ginger cake. Thus Judy ordered ginger cake. She didn't drink Darjeeling (6), so Ceylon tea and Dave drank Darjeeling. Kylie's Swiss roll order thus didn't go to Dave (6), so Judy. Thus Kylie received Madeira cake (3). Dave ordered Madeira (4) and got the chocolate cake ordered (6) by Wayne.
Thus (ordered, received):
Dave, Madeira, chocolate, Darjeeling;
Judy, ginger, Swiss roll, Ceylon;
Kylie, Swiss roll, Madeira, Earl Grey;
Samantha, carrot, ginger, Assam;
Wayne, chocolate, carrot, Lapsang Souchong.

No 43

A	A	C	B	B	C
B	B	A	C	A	C
C	A	C	B	B	A
B	C	A	A	C	B
A	B	B	C	C	A
C	C	B	A	A	B

No 44
The team in beige shirts and yellow socks isn't the Lemmings (clue 2), The Green Men or the Wanderers (clue 1) or The Tigers (3), so The Bulls, whose shorts (4) are black. The team in red shirts and red socks (5) isn't The Green Men or the Wanderers (1) or The Tigers (3), so The Lemmings. The Wanderers don't wear blue or white socks (3), so green. Their shirts aren't green (6), so orange (1) and The Green Men wear green shirts. The Tigers wear blue shirts. Their socks aren't blue (7), so white and (3) The Green Men wear grey shorts and blue socks. The Wanderers don't wear green or brown shorts (6), so white. The shorts

Solutions

worn by The Lemmings aren't brown (2), so green. Brown shorts are worn by The Tigers.

Thus (shirts, shorts, socks):

The Bulls, beige, black, yellow;
The Green Men, green, grey, blue;
The Lemmings, red, green, red;
The Tigers, blue, brown, white;
The Wanderers, orange, white, green.

No 45

The woman getting the silver has been left £120,000 (clue 2), so the one getting the Ming vases has been left £200,000 (clue 1) and Jean will get £180,000. Babs who will get the Rolls-Royce (3) had served for 2 more years than Deborah, who thus won't get the Ming vases (1). The woman getting the Ming vases isn't Jean or Georgina (1), so Rosie. The woman getting £150,000 has been left the bedstead (2), so Jean will get the paintings. Deborah hadn't served for 7 or 8 years (3), so won't get the bedstead (2). Thus Deborah will get the silver and Georgina the bedstead. Babs will get £100,000. The women who served for 4 and 5 years aren't Jean (1), Georgina (2) or Babs (3). Jean served for 2 years longer than Rosie (1) and Babs for 2 years longer than Deborah (3), so Jean and Babs served for 6 and/or 7 years. Thus Georgina served for 8 years. Deborah served for 5 years (2), so Babs for 7, Jean for 6 and Rosie for 4 years.

Thus:

Babs, £100,000, Rolls-Royce, 7 years;
Deborah, £120,000, silver, 5 years;
Georgina, £150,000, bedstead, 8 years;
Jean, £180,000, paintings, 6 years;
Rosie, £200,000, Ming vases, 4 years.

No 46 Odyssey

Carl left at 11.25 (clue 2), the man with a stomach upset left at 11.15 and the man who stayed on Tuesday left at 11.45. Dougal left at 11.15 (1) and the man with toothache at 11.35. The man who stayed on Tuesday had a dust allergy (5) and wasn't Sean (3). Tom stayed on Wednesday (3), so Wesley on Tuesday. The man who left at 11.20 on Monday (4) is thus Sean and Tom left at 11.35. The man who had a migraine on Thursday (6) is thus Carl, so Dougal stayed on Friday and Sean had an earache.

Thus:

Carl, Thursday, 11.25pm, migraine;
Dougal, Friday, 11.15pm, stomach upset;
Sean, Monday, 11.20pm, earache;
Tom, Wednesday, 11.35pm, toothache;
Wesley, Tuesday, 11.45pm, dust allergy.

No 47

In clues 1 and 5, the value of X is either 6, 8 or 12. If X=6, then (5) I and W are 2 and/or 3, so (1) U=4 and H=24. If X=8, then (5) I and W are 2 and/or 4, so (1) U=3 and H=24. If X=12, then (1) U=2 and H=24. Either way, H=24, so X isn't 12 (12). Either X=6, U=4 (1),

A=18 (12) and I and W are 2 and/or 3; or X=8, U=3 (1), A=16 and I and W are 2 and/or 4. The value of Z (9) is either 12, 13, 14, 15 or 16 and (above) the values 2, 3 and 4 are represented by either I, W and/or U, so (7) G=5 and D=25. The value of R is either 17 or 19 (4), so (14) R=17 and K=22. Thus (4) X=8. U=3 (1) and A=16 (12). Z is either 12 or 14 (9), so (3) B is either 7 or 9. Thus (10) Y is either 14 or 18. If Z=12, B=7 (3) and Y=14 (10); and if Z=14, B=9 (3) and Y=18 (10). So Z+Y is either 26 or 32; thus (2) V is either 13 or 16. Since A=16 (above), V=13 (2 and above), so Z=12, B=7 and Y=14. I=4 (9), so W=2 (5). O hasn't a value of 20 or 26 (11), so in clues 6 and 8 Q, C and J have values of either 1, 9 and/or 11; and the value of C (16) is thus 1. J=9 and N=10 (6), so (8) Q=11 and O=21. L=26 (11). M (15) is either 18 or 19 and P is either 19 or 20. In clue 13, the only possibility is that F=15, S=6 and P=19, so (above) M=18. E=20 and T=23 (16).

Thus:

A=16, B=7, C=1, D=25, E=20, F=15, G=5, H=24, I=4, J=9, K=22, L=26, M=18, N=10, O=21, P=19, Q=11, R=17, S=6, T=23, U=3, V=13, W=2, X=8, Y=14, Z=12.

No 48

Rob O'Connor was 3rd (clue 3). The jockey who was 1st isn't Sam Dawson or Will Parton (clue 1) or Les Cotter (2), so Dusty Miller. Thus he rode Lady Hayes's horse (4), so (3) Jon Keymer's horse was 5th and (7) Rob O'Connor rode Ann Bridges' horse. Wayward Lass was ridden by Sam Dawson and finished 2nd (6), so Les Cotter was 4th (2) and Will Parton 5th. Rosie Dawn was 1st (3), so Springwood was 4th (2). Abracadabra wasn't 5th (1), so 3rd and Striker was 5th. Springwood belongs to James Rasir (5), so Prince Felip's horse was 2nd.

Thus:

1st, Rosie Dawn, Lady Hayes, Dusty Miller;
2nd, Wayward Lass, Prince Felip, Sam Dawson;
3rd, Abracadabra, Ann Bridges, Rob O'Connor;
4th, Springwood, James Rasir, Les Cotter;
5th, Striker, Jon Keymer, Will Parton.

No 49

The 12-year-old lives at No 7 (clue 5). The 11-year-old doesn't live at No 11 or No 2 (clue 2) or No 4 (5), so No 8; thus she isn't Diane (4). So Diane is 12 (4) and the girl in Shelley Close is 15. She isn't Pamela or Katie (2) or Susan (3), so Cora. Susan lives in Keats Close (3). Pamela lives at No 11 (2), but not in Tennyson or Wordsworth Close (1), so Byron Close. The girl in Wordsworth Close isn't Katie (3), so Diane. Katie lives in Tennyson Close. The 14-year-old's house number is higher than Susan's (3). The 14-year-old isn't Katie (2), so Pamela and Cora lives at No 2. Katie isn't 13 (2), so 11. Susan is 13 and lives at No 4.

Solutions

Thus:
Cora, 15 years old, No 2, Shelley Close;
Diane, 12 years old, No 7, Wordsworth Close;
Katie, 11 years old, No 8, Tennyson Close;
Pamela, 14 years old, No 11, Byron Close;
Susan, 13 years old, No 4, Keats Close.

No 50

Whooper contains toffee (clue 1) and Jingle contains hazelnuts (clue 2). Thus the biscuit bar isn't Bingo or Scrummy (3), so Yum-Yum. The blue button is pressed for Bingo (3) and the orange button for the bar with peanuts (4), so Bingo contains caramel and Scrummy has peanuts. The green button isn't used for Jingle or Yum-Yum (2), so Whooper. Yum-Yum's button isn't red (5), so white and Jingle's is red. Yum-Yum doesn't sell for 97 cents (3), so Jingle sells for 91 cents (2), Whooper for 85 cents and Yum-Yum for 94 cents. Bingo sells for 97 cents (3), so Scrummy for 88 cents.
Thus:
Bingo, blue, 97 cents, caramel;
Jingle, red, 91 cents, hazelnuts;
Scrummy, orange, 88 cents, peanuts;
Whooper, green, 85 cents, toffee;
Yum-Yum, white, 94 cents, biscuit.

No 51

Remember throughout that pictures contain parts from 4 different animals (intro). The horse's body and cat's legs (clue 1) aren't with the head of the horse or cat. The kangaroo's head has the horse's tail (clue 2), so not the horse's body. The lion's head is with the kangaroo's body (clue 3), so the horse's body is with the mouse's head. The kangaroo's head and horse's tail (2) haven't the legs of the lion (4), so mouse. The lion's head and kangaroo's body (3) are thus with the horse's legs. The mouse's tail is with the lion's legs (4), so (by elimination) the horse's legs are with the cat's tail, the kangaroo's legs are with the lion's tail and the cat's legs are with the kangaroo's tail. Thus the mouse's body is with the lion's tail, the lion's legs are with the cat's body and the lion's body has the mouse's legs and horse's tail. The horse's tail is with the kangaroo's head (2), so the cat's body is with the horse's head and the cat's head has the mouse's body.
Thus (head, body, legs, tail):
Cat, mouse, kangaroo, lion;
Horse, cat, lion, mouse;
Kangaroo, lion, mouse, horse;
Lion, kangaroo, horse, cat;
Mouse, horse, cat, kangaroo

No 52

Cards total 82 (intro), so the 9 is missing. Card K is a diamond (clue 6), so cards C and I are hearts (intro) and A is a diamond. G isn't a spade (5), so E is a spade and G a club. D isn't a spade (clue 6), so a club. Thus B and L are spades (intro) and J is a club. F isn't a diamond (5), so a heart and H is a diamond. Card D (club, above) isn't the 3 (a heart, 2) and L isn't an ace (1), so D isn't the 2 (6). Thus D is the 4 (6), G the queen and L the jack. The 2 of clubs (2) isn't E (3), so J and (2) I is the 3 of hearts. Card F is the ace (4). Card C (a heart) isn't the 8 (1), so (5) B is the 5 and C the 10. Card H is the 7, K the 6 and E the 8 (3), so A is the king.
Thus:
KD 5S 10H 4C
8S AH QC 7D
3H 2C 6D JS

No 53

Lucille weighs 100kg (clue 1) and Polly Crowe weighs 96kg (clue 5). The woman who was 110kg is now 99kg (3), so Francesca Stafford (6) is now 105kg and was 115kg. The 92kg woman isn't Abigail (2), so Marian and Abigail is 99kg. Thus Abigail isn't Mrs Denby who was 106kg (4). Abigail's surname isn't Williams (2), so Norton. Marian was 101kg (5), so Lucille is Mrs Denby and Marian is Mrs Williams. Polly used to weigh 109kg.
Thus:
Abigail, Norton, 110kg, 99kg;
Francesca, Stafford, 115kg, 105kg;
Lucille, Denby, 106kg, 100kg;
Marian, Williams, 101kg, 92kg;
Polly, Crowe, 109kg, 96kg.

No 54 odyssey

Fred Grant is on the *Ariadne* (clue 4) and Ken McTavish skippers *Mirabelle* (clue 6), so Malcolm Evans and Bill Hayes (1) are on the *Coaster*. Jack Cooke sails with Liam Oates (6). Hank Jones is on *Golden Ghost* but not with Tim Weston (2), so Don Stack. The grinder with Ken McTavish isn't Jack Cooke (6), so Tim Weston; thus the trimmer on the *Mirabelle* isn't Jeff Thynne (2), so Alan French. Bob Naylor sails with Roy Collins (3), so Malcolm Evans' trimmer is Jeff Thynne. By elimination, Roy Collins' grinder is Fred Grant. Johnnie Bristow's isn't Don Stack (5), so Don Stack sails with Peter Davison and Johnnie Bristow's grinder is Jack Cooke. Roy Collins' yacht is the *Ariadne* (Fred Grant, above), so Johnnie Bristow's is *Silver Surfer*.
Thus:
Johnnie Bristow, *Silver Surfer*, Jack Cooke, Liam Oates;
Roy Collins, *Ariadne*, Fred Grant, Bob Naylor;
Pete Davison, *Golden Ghost*, Don Stack, Hank Jones;
Malcolm Evans, *Coaster*, Bill Hayes, Jeff Thynne;
Ken McTavish, *Mirabelle*, Tim Weston, Alan French.

No 55

Judy whose husband is Geoff (clue 2) is one year younger than Caroline. Raymond's wife is one year

Solutions

younger than Derek's wife (4), so Derek's wife isn't Caroline. Josephine is one year younger than Henry's wife (clue 5), so Henry's wife isn't Caroline. Caroline's husband isn't Milton (2), so Raymond. No woman is 34 (grid), so Caroline is 36, Judy is 35 (2) and Derek's wife is 37 (4). Josephine isn't 33 or 37 (5), so 32 and Henry's wife is 33. She isn't Geraldine (1), so Andrea. Geraldine is 37. Derek's wife is Geraldine (4), so Josephine's husband is Milton. Henry is one year younger than Derek (1), so Henry is one year older than Milton (6). Raymond is younger than Milton (2). Derek isn't 39 (3), so Derek is 38. Henry is 37 (1). Milton is 36 and Raymond is 35. Geoff is 39.

Thus:

Andrea, 33, Henry, 37;
Caroline, 36, Raymond, 35;
Geraldine, 37, Derek, 38;
Josephine, 32, Milton, 36;
Judy, 35, Geoff, 39.

No 56

The interview was on Monday morning (clue 3), so he saw the tailor on Tuesday (clue 1) and dated Kerry on Thursday. The French lessons were on the same day as his aunt's party but not Friday (5), so Wednesday or Thursday and he dated Kristel on Friday. The ju-jitsu lesson and date with Kathy (4) was thus on Wednesday, so he saw the doctor on Friday and had a French lesson on Thursday. His barber's appointment and date with Katya wasn't on Tuesday (2), so Monday. He saw Kim on Tuesday, when (6) he went to the dentist and he saw the chiropodist on Wednesday. He saw the optician on Friday.

Thus:

Monday, interview, barber, Katya;
Tuesday, tailor, dentist, Kim;
Wednesday, ju-jitsu lesson, chiropodist, Kathy;
Thursday, French lesson, aunt's party, Kerry;
Friday, doctor, optician, Kristel

No 57

By elimination, pieces 19 and 29 contain G (clue 3) and 28 and 33 (clue 4) contain B. Pieces 26 and 42 contain D (5). In line 7-43, the F is in either 7 or 37, so there's no F in piece 2. Thus pieces 2 and 47 (1) contain A, so 12 has an F and the A in line 7-43 is in 25. In 6-48, 34=A. In 7-43, the C is in either 7 or 43, so 1=D. Piece 9 contains either E or C, as does 14, so 8=A, 10=G and 11=D. By elimination, 38=A. In 7-43, the E is in either 37 or 43, so 36=B. In 2-44, the B and D are in either 16 or 44. In 36-42, the G is in 39. In 1-7, the G is in 6 and in 22-28, the G is in 23. Pieces 18 and 30 (2) don't (because of piece 35) contain B; so in 15-21, the B is in 16, thus 44=D and 20=D. The letter in 41 isn't F (6), so E. Thus 27=C, 48=F, 24=E, 9=C, 17=F, 37=F, 30=E, 18=E (2), 15=C, 43=E, 7=C, 14=E, 35=F, 32=C, 3=B, 4=F, 45=C and 46=B.

Thus:

D	A	B	F	E	G	C
A	C	G	D	F	B	E
C	B	F	E	G	D	A
F	G	E	A	D	C	B
G	E	D	C	B	A	F
B	F	A	G	C	E	D
E	D	C	B	A	F	G

No 58

The woman who bought shoe polish also bought fish or vegetables (clue 6), so Mrs Rather who bought bread or eggs (clue 7) also bought wax polish. Miss Braden bought hairspray (clue 2). The woman with shoe polish isn't Miss Atkins or Mrs Trotter (6), so Mrs Simpson, who thus bought fish (4). The one with meat isn't Miss Atkins or Miss Braden (3), so Mrs Trotter. Patsy who bought hairspray or a toothbrush isn't Mrs Rather or Mrs Simpson (above). Either Belinda or Margaret is Miss Braden (2) and either Greta or Margaret is Mrs Trotter (3), so Patsy is Miss Atkins, thus bought a toothbrush and (5) bread and Mrs Trotter bought a baking tray, so Mrs Rather bought eggs and Miss Braden vegetables. Mrs Trotter isn't Margaret (1), so Greta. Belinda didn't buy eggs (1), so isn't Mrs Rather. Mrs Rather isn't Ruth (7), so Margaret. Belinda is Miss Braden (2), so Ruth is Mrs Simpson.

Thus:

Belinda, Braden, vegetables, hairspray;
Greta, Trotter, meat, baking tray;
Margaret, Rather, eggs, wax polish;
Patsy, Atkins, bread, toothbrush;
Ruth, Simpson, fish, shoe polish.

No 59

The man with a birthday on 30th June, wedding anniversary on 19th July and child born on 21st August isn't Frank (clue 1), nor (because of their birthdays) is he Dave or Tom (clue 2) or Barry (4), so Simon. The man married on 10th July became a father on 1st August (4) and Barry on 8th August and the former's birthday is later than Barry's. Either Dave's birthday is on 29th and Tom's 22nd June (2) or Dave's is on 22nd and Tom's 15th June, ie either Dave's or Tom's is on the 22nd. The man with a child born on 14th August isn't Dave or Tom (2), so Frank. So his birthday is on 29th (2), Dave's on 22nd and Tom's on 15th June. Barry's is 14th June. Frank's anniversary is later than Tom's (2) but earlier than Barry's (4), so Frank's is 17th and Barry's 26th July. The man who became a father on 23rd August married on 7th July. He's Tom (3), so Dave married on 10th July.

Thus:

Barry, 14th June, 26th July, 8th August;
Dave, 22nd June, 10th July, 1st August;
Frank, 29th June, 17th July, 14th August;
Simon, 30th June, 19th July, 21st August;
Tom, 15th June, 7th July, 23rd August.

Solutions

No 60

				0	3				
		1	1	6	0				
		6	3	3	0				
	3	1	2	3	1	2	4	4	
1	1	5	4	5	6	6	2	3	0
4	6	5	3	4	0	0	3	2	4
	5	1	5	2	2	4	5	6	
		0	5	1	0				
		5	6	4	6				
			2	2					

No 61

One family bought 42 cans of orangeade (clue 1). The 40 cans weren't of blackcurrant (clue 2) or cola (3), so (4) cherryade and 43 were of lemonade. The Brooks shopped on Wednesday (3), so neither the Phelps nor Tysons shopped on Tuesday (2). Thus the Andrews shopped on Tuesday (5) and the Martins on Thursday. The Tysons shopped on Friday and the Phelps on Saturday. The 44 cans weren't bought on Saturday (1), so (2) the Phelps bought 41 cans of blackcurrant and the Tysons bought 40 (cherryade, above). The 44 cans thus contained cola, so (3) the Brooks bought lemonade. The Andrews family (Tuesday, above) thus bought 44 cans and the Martins bought 42.

Thus:

Andrews family, cola, 44 cans, Tuesday;
Brooks family, lemonade, 43 cans, Wednesday;
Martin family, orangeade, 42 cans, Thursday;
Phelps family, blackcurrant, 41 cans, Saturday;
Tyson family, cherryade, 40 cans, Friday.

No 62

Frank's table is either white or yellow (clue 1), so the table at Parrot Park which is either brown or green (clue 5) is Dean's and (4) Lance lives at Martin's Roost. The table at Parrot Park isn't on the east side (3), so south (2), Frank's is on the west side (1) and Ivor's is on the east side (3). Lance's (at Martins' Roost, above) isn't on the north side (3), so in the centre. Brian's is on the north side. Brian lives at Condor Cottage (3 and 6). Ivor (east side, above) lives at Eagles' Lair (3), so Frank at Finchley House. Lance's table is yellow or green (4), so Brian's is brown (7). The table at Parrot Park is green (5), so Lance's is yellow. Frank's is white (1), so the one at Eagles' Lair is black.

Thus:

Condor Cottage, Brian, north, brown;
Eagles' Lair, Ivor, east, black;
Finchley House, Frank, west, white;
Martins' Roost, Lance, centre, yellow;
Parrot Park, Dean, south, green.

No 63

Bear in mind throughout the times on the grid. The shortest (5 minutes) call wasn't to a father (clue 1), brother or cousin (clue 2), an aunt (3), grandfather (4), mother or sister (6), so an uncle. Deirdre called her cousin (2). Edward's call wasn't to his father, mother or aunt (3) and lasted for 6 or 13 minutes, thus wasn't to his grandfather (4) or sister (6), so brother. Deirdre's call (to a cousin) didn't last for 15 minutes (4), so (2) Edward's was 6 minutes and Deirdre's 8. Irma's lasted 5 minutes (3). The 12-minute call wasn't to a father (1), grandfather (4), mother or sister (6), so aunt. The 10-minute call wasn't to a father (1), mother or sister (6), so a grandfather and (4) Katherine's was 15 minutes. Felicity's was 12 minutes and the father was called for 13 minutes. The mother was called for 15 (6) and the sister for 16 minutes. Graham's call lasted for 13 (6), Joseph's 10 and Lynne's 16 minutes.

Thus:

Deirdre, cousin, 8 minutes;
Edward, brother, 6 minutes;
Felicity, aunt, 12 minutes;
Graham, father, 13 minutes;
Irma, uncle, 5 minutes;
Joseph, grandfather, 10 minutes;
Katherine, mother, 15 minutes;
Lynne, sister, 16 minutes.

No 64 *Gift of megi*

Tomato soup will be followed by duck (clue 2) and game soup by pork. Beef will follow mushroom soup (clue 3) and turkey and profiteroles are being served at No 1 (5), so the pea and ham soup at No 2 (1) will be followed by goose. By elimination, turkey follows asparagus soup. Those having beef don't live at No 3 (3) or No 4 (4), so No 5. The Christmas pudding at No 3 (5) won't follow pork (2), so duck. Thus No 4 will have pork, not with pavlova (2) or fruit salad (4), so mince pies. No 5 won't have fruit salad (4), so pavlova. No 2 will have fruit salad.

Thus:

1 Yule Terrace, asparagus, turkey, profiteroles;
2 Yule Terrace, pea/ham, goose, fruit salad;
3 Yule Terrace, tomato, duck, Christmas pudding;
4 Yule Terrace, game, pork, mince pies;
5 Yule Terrace, mushroom, beef, pavlova.

No 65

The woman whose partner arrived at 7.30 isn't Madge (clue 1), Phoebe (clue 2), Brenda (3) or Tammy (6), so Barbara. The one whose partner arrived at 7.40 isn't Madge (1), Brenda (3) or Phoebe (6), so Tammy and Barbara drank vodka and tonic. Phoebe didn't drink red wine, lager or martini (2), so a spritzer. Madge didn't drink lager (1) or red wine (2), so a martini and (5) read

Solutions

the *Daily Courier*. The woman with red wine wasn't Tammy (2), so Brenda. Tammy drank lager. She read the *Daily Times* (1) and Madge's partner arrived at 7.50. Brenda's partner arrived at 8.00 (2) and Phoebe's partner at 8.10. Brenda read the *Evening Extra* (4). Barbara read the *Night Mail* (3), so Phoebe read the *Daily News*.

Thus:

Barbara, *Night Mail*, vodka and tonic, 7.30pm;
Brenda, *Evening Extra*, red wine, 8.00pm;
Madge, *Daily Courier*, martini, 7.50pm;
Phoebe, *Daily News*, spritzer, 8.10pm;
Tammy, *Daily Times*, lager, 7.40pm.

No 66

5	9	7	8	9	6
1	2	9	1	8	3
3	4	5	6	7	8
2	3	7	2	6	5
4	7	6	9	5	8
1	2	4	3	4	1

No 67

Gabrielle woke Daniel 8 times (clue 2), so Glenda woke him 10 times (clue 5) and Edna's baby 6 times. Sandra's baby cried 8 times (1) and Simon 6 times. Doreen's baby woke 10 times (3) and Ginny's 9 times, so Melinda's baby woke 4 times. Ginny's baby isn't Christopher (4), so Bart. Christopher's mum is Melinda. Edna's flat has a number three higher than Ginny's (1), which is higher than Melinda's (4), which is higher than Sandra's (2), so Edna is at No 46, Ginny at No 43, Melinda at No 42 and Sandra at No 41. Doreen lives at No 45.

Thus:

Flat No 41, Gabrielle, Sandra, 8 times;
Flat No 42, Christopher, Melinda, 4 times;
Flat No 43, Bart, Ginny, 9 times;
Flat No 45, Glenda, Doreen, 10 times;
Flat No 46, Simon, Edna, 6 times.

No 68

Mitch didn't bring blueberries or sloes (clue 1), rosehips or elderberries (clue 4), so blackberries. Deborah didn't bring elderberries, blueberries or sloes (1), so rosehips. The blueberries weren't brought by Della (3) or Kenny (6), so Fiona. Della didn't bring elderberries (1), so sloes. Kenny brought elderberries. The hazelnuts weren't brought by Kenny (5) or Fiona (6). Hazelnuts weren't brought by the children surnamed Wood (6), Beeton or Mellard (7), so either Chester or Yates. Thus they weren't brought by Mitch (4) or (rosehips, above) Deborah (2), so by Della. Della's surname isn't Chester (3), so Yates. Kenny's surname isn't Beeton (5), Mellard or Wood (6), so Chester. Deborah's surname isn't Beeton or Wood (1), so Mellard. The Wood child

isn't Fiona (6), so Mitch. Fiona's surname is Beeton. Acorns weren't brought by Fiona or Deborah (1) or Mitch (3), so Kenny. Mitch didn't bring beechnuts (3) or walnuts (6), so chestnuts. Fiona didn't bring walnuts (6), so beechnuts. Deborah brought walnuts.

Thus:

Della, Yates, sloes, hazelnuts;
Deborah, Mellard, rosehips, walnuts;
Fiona, Beeton, blueberries, beechnuts;
Kenny, Chester, elderberries, acorns;
Mitch, Wood, blackberries, chestnuts.

No 69 *Odyssey Homecoming*

The Smiths paid £136,000 (clue 1), so the Lloyds paid £136,500 (clue 3) and the house with a conservatory was £138,500. Mr & Mrs Giles bought the house with a garage (2), thus paid either £137,250 or £138,000. Their house wasn't £750 more than the house with a patio (2), so the house which cost £750 more than that with a patio was also either £137,250 or £138,000. Thus the house with a patio didn't cost £137,250. Thus the one with a patio was £136,500 (Lloyds, above), another house was £137,250 and Mr & Mrs Giles paid £138,000. No 19 wasn't bought by the Smiths or Myers (1), the Gileses (2) or the Lloyds (4), so by Mr & Mrs Bates. No 15 wasn't bought by the Smiths or Gileses (1) or Lloyds (4), so by Mr & Mrs Myers. No 18 wasn't sold to the Smiths (1) or Lloyds (2), so to Mr & Mrs Giles and No 19 cost £137,250. Mr & Mrs Myers paid £138,500. No 19 hasn't a greenhouse (5), so double glazing. The Smiths' house has a greenhouse. It isn't No 17 (6), so No 16. Mr & Mrs Lloyd bought No 17.

Thus:

Mr & Mrs Bates, No 19, £137,250, double glazing;
Mr & Mrs Giles, No 18, £138,000, garage;
Mr & Mrs Lloyd, No 17, £136,500, patio;
Mr & Mrs Myers, No 15, £138,500, conservatory;
Mr & Mrs Smith, No 16, £136,000, greenhouse.

No 70

Eddie's partner is Martina (clue 2) and Stan's is Cynthia (clue 6). Dick whose interest is fishing met his partner in the bus station (1). Delores met her partner in a café (3) and Oona's interest is theology (4), so Dick's partner is Petula. Eddie's interest is philately (2). Theo's isn't botany or archaeology (5), so theology. Thus his partner is Oona (4) and Andy's is Delores. The couple who met in the park are interested in botany (5), so Andy's interest is archaeology and Stan's is botany. Oona didn't meet her partner in a bar (4), so the library. Eddie and Martina met in the bar.

Thus:

Andy, Delores, café, archaeology;
Dick, Petula, bus station, fishing;
Eddie, Martina, bar, philately;
Stan, Cynthia, park, botany;
Theo, Oona, library, theology.

Solutions

No 71
Remember throughout that each person has 3 different favourites (intro). The person who places cricket 2nd places football 3rd (clue 1) and the one who places snooker 2nd places boxing 3rd (clue 3). The one whose favourite is tennis places football 2nd (4). The one whose favourite is cricket places tennis 2nd (6), thus (by elimination) snooker 3rd. So the one whose favourite is tennis places cricket 3rd and the one whose 2nd favourite is boxing places tennis 3rd. Thus the one whose favourite is boxing places football 3rd, the one whose favourite is snooker places boxing 2nd and the one whose favourite is football places boxing 3rd. Deanna's favorite isn't boxing (1) nor (2 and above) cricket, football or snooker (2), so tennis (football 2nd, cricket 3rd). The person who favours football 1st snooker 2nd and boxing 3rd (above) isn't Arthur (2), Teresa or Vincent (3), so Paul. Arthur's 3rd favourite isn't football (2), so his favourite isn't boxing and his 2nd favourite isn't cricket (above). Thus cricket is the 2nd favourite of either Teresa or Vincent. Vincent's favourite isn't cricket (6), so his 2nd favourite isn't tennis (above). If Vincent's 2nd is boxing, then his favourite is snooker (above) and boxing is the favourite of Teresa. But Teresa's favourite is different to Vincent's 2nd (5). Thus Vincent's 2nd is cricket, so his favourite is boxing. Teresa's favourite isn't cricket (5), so snooker. Arthur's favourite is cricket.

Thus (1st, 2nd, 3rd favourite):
Deanna, tennis, football, cricket;
Arthur, cricket, tennis, snooker;
Paul, football, snooker, boxing;
Teresa, snooker, boxing, tennis;
Vincent, boxing, cricket, football.

No 72 *Gift of magi*
The amount given on Tuesday wasn't $1.00 (clue 4), so $1.20 and $1.00 was given to the driver's collection (clue 2). The driver's collection wasn't on Wednesday (1), so Friday (4) for the 'get well soon' gift and the administrator's collection was on Wednesday. The $0.50 for the HR manager's birthday was on Thursday (1) and Tuesday's was for the receptionist leaving to have a baby. Monday's was for the wages clerk. The administrator isn't getting married (3), so the $1.50 was for the administrator's retirement (4). Thus $0.80 was given for the wages clerk's marriage gift.
Thus:
Monday, wages clerk, $0.80, marriage;
Tuesday, receptionist, $1.20, baby;
Wednesday, administrator, $1.50, retirement;
Thursday, HR manager, $0.50, birthday;
Friday, driver, $1.00, get well soon.

No 73
The person with green pillowcases and beige sheets (clue 3) isn't Moira whose pillowcases are the same colour as Leonora's duvet (clue 4), so either blue or purple. No-one has a beige duvet, so Clarice's sheets aren't beige (1), thus her pillowcases aren't green and Moira's sheets (4) aren't green. So Moira's sheets and Clarice's pillowcases (4) are (by elimination) pink. Moira's duvet is yellow (3), so Yuri's duvet and Clarice's sheets (1) are orange. Clarice's duvet isn't white (2), so the white duvet is Jeffrey's and (5) he hasn't yellow sheets. The person with yellow sheets isn't Yuri (1), so Leonora. Yuri (orange duvet, above) hasn't green sheets (2), so beige (with green pillowcases, 3). Jeffrey's sheets are green and (1) his pillowcases are beige. The person with the blue duvet hasn't blue pillowcases (6), so purple. By elimination, this person is Leonora, so Clarice's duvet is purple and Moira's pillowcases are blue.
Thus (duvet, pillowcases, sheets):
Clarice, purple, pink, orange;
Jeffrey, white, beige, green;
Leonora, blue, purple, yellow;
Moira, yellow, blue, pink;
Yuri, orange, green, beige.

No 74
The value of B is either 2, 3, 4 or 5 (clue 2). B+C=Y (clue 8), Y=K+1 (14) and K=BxB (2), so C=(BxB)−B, +1. Thus if B=2, then C=3 and there are no values for R and P (1). Similarly, if B=3, then C=7 and clue 1 doesn't work. If B=4, C=13 and clue 1 doesn't work. Thus B=5 and K=25 (2). Y=26 (14). C=21 (8). T=16 (7). R and/or P are 3 and/or 7 (1). Z and/or Q are 2 and/or 8 (3). V isn't 1 (4), thus V=4 (13), S=6 (4) and M=24. L isn't 2, 3, 4, 6 or 7 (above) and F isn't 24, 25 or 26. Thus L=1 and F=17 (13). R=3 (6), N=18, P=7 (1) and D=11 (9). I is at least 9, so (5) Q=2 and (above) Z=8. Thus I=10 and E=20 (5). The value of A is either 22 or 23 (11), as is that of W (10). If A=22, then J=14 (11) and W can't be 23 (10). Thus A=23 and J=15 (11), so W=22. X=12, G=9 (12) and H=13 (10). U=19 and O=14 (15).
Thus:
A=23, B=5, C=21, D=11, E=20, F=17, G=9, H=13, I=10, J=15, K=25, L=1, M=24, N=18, O=14, P=7, Q=2, R=3, S=6, T=16, U=19, V=4, W=22, X=12, Y=26, Z=8.

No 75
Jolene cleaned her dining room (clue 1) and the cellar was cleaned on Wednesday (clue 6). Cissy was helped by Midge on Tuesday but not in the kitchen or lounge (3), so bathroom and (5) the kitchen was done on Monday. Midge cleaned on Monday and was helped by Davina (4). Jolene helped on Friday (2), so Tanya helped Jolene (1) on Thursday. Jolene didn't help Tanya (intro), so Tanya was helped by Cissy. By elimination, this was on Wednesday, so the lounge was cleaned on Friday.
Thus:
Cissy, Tuesday, Midge, Bathroom;
Davina, Friday, Jolene, lounge;
Jolene, Thursday, Tanya, dining room;
Midge, Monday, Davina, kitchen;
Tanya, Wednesday, Cissy, cellar.

Solutions

No 76 *Thank you m'm*

The total haul was $450,000 (intro), so Mr Swindler got either $50,000 or $70,000 (clue 3), thus he isn't Connie (clue 1) or Lonnie (clue 2). Donnie's surname is Blank (5), so Ronnie's is either Check or Forge (2) and Johnnie is thus Mr Swindler. The planner got $130,000 (5). Johnnie wasn't the safe-blower or driver (3) or gunman (1), so was the look-out. Connie got $40,000 more than Mr Check the gunman (1), so Ronnie isn't Mr Check (2), thus he's Mr Forge and Lonnie is Mr Check, so Connie is Mr Cash. The planner ($130,000) wasn't Donnie (5), so Connie. Thus Lonnie got $90,000 (1) and Ronnie $50,000. Johnnie thus got $70,000. Ronnie wasn't the driver (4), so the safe-blower. Donnie was the driver.

Thus:

Connie, Cash, planner, £130,000;
Donnie, Blank, driver, $110,000;
Johnnie, Swindler, look-out, $70,000;
Lonnie, Check, gunman, $90,000;
Ronnie, Forge, safe-blower, $50,000.

No 77

No man leaves at 10.30 (grid). The man who leaves at 9.30 doesn't have waffles or eggs and bacon (clue 1), boiled eggs (clue 2) or kedgeree (3), so kippers. The man who spends 12 minutes eating leaves at 10.00. The man with eggs and bacon takes longer than 12 minutes to eat (1), so he leaves at 11.00 and the one who has waffles leaves at 12.00. No man eats for 15 minutes (grid), so the one who has eggs and bacon doesn't eat for 16 (1). The man who eats for 16 minutes thus leaves at 9.30 (2) and the one who has boiled eggs leaves at 10.00. The man who has kedgeree leaves at 11.30. The man with eggs and bacon takes 14 minutes and the one with waffles 13 minutes (1), so the man with kedgeree takes 17 minutes and (2) eats at 8.00. The man with eggs and bacon eats at 7.30 (3), so the one with waffles at 6.30 (1). The man with kippers eats at 8.30 (4), so the one with boiled eggs eats at 9.00.

Thus:

Boiled eggs, 9.00am, 12 minutes, 10.00am;
Eggs and bacon, 7.30am, 14 minutes, 11.00am;
Kedgeree, 8.00am, 17 minutes, 11.30am;
Kippers, 8.30am, 16 minutes, 9.30am;
Waffles, 6.30am, 13 minutes, 12.00 noon.

No 78

Card D was called immediately after G (clue 2), so D wasn't called 13th (clue 3). Card I wasn't called immediately after A (3), so A wasn't 13th (3). Thus F was 13th (3), M 12th and D 11th, so G was 10th (2). The card called 8th was thus C (4), J was 3rd and E 6th. L was 14th (5), K 1st and O 15th (last). A was 4th and B 7th (1). H was 2nd (4). Card I wasn't 5th (2), so 9th and N was 5th.

Thus:

1st K, 2nd H, 3rd J, 4th A, 5th N, 6th E, 7th B, 8th C, 9th I, 10th G, 11th D, 12th M, 13th F, 14th L, 15th O.

No 79 *R & J Honeymoon*

Suzie from Australia arrived on Wednesday (clue 2) and Mee-Ling from Japan arrived on Thursday (clue 4). Dave arrived on Saturday (3), so Pete from the USA who didn't arrive on Friday (1) came on Tuesday. Amanda arrived on Tuesday (5) and Lee on Thursday. Dave's wife isn't Ellen (3), so Wendy. Thus Ellen arrived on Friday. Jack isn't from Denmark or Australia (2), so Ireland; and (by elimination) he's married to Ellen. Thus Dave is from Denmark and Hugh's wife is Suzie.

Thus:

Dave, Wendy, Saturday, Denmark;
Hugh, Suzie, Wednesday, Australia;
Jack, Ellen, Friday, Ireland;
Lee, Mee-Ling, Thursday, Japan;
Pete, Amanda, Tuesday, USA

No 80

The car with the globe design which made 3 pit stops (clue 2) isn't gold (clue 1), black (3), red (4) or yellow (7), so blue. The red car's design isn't red stars (4), pink swirls or green stars (5), so white stripes. Thus the car with pink swirls made 4 pit stops (5 and 6). It isn't gold (1) or black (3), so yellow. The gold car made 6 pit stops (1). The red car made 7 (4) and the gold car has red stars. By elimination, the black car has green stars and made 5 pit stops, so (3) the blue car completed 17 laps. The black car completed 18 laps (7), so the yellow car 15 (5) and the red car 14 laps. The gold car completed 19 laps.

Thus:

Black, green stars, 18 laps, 5 pit stops;
Blue, globe, 17 laps, 3 pit stops;
Gold, red stars, 19 laps, 6 pit stops;
Red, white stripes, 14 laps, 7 pit stops;
Yellow, pink swirls, 15 laps, 4 pit stops.

No 81 *The Necklace*

Billy found Mr Barlow's item (clue 4) and Harry found something on Tuesday (clue 5), but not the umbrella. Miss Cooke's item was found on Friday (7), so Mr Porter's item was found on Wednesday (6) and the umbrella on Monday. Mr Barlow's item wasn't the umbrella (4), so Bill's find was on Thursday and the pen was found on Friday. Harry's find doesn't belong to Mr Thomas (5), so Mrs Jarvis. By elimination, Mr Thomas's item was found on Monday. Mr Porter's item wasn't found by Lucien or Tina (6), so Willow. Friday's find wasn't made by Lucien (1), so Tina. Mr Thomas's item was found by Lucien. The book wasn't found by Billy or Willow (3), so Harry. Willow found the watch (2), so Billy found the calculator.

Thus:

Billy, Thursday, calculator, Mr Barlow;
Harry, Tuesday, book, Mrs Jarvis;
Lucien, Monday, umbrella, Mr Thomas;
Tina, Friday, pen, Miss Cooke;
Willow, Wednesday, watch, Mr Porter.

Solutions

No 82 *Speckled Band*

The 6'1" man didn't have the silver bracelet (clue 2), gold ring (clue 3), gold watch (4) or silver locket (5), so sunglasses and the 34-year-old (2) is 6'0". No man is 5'11" (grid), so the 6'1" man didn't say his item was from his girlfriend (2). Nor did he say it was from his grandfather or mother (1). No man is 38 (grid), so the 6'1" man didn't say his item was from his uncle (4), so from his auntie. The 34-year-old man didn't have a silver bracelet (2), gold watch (4) or silver locket (5), so a gold ring, thus (3) the 6'1" man is 32. The man with the gold watch is 36 (4) and the 40-year-old said his gift was from an uncle. The 5'8" man didn't say his item was from his uncle (4) or mother (5), so grandfather and (1) the 40-year-old is 5'9". The 36-year-old (gold watch, above) is 5'8" (4), so the 42-year-old is 5'10". He didn't say his item was from his girlfriend (2), so his mother. The 34-year-old said his item was from his girlfriend. He's 6'0" (above), so the 5'10" man had the silver bracelet (2). The 40-year-old thus had a silver locket.

Thus:
32-year-old, 6'1", sunglasses, auntie;
34-year-old, 6'0", gold ring, girlfriend;
36-year-old, 5'8", gold watch, grandfather;
40-year-old, 5'9", silver locket, uncle;
42-year-old, 5'10", silver bracelet, mother.

No 83 *1st Week*

Mr Cameron went to Hill Rise School (clue 2) and Joe's surname is Bush (clue 4). Mr Dickins's tie had a colour in common with Robbie's (4), so Clifford who (3) attended Denne Road (and whose tie had no colours in common with Robbie's) isn't Mr Dickins. Nor is he Mr Shaw (3), so he's Mr Smythe. The man who went to East Park isn't surnamed Bush or Dickins (4), so Shaw, whose tie (3) was black/purple. Robbie didn't go to East Park (4), so he's Mr Cameron. Thus Joe Bush went to St Christophe's (2 and 4) and Benny is Mr Dickins. Mike is Mr Shaw and Benny went to Bell Hill. Green and white are colours which feature in one tie each. Thus (4) Robbie's was either purple/blue or blue/red. Benny's had no red (1) nor (2 and above) was it green/black, thus it was purple/blue, Robbie's was blue/red and (4) Joe's was red/white. Clifford's was green/black.

Thus:
Benny, Dickins, Bell Hill, purple/blue;
Clifford, Smythe, Denne Road, green/black;
Joe, Bush, St Christophe's, red/white;
Mike, Shaw, East Park, black/purple;
Robbie, Cameron, Hill Rise, blue/red.

No 84

The letter in pieces 2 and 13 (clue 1) is (by elimination) F and that in pieces 31 and 49 is D (clue 4); thus 41=G. The letter in pieces 20 and 7 (3) is B; thus 6=A and (in column 6-48) 27=D. In row 8-14, the D isn't in piece 11 (6), so it's in 8. The letter in 33 and 37 is E (5), so

19=C, 1=C and 17=F. In 36-42, 39=D; thus in 15-21, 16=D. The letter in 3 and 12 is G (2); thus 4=E. By elimination, 18=G and 11=C. In row 36-42, 38=C, so 44=C and 28=C. In 22-28, 23=G. In 29-35, 35=G. In 2-44, 30=A. Piece 14=A (6); so in 7-49, 21=E and (in 8-14) 10=E. Thus 15=A, 36=B and 40=A. Piece 29=F, so 22=E. Piece 24=B, 45=A, 26=F, 47=B, 46=F and 32=B.

Thus:

C	F	G	E	D	A	B
D	B	E	C	G	F	A
A	D	F	G	C	B	E
E	G	B	A	F	D	C
F	A	D	B	E	C	G
B	E	C	D	A	G	F
G	C	A	F	B	E	D

No 85

Remember throughout that no block houses 43 men or 45 women (grid). There are either 46 women at Clinton Court and 44 at Lincoln Court (clue 3) or 48 at Clinton Court and 46 at Lincoln Court, ie the 46 women live at either Clinton Court or Lincoln Court. Carter Court hasn't 43 women (clue 5), so 47 (1) and there are 48 in block B. Block A is Carter Court (5). Block B has 45 men (1). The block with 43 women isn't Kennedy Court (2), so Bush Court. Bush Court isn't D or E (4), so C. Lincoln Court is E and Clinton Court D (3), so Kennedy Court is B. Thus Clinton Court has 46 women (3) and Lincoln Court has 44 women (2). Block A has 44 men (2). Clinton Court has more men than Lincoln Court which has more men than Bush Court (4), so there are 42 men at Clinton Court, 41 at Lincoln Court and 40 men at Bush Court.

Thus:
A, Carter Court, 44 men, 47 women;
B, Kennedy Court, 45 men, 48 women;
C, Bush Court, 40 men, 43 women;
D, Clinton Court, 42 men, 46 women;
E, Lincoln Court, 41 men, 44 women.

No 86

The youngest (born 1996) isn't Stephen (clue 1), so Danny (a boy, clue 2) whose birthday is the 16th. Naomi was born in 1992 (6) and Louisa was born in June (7). Naomi wasn't born on the 17th (4). Stephen is older (1) than the child born on 17th July, who is (by elimination) Christine. She wasn't born in 1993 (4) or 1994 (5), so 1995. The 1993 child was born in September (4), so is Stephen. Danny was born in August (3) and Naomi in October. By elimination, Louisa was born in 1994. Stephen wasn't born on the 16th or 15th (1), so 13th. Naomi was born on the 14th (4), so Louisa on the 15th.

Thus:
Christine, 17th, July, 1995;
Danny, 16th, August, 1996;
Louisa, 15th, June, 1994;
Naomi, 14th, October, 1992;
Stephen, 13th, September, 1993.

Solutions

No 87

The man run out made 11 runs (clue 3) and wasn't batsman No 5 (clue 1), so No 8 (3) and No 6 was caught out. Roger was given out for obstruction (2), so he was batsman No 3 (5) and Willie was No 5. The man stumped wasn't Willie (5), so was No 2 and Willie was given out lbw. Ambrose made either 5 or 9 more runs than Willie (1) and Des made one more run than Roger (2), who (being No 3, above) made more runs than Willie (4). So Roger made 10, Des 11, Ambrose 15 and Willie 6 runs. Thus Jamie made 5 runs. Jamie wasn't No 2 (6), so No 6 and Ambrose was No 2.

Thus:

No 2, Ambrose, 15 runs, stumped;
No 3, Roger, 10 runs, obstruction,
No 5, Willie, 6 runs, lbw;
No 6, Jamie, 5 runs, caught out;
No 8, Des, 11 runs, run out.

No 88 *R 95*

Mark's story is set in Wellington (clue 4) and a MAN (thus not Ursula) surnamed Findlay set his book in Adelaide (clue 6). Angela whose surname is Hammond (1) didn't set hers in London or Sydney, so New York: thus it's *Waiting in New York* (2). Ursula's story isn't set in London (3), so Sydney. The story set in London wasn't written by Luke (3), so Steven. Luke's is thus set in Adelaide, so he's Mr Findlay (6). Steven's surname isn't Walsh (3) or Brooker (5), so Packer. Ursula's isn't Walsh (3), so Brooker, thus her book begins *Steamy In* (5). Mark's surname is Walsh. Luke's book's title doesn't begin with *Adoration In* (6) or *Passion In* (7), so *Wedding In*. Steven's doesn't begin with *Adoration In* (7), so *Passion In*. Mark's begins with *Adoration In*.

Thus:

Angela, Hammond, *Waiting In*, *New York*;
Luke, Findlay, *Wedding In*, *Adelaide*;
Mark, Walsh, *Adoration In*, *Wellington*;
Steven, Packer, *Passion In*, *London*;
Ursula, Brooker, *Steamy In*, *Sydney*.

No 89 *Trojan War*

The RFC man was decorated in 1916 (clue 4) and the DCM was awarded in 1917 (clue 5), so the DSO was awarded in 1916 (1) and Henry in the Cavalry was decorated in 1914. The DCM wasn't given to the man in the Artillery (5) or Guards (6), so Infantry. William's 1918 medal (7) wasn't the Military Cross or Victoria Cross, so the Military Medal. He wasn't in the Guards (6), so Artillery. The Military Cross wasn't given in 1914 (2), so 1915 and the Victoria Cross was given in 1914. Albert was in the Guards (3), so was decorated in 1915. George wasn't in the Infantry (5), so RFC and Frederick was in the Infantry.

Thus:

Albert, 1915, Military Cross, Guards;
Frederick, 1917, DCM, Infantry;
George, 1916, DSO, RFC;
Henry, 1914, Victoria Cross, Cavalry;
William, 1918, Military Medal, Artillery.

No 90 *Gift of Magi*

The alarm clock is in the bedroom and the carriage and grandfather clocks were both slow (clue 3). The clock in the hall, which is fast isn't the wall-clock (clue 4), so the cuckoo-clock. The lounge clock was accurate (2), so it's the wall-clock. The cuckoo-clock was wrong by 7 minutes (5), thus was 7 minutes fast and the alarm clock was (by elimination) 12 minutes fast. The grandfather clock wasn't adjusted at 9.30 (3), so the 12-minute slow clock adjusted at 9.30 (6) is the carriage clock and the grandfather clock was 7 minutes slow. The carriage clock isn't in the study (1), so dining room and the grandfather clock is in the study. The cuckoo-clock (hall, above) was corrected at 8.00 (4) and the wall-clock at 7.00. The grandfather clock was corrected at 6.30 (3) and the alarm clock at 8.30.

Thus:

Alarm clock, bedroom, 8.30pm, 12 minutes fast;
Carriage clock, dining room, 9.30pm, 12 minutes slow;
Cuckoo-clock, hall, 8.00pm, 7 minutes fast;
Grandfather clock, study, 6.30pm, 7 minutes slow;
Wall-clock, lounge, 7.00pm, accurate

No 91

The boy who got 10 toffees isn't Rupert (clue 2), Mark (clue 3), Graeme or Francis (4), so Adam. Rupert didn't get 4 or 6 toffees (2) or 12 (3), so 8. The boy who got 12 isn't Graeme or Mark (3), so Francis. Graeme didn't get 4 (2), so 6 and Mark got 4. The boy whose favourite is English and least favourite is maths isn't Adam or Rupert (1). Physics isn't the favourite of the boy whose least favourite is French (2). The boy whose least favourite is French doesn't favour art or geography (2), so chemistry. He isn't Mark, Rupert or Graeme (2) or Francis (3), so Adam. In clue 3, Graeme is the boy whose least favourite is literature. In clue 2, Francis is the boy whose favourite is physics, thus Mark is the boy whose favourite is English and least favourite is maths. In clue 1, Francis is the boy whose least favourite is history and Graeme is the boy whose favourite is art. So Rupert's favourite is geography and his least favourite is English.

Thus:

Adam, 10 toffees, chemistry, French;
Francis, 12 toffees, physics, history;
Graeme, 6 toffees, art, literature;
Mark, 4 toffees, English, maths;
Rupert, 8 toffees, geography, English.

Solutions

No 92

3	6	1	9	3	9
1	4	6	7	8	2
5	8	2	4	6	5
8	7	6	5	4	3
7	5	4	3	2	7
8	9	1	9	1	2

No 93

Maisie shopped at Deal & Marsh and hasn't odd-sized feet (clue 1), nor is she petite/plump or petite/slim (clue 2). Wilma who shopped at The Supplier isn't petite/slim or tall/slim (6). The petite/slim woman didn't go to Geckle & Sons (4) or B T Nolan (5), so Corbett's. She isn't Nicky (3) or Fleur (7), so Victoria. Nicky didn't shop at B T Nolan (3), so Geckle & Sons. Thus Fleur went to B T Nolan and (7) bought a coat. The woman with odd-sized feet bought trainers and isn't Maisie (1) or Nicky (3), so Wilma. The petite/plump woman isn't Fleur (5), so Nicky. The tall/slim woman isn't Fleur (7), so Maisie and Fleur is tall/plump. The jacket wasn't bought by Maisie or Victoria (4), so Nicky. Maisie didn't buy a dress (2), so trousers. Victoria bought the dress.

Thus:

Fleur, coat, B T Nolan, tall/plump;
Maisie, trousers, Deal & Marsh, tall/slim;
Nicky, jacket, Geckle & Sons, petite/plump;
Victoria, dress, Corbett's, petite/slim;
Wilma, trainers, The Supplier, odd-sized feet.

No 94

The family with vegetable soup and semolina lives next door to the ones with minestrone (clue 2) AND next door to the ones with asparagus soup (1), thus not at No 9. The family with asparagus soup lives between two others (1), so not at No 9. The ones at No 9 didn't have leek and potato (2) or French onion soup (3), so minestrone. They ate duck (2) and those at No 7 had vegetable soup and semolina. No 5 had asparagus soup (1) and No 3 had pork. No 5 had rice (3), No 1 had French onion soup and No 7 had chicken. By elimination, No 3 had leek and potato soup. No 5 didn't have beef (4), so lamb and No 1 had beef. Sago wasn't eaten at No 9 (2) or No 1 (4), so No 3. No 9 didn't have tapioca (2), so macaroni. No 1 had tapioca.

Thus:

No 1, French onion, beef, tapioca;
No 3, leek and potato, pork, sago;
No 5, asparagus, lamb, rice;
No 7, vegetable, chicken, semolina;
No 9, minestrone, duck, macaroni.

No 95 *Odyssey (Ship wreck)*

No-one woke at 2.50 (grid). Harry didn't wake at 3.00 (clue 2), so either Scott woke at 2.35 and Harry at 2.40 (clue 5) or Scott woke at 2.40 and Harry at 2.45: ie the one woken at 2.40 was either Harry or Scott. Thus Olga woke at 3.00 (4) and Neil at 2.55. The person surnamed O'Brien isn't Neil (2) or Olga (4),

so Harry didn't wake at 2.45 (2). Thus Harry woke at 2.40, Scott at 2.35 (5) and Marjorie at 2.45. Marjorie is thus O'Brien (2). The holiday dream wasn't Harry's (6), so Scott's (1) and Harry's surname is Nye. Neil's isn't Masters or Standish (4), so Hilton, thus (3) he dreamt of his wedding. The man who dreamt of an inheritance (2) is thus Harry. Masters who dreamt of a new house (7) is thus Olga, so Scott's surname is Standish and Marjorie dreamt of film stardom.

Thus:

Harry, Nye, 2.40am, inheritance;
Marjorie, O'Brien, 2.45am, film stardom;
Neil, Hilton, 2.55am, wedding;
Olga, Masters, 3.00am, new house;
Scott, Standish, 2.35am, holiday

No 96

C	C	A	B	B	A
B	B	A	C	C	A
A	B	C	A	B	C
C	A	B	A	C	B
A	C	B	B	A	C
B	A	C	C	A	B

No 97

The woman who stripped walls on Monday did so for either 4 or 4½ hours (clue 4) and isn't Sue. Nor is she Selina or Simone (2) or Sonia (3), so Sally. Thus she worked for 4½ hours (1) and Sue for 6½ hours (4). Simone was in the lounge (2). The woman who stripped her conservatory isn't Sally (Monday, above), Selina or Sue (4), so Sonia. The one who spent 4 hours in the bathroom (1) was thus Selina. She isn't the woman who spent one hour less stripping walls than Simone (2), so Simone worked for 6 hours and Sonia for 5. Thus Sonia's day off was two days before Selina's (2) and the day after Sue's (2). So Sonia's was on Wednesday, Selina's on Friday and Sue's on Tuesday. Simone was thus off work on Thursday. The woman who stripped her kitchen isn't Sue (5), so Sally. Sue stripped her bedroom.

Thus:

Sally, Monday, 4½ hours, kitchen;
Selina, Friday, 4 hours, bathroom;
Simone, Thursday, 6 hours, lounge;
Sonia, Wednesday, 5 hours, conservatory;
Sue, Tuesday, 6½ hours, bedroom.

No 98

When Phil and Dana played (clue 1), the second woman wasn't Antonia (clue 3) or Alison (4), Stephanie or Josie (5), so Laura who (6) was at the same session as Frederick. When Betsy and Hank played, the first man wasn't Ian or Bruce (2) or Miles (3), so Ted. Caroline played with Alison (4). Stephanie and Ian (6) didn't play with Jessica (5), so Roseanne. Thus

Solutions

Antonia played with Jessica and (3) Jeff and Miles. By elimination, Bruce played with Caroline. Roseanne wasn't at the same session as Clive (7), so Bernard. Thus Caroline was at the same session as Clive.

Thus:
Bruce, Caroline, Clive, Alison;
Frederick, Dana, Phil, Laura;
Ian, Roseanne, Bernard, Stephanie;
Miles, Jessica, Jeff, Antonia;
Ted, Betsy, Hank, Josie

No 99

The 22-year-old isn't Sharon or Thomas (clue 2), Arthur (clue 3) or Steve (4), so Pamela. The 30-year-old isn't Thomas (2) Arthur (3) or Steve (4), so Sharon. The 46-year-old is sketching the flagon (1). The armour in the Tudor room (3) is being sketched by someone 8 years older than the artist in the Indian section, but younger than Arthur, so either the person in the Tudor room is 30 and the one in the Indian room is 22, or the one in the Tudor room is 38 and the one in the Indian room is 30: thus the 30-year-old (Sharon, above) is either in the Indian or Tudor room. Arthur is sketching pots. The sword in the Victorian room (4) isn't being sketched by Steve or Pamela, so Thomas. Steve is in the Egyptian room (4), so Arthur is in the Roman room, Pamela (aged 22) is in the Indian room and Sharon in the Tudor room. The 46-year-old sketching the flagon (1) is (by elimination) Steve. So Thomas is 38 (4) and Arthur is 54. Pamela is sketching jewellery.

Thus:
Arthur, 54 years old, pots, Roman;
Pamela, 22 years old, jewellery, Indian;
Sharon, 30 years old, armour, Tudor;
Steve, 46 years old, flagon, Egyptian;
Thomas, 38 years old, sword, Victorian.

No 100

Cards total 80 (intro), so the jack is missing. G has a value one lower than F (clue 2), which has a value one lower than C (clue 3), which has a value one lower than B (1). C has a value two lower than I (4). If F's value is 2, then (above) B's is 4, leaving no value for E (2); and if F's value is 3, then (above) I's value is 6, leaving no value for E (2). So F is the 4, G the 3 (2), C the 5 (3), B the 6 (1) and I the 7 (4). A is the queen (1), E the 8 (2) and L the 10 (3). K is the 2 (5) and J the 9. H is the ace (5) and D the king of (6) clubs. Cards L and B are spades (intro) and J is a club. G (a 3, above) isn't a spade (6), so a club and E is a spade. H isn't a diamond (6), so a heart and F is a diamond. I isn't a diamond (4), so I and C are hearts and A and K are diamonds.

Thus:
QD 6S 5H KC
8S 4D 3C AH
7H 9C 2D 10S

No 101

Pamela's 2nd number wasn't 45 (clue 4), so the number chosen as 3rd by Wilhelmina, 1st by Jacqueline and 2nd by Pamela (clue 5) is 20. Jacqueline's 2nd and Henrietta's 3rd wasn't 45 (3), so 36. The woman who chose 37 2nd isn't Ariadne (1) or Henrietta (2), so Wilhelmina. The number chosen by Henrietta 1st and Ariadne 2nd (1) was thus 45. Wilhelmina's 1st and Henrietta's 2nd (2) was 16. Pamela's 3rd was 41 (4), so her 1st was 12 and Ariadne's 1st was 41. Ariadne's 3rd wasn't 45 (her 2nd choice, above), so 12. Jacqueline's 3rd was 45.

Thus (first, second, third):
Ariadne, 41, 45, 12;
Henrietta, 45, 16, 36;
Jacqueline, 20, 36, 45;
Pamela, 12, 20, 41;
Wilhelmina, 16, 37, 20.

No 102

Valentina got a bracelet (clue 3) and Bella a ring (clue 4). Jo didn't get the necklace or brooch (5), so earrings. Kate didn't get the brooch (2), so a necklace and Rebecca got the brooch and (5) candle. Kate's boyfriend is Eric (2). Valentina didn't get lilies, roses or wine (3), so chocolates. Her boyfriend isn't Clifford (3), Nigel or Frank (6), so Timothy. Jo didn't get lilies or roses (1), so a bottle of wine. Clifford gave lilies (3), thus to Bella and Eric gave the roses. Rebecca didn't get her candle from Nigel (6), so Frank. Jo's boyfriend is Nigel.

Thus:
Bella, ring, lilies, Clifford;
Jo, earrings, wine, Nigel;
Kate, necklace, roses, Eric;
Rebecca, brooch, candle, Frank;
Valentina, bracelet, chocolates, Timothy.

No 103

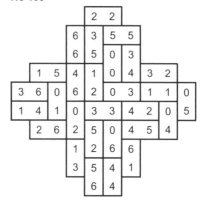

Solutions

No 104 *R ?J*

Tuesday's gardener worked for either 3½ or 4 hours (clue 5), so Boris who dug for either 2 or 3 hours (2) did so on Friday. Peter dug on Tuesday (4), so Lisa on Monday (1). John is the gardener surnamed Raikes who dug on Wednesday (3), so Cathy dug on Thursday. Peter's surname is Mower (4), so Lisa's is Trowell (1). Cathy's surname is Forke (2), so Boris' is Spayde. Boris thus dug for 3 hours (6), so John for 3½ (3) and Peter for 4 hours (5). Cathy (Thursday, above) dug for 2 hours (6), so Lisa for 2½ hours.

Thus:

Boris, Spayde, 3 hours, Friday;
Cathy, Forke, 2 hours, Thursday;
John, Raikes, 3½ hours, Wednesday;
Lisa, Trowell, 2½ hours, Monday;
Peter, Mower, 4 hours, Tuesday.

No 105

The 1,250-word essay wasn't written by Dick (clue 1), Mike (clue 2), Lucy (3) or Hugh (4), so Fenella. The 1,340-word essay wasn't on commerce (1), travel (2), theatre (3) or music (4), so birds. The 1,320-word essay wasn't written by Dick (1), nor (since none was of 1,300 words) by Mike (2) or Hugh (4), so Lucy. The one on birds wasn't written by Dick (1) or Mike (2), so Hugh. Lucy's was on music (4). Mike's wasn't on travel or commerce (2), so the theatre. Dick's was thus on travel (1) and Fenella's on commerce. Dick's was of 1,270 words (2) and Mike's of 1,290 words. Dick's was ranked 33rd (3), so Lucy's was 32nd (1). Hugh's was 28th (4) and Fenella's was 31st, so Mike's essay was ranked 29th.

Thus:

Dick, travel, 1,270 words, 33rd;
Fenella, commerce, 1,250 words, 31st;
Hugh, birds, 1,340 words, 28th;
Lucy, music, 1,320 words, 32nd;
Mike, theatre, 1,290 words, 29th.

No 106

AxA (clue 1) is less than 52, so A is one of either 2, 3, 4, 5, 6 or 7. G+L is equal to E+Z (clue 5), which is equal to D+U (8), which is equal to GxF (9). So AxA=GxF (1). SxK is also equal to E+Z (11) and so equal to GxF (above). JxH (3) is equal to R+P, so is also equal to AxA (13 and above). Neither 4, 9, 16, 25 nor 49 has four sets of factors, so A=6, and S, K, G, F, J and H are 2, 18, 3, 12, 4 and/or 9. C=5 (2) and U=25. D=11 (8 and above), so G is at least 10 (1). G+L=36 (1), so G isn't 18, so G=12 (above), L=24 (1) and F=3 (9). K isn't 18, 9, or 4 (12), so K=2 and S=18 (11). J is either 4 or 9 (above), so P−Y is 22 (6), thus J=4 and H=9 (3). Y=1 and P=23 (6). R=13 (3). M=26 (12). E and Z add up to 36 (5) and Ex5=ZxB (7), so E and/or Z aren't 14, 16, 17; so E=21 and Z=15. B=7 (7). The smallest numbers remaining are 8 and 10, so O is at least 10 (15). X is at least 8, so (10) V=22, X=8, O=14; and I=10 (15). N=17 and W=19 (4). Q=20 and T=16 (14).

Thus:

A=6, B=7, C=5, D=11, E=21, F=3, G=12, H=9, I=10, J=4, K=2, L=24, M=26, N=17, O=14, P=23, Q=20, R=13, S=18, T=16, U=25, V=22, W=19, X=8, Y=1, Z=15.

No 107 *1st week*

Either Doreen or Gill is Mrs Ross (clue 8), so the woman studying accounting is Mrs Lind (clue 1). Anne's husband is Stuart or Grant (clue 5), so she isn't Mrs Lind (2). Thus Kay is Mrs Lind (1), Doreen is studying computing and has the surname Muckle (3) and Gill is Mrs Ross (8). Kay's husband (accounting) isn't Kelvin (6), so James (2) and Thomas is Mr Ross. Doreen's husband (computing) isn't Kelvin (6) or Stuart (7), so Grant. Kelvin is Mr White (6). The couple studying literature aren't surnamed Packard (4) or White (6), so Ross (Thomas/Gill, above). Stuart is studying Spanish (7), so Kelvin is studying painting. By elimination, Stuart is Mr Packard. His wife isn't Mandy (4), so Anne. Mandy is studying painting.

Thus:

Accounting, James, Kay, Lind;
Computing, Grant, Doreen, Muckle;
Literature, Thomas, Gill, Ross;
Painting, Kelvin, Mandy, White;
Spanish, Stuart, Anne, Packard.

No 108

No man was born in September (grid) and the man born in November doesn't have brown or ginger hair (clue 5), so (clue 4) the man with ginger hair was born in July and the one with brown hair in August. No man is 5'10" (grid), so the man with ginger hair isn't 5'11" or 5'7" (3). Nor is he 6'0" (2) or 5'8" (5), so he's 5'9". The man born in November is 5'8" (5) and the one with brown hair is 5'7". Raymond's birthday is one month after that of the man one inch shorter than the grey-haired man (6), so (since no man's birthday is one month after that of the 5'7" man), the grey-haired man isn't 5'8". Since no man is 5'10", the grey-haired man isn't 5'11" (6), so 6'0" and Raymond's birthday is one month after the 5'11" man's. Thus Raymond was born in November, the 5'11" man in October and (by elimination) the 6'0" man in December. The man with blond hair is 5'11" (2), so Raymond's hair is black. Tommy was born in July (1) and Malcolm in December. Abraham's hair isn't brown (4), so blond and Walter's is brown.

Thus:

Abraham, October, blond, 5'11";
Malcolm, December, grey, 6'0";
Raymond, November, black, 5'8";
Tommy, July, ginger, 5'9";
Walter, August, brown, 5'7".

No 109 *Open Window*

The Whites have 2 children (clue 6) and the Browns who went to Italy have 4, so stayed in a farmhouse

Solutions

(clue 3). The Blacks have one child (5), so (1) the Greens have 3 and the Grays who stayed in a guesthouse have none. The tent holiday in France wasn't chosen by the Greens or the Blacks (5), so the Whites. The Greens didn't go to Belgium (1) or Greece (2), so Portugal. They didn't stay in a caravan (4), so a hotel and the Blacks had a caravan: not in Greece (4), so Belgium. The Grays went to Greece.

Thus:
Mr & Mrs Black, Belgium, caravan, 1 child;
Mr & Mrs Brown, Italy, farmhouse, 4 children;
Mr & Mrs Green, Portugal, hotel, 3 children;
Mr & Mrs Gray, Greece, guesthouse, 0 children;
Mr & Mrs White, France, tent, 2 children.

No 110

Mr Wynde painted his fence (clue 1), Mr Sheik washed his car (clue 3) and Mr Hardy mended his shed roof (4), so Mr Shivra was sweeping paths (2) and Mr Tufnut chopped firewood. Mr Shivra worked on the day the temperature was -1°C (2) and Mr Tufnut on the day it was -3°C so (4) it was -2°C when Mr Hardy worked and -4°C on Wednesday. Mr Sheik worked on Saturday (3), so when it was -5°C. Mr Wynde thus worked on Wednesday. Mr Shivra worked on Friday (2) and Mr Tufnut on Thursday. Mr Hardy worked on Tuesday.

Thus:
Tuesday, Mr Hardy, mending shed roof, -2°C;
Wednesday, Mr Wynde, painting fence, -4°C;
Thursday, Mr Tufnut, chopping firewood, -3°C;
Friday, Mr Shivra, sweeping paths, -1°C;
Saturday, Mr Sheik, washing car, -5°.

No 111

A	C	B	B	A	C
A	C	B	C	A	B
C	B	A	C	B	A
C	A	A	B	B	C
B	B	C	A	C	A
B	A	C	A	C	B

No 112 *Mask of Red Death*

The 11.00 return was to the Party Shop (clue 5). The 10.20 return wasn't to Choose Who (clue 1), Witching Hour (2) or Katy's Hire (4), so Dressage and (2) was hired out at 10.30, thus was kept for 24 hours and 10 minutes. The item from the Witching Shop was kept for less time than this (2), so was hired out at 11.20 and returned at 11.20. Katy's Hire hired out at 11.10 (4), so the Party Shop at 10.50 (5) and Choose Who at 10.30. The item from Choose Who was returned 10 minutes after a costume not from Katy's Hire (1). So The Katy's Hire costume was returned at 11.40, the Choose Who costume at 11.30 and the Darth Vader costume (1) at 11.20. The Frankenstein costume was from Choose Who (4). The witch costume was returned at 10.30 and the mummy costume at 11.00 (3), so the Dracula costume was from Katy's Hire.

Thus:
Darth Vader, Witching Hour, 11.20am, 11.20am;
Dracula, Katy's Hire, 11.10am, 11.40am;
Frankenstein, Choose Who, 10.30am, 11.30am;
Mummy, Party Shop, 10.50am, 11.00am;
Witch, Dressage, 10.20am, 10.30am.

No 113

The $65 kit wasn't the bar stools (clue 6), so the bar stools kit cost $68 (1) and had 10 pieces. The kit missing 12 screws wasn't for the bar stools, bed or table (3) or wardrobe (6), so the bookcase. It hadn't 8 or 9 pieces (5) or 6 (7), so 7 pieces and (5) the wardrobe kit had 9. The bed kit had 8 pieces (3), so the table had 6. The $72 item needed 14 screws (2). The bar stools kit (10 pieces) didn't need 21 (1) or 20 (7), so 15. The $65 kit thus needed 12 screws (6), so was the 7-piece bookcase. Thus the wardrobe kit cost $70 (2) and the bed kit $72. The table kit was $73. It didn't need 21 screws (4), so 20 and the wardrobe needed 21 screws.

Thus:
Bar stools, $68, 10 pieces, 15 screws;
Bed, $72, 8 pieces, 14 screws;
Bookcase, $65, 7 pieces, 12 screws;
Table, $73, 6 pieces, 20 screws;
Wardrobe, $70, 9 pieces, 21 screws

No 114

Remember that each picture is made up of different parts. Kate's head is in the same picture as Bob's legs (clue 1), thus not Bob's feet. Tom's body and Bob's feet aren't with Liz's head (2), so Kylie's: and thus isn't Kate's legs (5), so Liz's. Bob's body isn't with Tom's head (4), so Liz's. Tom's legs aren't with Bob's head (3), so Liz's. Kate's legs are with Kylie's body (5), so Kate's head is with Liz's body. By elimination, Kate's body is with Kylie's legs. So Kate's feet are in the same picture as Liz's head, Kylie's feet are in the same picture as Kate's head and Tom's feet are in the same picture as Bob's head. Thus Liz's feet are in the same picture as Tom's head, not with Kylie's legs (6), so Kate's. Kate's body is thus with Bob's head.

Thus (head, body, legs, feet):
Bob, Kate, Kylie, Tom;
Tom, Kylie, Kate, Liz;
Kylie, Tom, Liz, Bob;
Liz, Bob, Tom, Kate;
Kate, Liz, Bob, Kylie.

No 115

One child had Wheeties for breakfast and Krispo after school (clue 1) and the child with Brownies for breakfast drank water (clue 3). The one who drank milk had Cococrunch for breakfast but not Crumbler (5) or Cococrunch (intro) after school, so Wheeties. The one with coffee and Brownies after school (2) didn't have Crumbler for breakfast (7), so Krispo. Thus the one with Crumbler for breakfast had Cococrunch after school

Solutions

and the one with Crumbler after school had Brownies for breakfast. Patrick drank milk or tea (6), so Thomas had Brownies for breakfast. Emma's breakfast wasn't Krispo (2), Cococrunch or Crumbler (4), so Wheeties. Dean's breakfast wasn't Krispo or Crumbler (8), so Cococrunch. Patrick's wasn't Krispo (6), so Crumbler and Julia's breakfast was Krispo. Since Dean drank milk (above), Patrick drank tea (6) and Emma drank orange juice.

Thus:
Dean, Cococrunch, milk, Wheeties;
Emma, Wheeties. orange juice, Krispo;
Julia, Krispo, coffee, Brownies;
Patrick, Crumbler, tea, Cococrunch;
Thomas, brownies, water, Crumbler.

No 116
Pieces 13 and 33 contain F (clue 2). Pieces 1 and 42 contain A (clue 1). The A in the diagonal line 7-43 is in piece 31. Pieces 15 and 48 contain B (clue 3). Pieces 9 and 45 contain C (7). Piece 49=D and 25=B. The B in row 8-14 is in 10. Pieces 43 and 47 contain G and/or E so 44 and 46 have A and/or F. The B in 36-42 is in 40. The remaining B is in 2. The A in 22-28 is in 27 (clue 5). Since 43 and 47 have G and/or E, 19 hasn't G, so (7) 19=D. Piece 37=E, 43=G and 7=C. Piece 47 contains an E, 5=G and 26=C. The G in 3-45 is in 24. The D in 22-28 is in 23. Piece 30=G. Piece 36=F, 22=E, 38=D, 39=C and 3=F. Pieces 4 and 32 contain E and/or D, so 11=G, 14=E, 28=F and 21=G. The C in 15-21 is in 20. Piece 44=A (clue 6), 46=F, 18=A and 16=F. Piece 34=D (4), 6=E, 4=D and 32=E.

Thus:

A	B	F	D	G	E	C
D	C	B	G	A	F	E
B	F	E	A	D	C	G
E	D	G	B	C	A	F
C	G	A	E	F	D	B
F	E	D	C	B	G	A
G	A	C	F	E	B	D

No 117 *Short Story*
Arthur made tea (clue 4), the person who fetched lager has a grey bookmarker (clue 5) and Pauline fetched lemonade (6). Jennifer has a green bookmarker and didn't get the coffee (1), so chocolate. Sharon's bookmarker is red (3), so she got the coffee and Tommy got the lager. Pauline read the biography (6), so the person with a yellow bookmarker who read the western (2) is Arthur and Pauline's bookmarker is black. Sharon read the whodunnit (3). The autobiography wasn't read by Jennifer (1), so Tommy and Jennifer read a romance.

Thus:
Arthur, western, yellow, tea;
Jennifer, romance, green, chocolate;
Pauline, biography, black, lemonade;
Sharon, whodunnit, red, coffee;
Tommy, autobiography, grey, lager.

No 118
Stella bought the iron (clue 1). Sam didn't buy the coffee percolator or kettle (clue 2). The holder of ticket 126 got what Sam bought (2) and the holder of 124 got the drill (4), so Sam didn't buy the drill. Thus Sam bought an alarm clock. The person with ticket 124 bought the kettle/got the drill (4) and the person with ticket 126 got the alarm clock (2), so Ian had either ticket 124 or 126 (3) and the percolator was bought by the person with either 125 or 127 who got what Pippa had bought: thus not the drill (4), so the kettle. Pippa thus had ticket 124, so Ian had 126 and (3) the holder of 127 bought the percolator. By elimination, Cordelia bought the percolator and Ian bought the drill, Sam received the iron and Stella received the percolator. Ticket 123 was thus Sam's (1) and Stella had 125.

Thus:
Cordelia, ticket 127, percolator, kettle;
Ian, ticket 126, drill, alarm clock;
Pippa, ticket 124, kettle, drill;
Sam, ticket 123, alarm clock, iron;
Stella, ticket 125, iron, percolator.

No 119
No-one bought 11 bottles of wine. Nancy didn't buy 5 bottles of wine (clue 1), so Amanda bought 13 (clue 3) and Nancy 9 bottles of wine. Mary bought 7 (1) and June 15 (2), so Fiona bought 5 bottles of wine. No-one bought 8 bottles of spirits. Nancy didn't buy 12 bottles of spirits (2), so Nancy bought 10 and Mary bought 4 (3). Fiona bought 2 (1) and Amanda 12 (2), so June bought 6 bottles of spirits. Fiona didn't buy 15 bottles of beer (1) and Mary didn't buy 35 (2), so Mary bought 30 (3) and Fiona 20 of beer. June bought 15 (1) and Nancy 35 (2), so Amanda bought 25 bottles of beer.

Thus (beer, spirits, wine):
Amanda, 25, 12, 13;
Fiona, 20, 2, 5;
June, 15, 6, 15;
Mary, 30, 4, 7;
Nancy, 35, 10, 9.

No 120 *Open Window*
Mr Bishop paid £305 (clue 2), so Mrs Carter paid £299 (clue 3) and Mr Ford paid £199 for (1) the Madrid break. Martina thus sold Mr Wilton the £249 break (4) and Miss Anderson's Paris break was £205. Richard's client who bought a break in Stockholm (6) wasn't Mr Bishop (2), so Mrs Carter. By elimination, the client for whom Louise arranged the Rome break (5) is Mr Bishop, so Mr Wilton bought the Lisbon break. Dennis' client wasn't Miss Anderson (4), so Mr Ford. Gina served Miss Anderson.

Thus:
Miss Anderson, Gina, Paris, £205;
Mr Bishop, Louise, Rome, £305;
Mrs Carter, Richard, Stockholm, £299;
Mr Ford, Dennis, Madrid, £199;
Mr Wilton, Martina, Lisbon, £249.

Solutions

No 121 *Most Dangerous Game*

Timmy's pet is Nora (clue 3), the ant is Digger (clue 4) and Colin's pet is Bilbo (5). George's snail (1) isn't Horace (2), so Speedy. Digger doesn't belong to Joe (6), so Will and Joe's pet which came 2nd is Horace. The ladybird was 1st (6), so Horace who isn't a slug (2) is the caterpillar. Bilbo finished one place ahead of Speedy (5) who wasn't 4th, so Speedy was 5th and Bilbo 4th. Will's pet was thus 3rd and the ladybird belongs to Timmy. Colin's pet is a slug.
Thus:
Colin, slug, Bilbo, 4th;
George, snail, Speedy, 5th;
Joe, caterpillar, Horace, 2nd;
Timmy, ladybird, Nora, 1st;
Will, ant, digger, 3rd.

No 122 *R & J*

No theatre has 7 shows per week (grid). The man in 8 shows works as a salesman (clue 2), so the waiter performs 6 times (clue 4) and Jack appears 4 times at the Albion. Jeff is the gardener (2). Jack isn't the driver (3), so the chef. The Old Mill has 8 shows per week (3) and the driver appears in 9 at (1) the Gaeity. Jeff is thus in 5 shows, not at the Alhambra (2), so the Criterion and there are 6 shows at the Alhambra. John isn't at the Old Mill or Alhambra (2), so the Gaeity. Jason isn't the waiter (4), so he's at the Old Mill and Jude is at the Alhambra.
Thus:
Albion Theatre, 4 performances, Jack, chef;
Alhambra Theatre, 6 performances, Jude, waiter;
Criterion Theatre, 5 performances, Jeff, gardener;
Gaeity Theatre, 9 performances, John, driver;
Old Mill Theatre, 8 performances, Jason, salesman.

No 123 *The Necklace*

Kitchenware is on the 2nd floor (clue 1) and Jill shopped on the 1st. Sue was on the 4th (3) and Conrad on the 3rd (4), so Hannah who bought linen (3) was on the 5th and (2) saved 50%. Robert who saved 40% (5) was on the 2nd floor. The person who bought menswear saved 10% and wasn't on the 3rd floor (2), so isn't Conrad. Thus Jill saved 30% and Conrad 20% (1), so Sue bought menswear. Jill bought stationery (5), so Conrad bought leatherwear.
Thus:
Conrad, leatherwear, 3rd floor, 20%;
Hannah, linen, 5th floor, 50%;
Jill, stationery, 1st floor, 30%;
Robert, kitchenware, 2nd floor, 40%;
Sue, menswear, 4th floor, 10%.

No 124 *The Waltz*

Elaine partnered Des (clue 2). Barbara didn't dance with Shane (clue 4), Keith (6) or Ritchie (7), so Morgan. Marilyn's partner wasn't Keith (1) or Shane (4), so Ritchie. No-one danced for 3 hours 30 minutes (grid). The woman who danced for 3 hours 15 minutes isn't Alison or Elaine (3), Barbara (5) or Marilyn (7), so Lola, who (by elimination) partnered either Keith or Shane. She isn't 22 or 23 (1), so both she and the 23-year-old (5) danced for less time than Morgan (and Barbara, above). Thus Barbara didn't dance for 3 hours 45 minutes. Marilyn danced for longer than 4 hours (7), so Elaine for 3 hours 45 minutes (3) and Alison for 4 hours. Barbara didn't dance for 4 hours 15 minutes (6), so 4 hours 30 minutes and Marilyn for 4 hours 15 minutes. Each woman is the same age as her partner (intro), so Ritchie/Marilyn are 2 years younger than Lola (1) and one year younger than Keith (6). Thus Keith's partner was Alison and Lola's was Shane. Ritchie is one year younger than Keith (6) and two years younger than Shane. Des is also younger than Keith (2), as (6) is Morgan (Barbara's partner). Thus Shane is 26, Ritchie 24 and Keith 25. Morgan is 22 (5). Des is 23.
Thus:
Des, Elaine, 23, 3 hours 45 minutes;
Keith, Alison, 25, 4 hours;
Morgan, Barbara, 22, 4 hours 30 minutes;
Ritchie, Marilyn, 24, 4 hours 15 minutes;
Shane, Lola, 26, 3 hours 15 minutes.

No 125

In clue 5, the card called 3rd was J or L. If J was 3rd, then A or I was 15th (last); and if L was 3rd, then H was 15th. The card called 12th was I or K (clue 5): so either K was 12th, L 3rd and H 15th; or I was 12th, J 3rd and A 15th. In clue 4, the card called 1st was J or O, the one called 9th was D, H or M and the one called 10th was E, I or N. If I was 10th, then H was 9th and J 1st (4), so L was 3rd and K 12th (5) – but then H would also be 15th, so that won't work. Thus E or N was 10th, so D or M was 9th (4) and O was 1st. Card L wasn't 3rd (3), so J was 3rd. Thus I was 12th (5) and A 15th. M was 8th (1) and C was 11th; thus (4 and above) E was 10th and D 9th. K was 7th (2) and L 13th, so F (same suit as K) was 6th. G was 5th (3). The card called 2nd isn't a club (1), so is B. N was called 4th (5) and H 14th.
Thus:
1st O, 2nd B, 3rd J, 4th N, 5th G, 6th F, 7th K,
8th M, 9th D, 10th E, 11th C, 12th I, 13th L,
14th H, 15th A.

No 126

The child with 55 (fewest) points wasn't Shelley (clue 2), Danny (clue 4), Bob or Marc (5), so Rose. No child had 63 points. The one with 68 wasn't Danny (4), Bob or Marc (5), so Shelley. The child with 70 points didn't have chicken (1), tuna (2) egg/cress (4) or salmon (5), so tomato sandwiches, thus wasn't Danny (4). So Marc had tomato and Bob got 65 points (5). Danny got 60 points (4) and Rose (55 points) had egg and cress sandwiches. Danny had salmon (5). Shelley had chicken (1), so Bob had tuna. Bob's test was on chemistry (2) and Rose's was on history (3). Marc's was on physics (3), Shelley's was on spelling and Danny's was on maths.

294

Solutions

Thus:
Bob, 65 points, chemistry, tuna;
Danny, 60 points, maths, salmon;
Marc, 70 points, physics, tomato;
Rose, 55 points, history, egg/cress;
Shelley, 68 points, spelling, chicken.

No 127 *The Odyssey*

Roger was 4th (clue 4). Catherine wasn't 1st (clue 1) or 5th (2). Brian bought a notepad (5). Catherine didn't buy a newspaper (1), map, (2) or comic (bought by a man, 3), so a magazine. Since she was either 2nd or 3rd (above) the newspaper was bought either 1st or 2nd (1) and the map either 3rd or 4th (2). Brian wasn't 5th (5), so the person who was 5th bought a comic and (3) is a man, thus is Stanley. Stanley's postcard showed the lake (6). By elimination, Roger bought the map, so Catherine was 3rd (2) and the 2nd person bought a newspaper and mountain postcard (1), so is Edna. Brian was 1st. The WOMAN who bought the beach postcard (3) is Catherine. Roger's postcard hadn't a picture of the castle (4), so the park. Brian's showed the castle.

Thus:
Brian, castle, notepad, 1st;
Catherine, beach, magazine, 3rd;
Edna, mountain, newspaper, 2nd;
Roger, park, map, 4th;
Stanley, lake, comic, 5th.

No 128

1	6	7	8	9	3
9	8	3	7	8	1
4	5	7	6	9	8
1	6	2	5	3	4
5	2	9	4	7	2
6	5	4	3	2	1

No 129 *Speckled Band*

Dean Bradley was in the South Bronx (clue 6). Sam hunted Clyde Warner on Monday (clue 5), but not in Greenwich Village (2), Brooklyn (4), or Harlem (5), so Manhattan, thus Clyde Warner is the bigamist (3). Sam was in Greenwich Village on Friday (2) and tried to trace a missing person on Saturday, but not in Brooklyn. Ray Schultz was wanted for theft (1). The forger isn't Dean Bradley or Arnie Meyer (6), so Harry Knorr. He wasn't hunted on Thursday (4), so on Friday and Sam was in Brooklyn on Thursday. Arnie Meyer was sought on Sunday (4). By elimination, Ray Schultz was sought for theft (1) on Thursday; and Arnie Meyer was wanted for blackmail and sought on Sunday in Harlem, thus Dean Bradley was sought on Saturday.

Thus:
Thursday, Brooklyn, Ray Schultz, theft;
Friday, Greenwich Village, Harry Knorr, forgery;
Saturday, S Bronx, Dean Bradley, missing person;
Sunday, Harlem, Arnie Meyer, blackmail;
Monday, Manhattan, Clyde Warner, bigamy.

No 130 *Secret Life Walter Mitty*

Jim Turner served with the 17th/21st Lancers (clue 2). The Petty Officer was in the Royal Navy and the Flight Sergeant was in the RAF (clue 3). Alf Daley the handyman wasn't in the Royal Navy or RAF (clue 3) or Royal Marines (4), so the Parachute Regiment. He wasn't a Corporal (2) or Sergeant (4), so Lieutenant. The butler who was a Sergeant wasn't in the Royal Marines (4), so the 17th/21st Lancers. Percy Abbott, ex-Royal Marines (4) was thus a Corporal, so was the chauffeur (2). The Petty Officer was in the Royal Navy and the footman joined the RAF (3), so the ex-gardener was in the Royal Navy. Len Foster was thus the footman (1), so Cyril Moone was the gardener.

Thus:
Percy Abbott, chauffeur, Royal Marines, Corporal;
Alf Daley, handyman, Parachute Regiment, Lieutenant;
Len Foster, footman, RAF, Flight Sergeant;
Cyril Moone, gardener, Royal Navy, Petty Officer;
Jim Turner, butler, 17th/21st Lancers, Sergeant.

No 131

No-one went to bed at 11.15 (grid). The person who went to bed at 11.45 (latest) wasn't Raymond (clue 1), Judith (2), Lou or Lavinia (3), so Kenneth. The one who drank whisky went to bed at either 10.30 or 10.45 (3) and didn't borrow the science fiction (1), romance or history (2) or biography (4), so mystery book. The one who went at 11.45 didn't borrow the science fiction (1), romance or history (2), so biography. The one who went to bed at 10.45 drank whisky (3). Judith borrowed the romance but didn't go to bed at 10.30 (2). The person who borrowed the science fiction book didn't go at 10.30 (1), so the one who borrowed the history book went at 10.30 and (2) Judith at 11.00. The one who drank brandy and borrowed the science fiction book (1) went at 11.30 and the one who drank rum at 11.45. The one who borrowed the history book didn't drink sherry (2), so port. The one who borrowed the romance drank sherry. The person who drank whisky isn't Lou or Lavinia (3), so Raymond. Lavinia didn't go to bed at 10.30 (4), so 11.30 and Lou at 10.30.

Thus:
Biography, Kenneth, rum, 11.45pm;
History, Lou, port, 10.30pm;
Mystery, Raymond, whisky, 10.45pm;
Romance, Judith, sherry, 11.00pm;
Science fiction, Lavinia, brandy, 11.30pm.

No 132

Andrew's surname is Donkin (clue 1) and Leonard is a window cleaner (clue 3). The clerk surnamed Unwin isn't Elizabeth or Gordon (5), so Cheryl. Andrew isn't a nurse (1) or a teacher (6), so a train driver. He didn't want to be a film star (1), chemist or lawyer (4) or astronaut (6), so a surgeon. Leonard didn't want to be a film star (1), lawyer (3) or chemist (5), so an astronaut. His surname isn't Warburton (2) or Fisher (3), so Klein. Elizabeth's surname isn't Fisher (6), so Warburton and

Solutions

Gordon's is Fisher. The nurse who had wanted to be a film star isn't Elizabeth (2), so Gordon. Elizabeth is a teacher. Cheryl didn't want to be a lawyer (3), so a chemist. Elizabeth planned to be a lawyer.

Thus:

Andrew, Donkin, surgeon, train driver;
Cheryl, Unwin, chemist, clerk;
Elizabeth, Warburton, lawyer, teacher;
Gordon, Fisher, film star, nurse;
Leonard, Klein, astronaut, window cleaner

No 133

The following are all multiples of F: N (clue 5), P (clue 7), M (9), A (10), R (11) and X (13), so F is 2 or 3. The following are all multiples of Y: T (1), O (3), C (6), K (8), R (11) and Z (12), so Y is also 2 or 3. Thus R=6 (11). O is 12 or 18 (3), so O is also a multiple of F, thus F=2 and Y=3. O=18 (3). G is either 4, 5, 7 or 8 (6), as are I (1), Q (8) and U (12). So B=20 (4), I and G are 4 and/or 5. A isn't 8 (above), so A=10 (10), G=5 and I=4. T=12 (1) and C=15 (6). Z (12) and K (8) are 21 and/or 24. N (5) and M (9) are 14 and/or 16. P (7) and X (13) are 22 and/or 26. P isn't 26 (2), so P=22, J=11 (7), W=13 and X=26 (13). D=23 (2) and H=1. U is either 7 or 8 (above) and S is at least 9 (14), so E=25, U=8, S=9, Q=7 (8), K=21, N=16 (5), M=14 (9), Z=24 (12). L=19 and V=17 (15).

Thus:

A=10; B=20; C=15; D=23; E=25; F=2; G=5; H=1; I=4;
J=11; K=21; L=19; M=14; N=16; O=18; P=22; Q=7;
R=6; S=9; T=12; U=8; V=17; W=13; X=26; Y=3; Z=24.

No 134 *Odyssey & Most Dangerous Game*

Gayle Portman plays hockey (clue 3). The softball player isn't Teri, Trina or Odette (clue 1), so Marianne. Odette is at No 1 or No 5 (1) as is Trina (2). Marianne isn't ii at No 6 (1) or No 2 (2), so No 9. Gayle isn't at No 6 (3), so No 2. Since Gayle plays hockey, Trina is at No 5 (2) and Teri at No 6 plays table tennis. Odette is at No 1. Trina is Johnson (3) and doesn't play badminton, so netball. Odette plays badminton. Teri's surname isn't King or Wild (2), so Lessing. Odette's is King (1) and Marianne's is Wild.

Thus:

Gayle, Portman, No 2, hockey;
Marianne, Wild, No 9, softball;
Odette, King, No 1, badminton;
Teri, Lessing, No 6, table tennis;
Trina, Johnson, No 5, netball.

No 135

The people who got 12 and 16 ('one fewer') on Monday are Nellie (clue 4) and/or Corinne (clue 5). The one who got 13 on Monday wasn't Kevin (3) or Jack (6), so Thelma. Corinne didn't get 12 on Monday (5), so 16 and Nellie got 12. Thelma got one more than Jack on Tuesday (4), so (1) Jack got one more than Corinne on Monday, thus Jack got 17 and Kevin 19 on Monday. The people who got 15 and 18 on Wednesday didn't get 'one fewer', so aren't Nellie (5) or Corinne (7). On Tuesday, Kevin didn't get 16 (2), so either 14 or 15 on Tuesday (3) and 13 or 14 on Wednesday. So Jack and/or Thelma got 15 and/or 18 on Wednesday. Thus Thelma got 15 (6), Jack 18 and Nellie 17 (5). Corinne thus got 13 on Wednesday (7), and Kevin 14. Kevin got 15 on Tuesday (4). Thelma didn't get 14 (2), so 13. Thus Jack got 12 and Corinne 14 on Tuesday.

Thus (Monday, Tuesday, Wednesday):

Corinne, 16, 14, 13;
Jack, 17, 12, 18;
Kevin, 19, 15, 14;
Nellie, 12, 16, 17;
Thelma, 13, 13, 15.

No 136

No 137

Diane has bought cuff-links (clue 2). Ruth who is taking her husband to a restaurant hasn't bought a jumper (clue 3) a briefcase (1) or golf clubs (2), so a watch. The only place for Ruth in clue 1 is as Ron's wife. Leslie is going to the casino (1), so in clue 2, he's either the man getting golf clubs or the one getting cuff-links. Thus the only place for Leslie in clue 3 is as Florence's husband, so (2) he's getting golf clubs. Meryl isn't giving the briefcase (1), so a jumper. Shirley is giving the briefcase. The woman taking her husband to a dance isn't Meryl or Shirley (1), so Diane. The only place for Diane in clue 3 is as Geoff's wife. Meryl (jumper, above) isn't taking her husband to the cinema (3), so the theatre. He isn't Bill (2), so Oliver. Shirley is thus taking Bill to the cinema.

Thus:

Diane, Geoff, cuff-links, dance;
Florence, Leslie, golf clubs, casino;
Meryl, Oliver, jumper, theatre;
Ruth, Ron, watch, restaurant;
Shirley, Bill, briefcase, cinema

No 138

No patient was seen at 3.00 (grid). The person with a sprained wrist was seen 15 minutes later than Caroline

Solutions

(clue 1) and the person with a broken finger was seen 15 minutes later (clue 4) than Rosemary who had a cut on her arm. Thus Rosemary wasn't seen 15 minutes later than Caroline; so these are 4 different people. Freddy had a splinter (2), thus (by elimination) Caroline had the eye injury. She wasn't seen at 2.15 or 2.30 (3), so at 3.15 (1) and the person with a sprained wrist was seen at 3.30. Dr Stitchett saw someone at 2.45 (3), so Dr Makebetter saw someone at 2.15 (5) and Edward was seen at 2.45, thus Simon was the person with the sprained wrist (1) seen at 3.30, Edward had a broken finger and (4) Rosemary was seen at 2.30. By elimination, Freddy was seen at 2.15. Dr Plarster didn't treat Caroline or Simon (6), so Rosemary. Dr Gedwell didn't treat Caroline (1), so Simon and Caroline was seen by Dr Kurem.

Thus:

Caroline, eye injury, Dr Kurem, 3.15 pm;
Edward, broken finger, Dr Stitchett, 2.45 pm;
Freddy, splinter, Dr Makebetter, 2.15 pm;
Rosemary, cut on arm, Dr Plarster, 2.30 pm;
Simon, sprained wrist, Dr Gedwell, 3.30pm.

No 139

Cards total 78 (intro), so the king is missing. Card I has a value two lower than K, which has a value two lower than G (clue 1), which has a value two lower than C, which has a value two lower than B, which has a value two lower than A (clue 2). The 3 is directly next to and below the 7 (clue 4), so K isn't the 3 (clue 1). Thus card I is the 2, K the 4, G the 6, C the 8, B the 10 and A the queen. E is the 9 (4), F is the 7 and J the 3. H is the jack (3). D isn't the ace (4), so the 5 and L is the ace. Since F is a club and J a heart (4), H is a spade (intro), B and L are diamonds and D is a heart. Card I isn't a spade (1), so a club, thus A and K are spades (intro) and C is a club. G isn't a heart (3), so a diamond and E is a heart.

Thus:

QS 10D 8C 5H
9H 7C 6D JS
2C 3H 4S AD

No 140 *Odyssey / most Dangerous Game*

Samantha is 17 (clue 4). The 21-year-old (oldest) isn't Victoria (clue 2), Rachel (3) or Josie (5), so Jill. Samantha's vest isn't green (2), pink (3), yellow (4) or blue (5), so red. Jill's isn't blue or pink (3). Thus the 20-year-old isn't Rachel (2) or Josie (5), so Victoria. Jill's vest is green (2). Josie isn't 19 (5), so 18 and Rachel is 19 and her vest is blue. Victoria's vest is pink (3), so Josie's is yellow and Josie is 3rd, so Rachel is 2nd (5). Victoria is 4th (1) and Jill is 1st, so Samantha is 5th.

Thus:

Jill, 21 years old, 1st, green;
Josie, 18 years old, 3rd, yellow;
Rachel, 19 years old, 2nd, blue;
Samantha, 17 years old, 5th, red;
Victoria, 20 years old, 4th, pink.

No 141 *Short Story*

Alistair was at the boating lake (clue 1), Stephanie in the rose garden (clue 2) and Ginny on the main lawn (5). The person by the bowling green read a tour brochure (4), thus isn't Felix (3), so Nina and Felix read his newspaper (3) by the fish pond. Felix works at Dibleigh's. The person with the trade journal works at Tesbury's and isn't Stephanie or Alistair (1), so Ginny. The one who read the magazine works at the Dress Shop and isn't Stephanie (2), so Alistair. Stephanie read a novel. She works at Cotter & Co (6) and Nina works at Falstaff's.

Thus:

Alistair, boating lake, magazine, Dress Shop;
Felix, fish pond, newspaper, Dibleigh's;
Ginny, main lawn, trade journal, Tesbury's;
Nina, bowling green, tour brochure, Falstaff's;
Stephanie, rose garden, novel, Cotter & Co.

No 142

The 7.00 programme isn't on Channel 4 (clue 1), Channel 9 or Channel 2 (clue 2) or Channel 6 (3), so Channel 1 and (5) so *Sportsworld*. It isn't watched by Pam (1), John (3), Julia or Kathy (5), so Owen. The 8.00 programme isn't on Channel 4 (1), Channel 9 (2) or Channel 6 (3), so Channel 2 and (2) the Channel 9 programme is at 8.30. *News Talk* isn't on Channel 4 or Channel 6 (1), so it's either 8.00 or 8.30. Pam doesn't see the 9.00 or 10.00 programmes (1), thus she watches at 8.00 and *News Talk* is at 8.30. *In The Garden* is thus at 8.00 (3). The person who watches *Cook With Joe* isn't Julia or Kathy (4), so John. John doesn't watch Channel 6 (3), so Channel 4. By elimination, *Nature Today* is on Channel 6. Kathy thus watches *Nature Today* (6) and Julia watches *News Talk*. It isn't shown half-an-hour earlier than *Nature Today* (6), so *Cook With Joe* starts at 9.00 and *Nature Today* at 10.00.

Thus:

John, *Cook With Joe*, Channel 4, 9.00 pm;
Julia, *News Talk*, Channel 9, 8.30 pm;
Kathy, *Nature Today*, Channel 6, 10.00pm;
Owen, *Sportsworld*, Channel 1, 7.00 pm;
Pam, *In The Garden*, Channel 2, 8.00 pm.

No 143

B	A	C	B	C	A
A	A	C	B	B	C
B	C	A	C	A	B
C	B	B	C	A	A
C	C	A	A	B	B
A	B	B	A	C	C

No 144

The person with 2,633 stamps doesn't collect on the theme of fish or flowers (clue 2), inventions or birds (clue 4), so transport. The one with 1,090 doesn't collect on invention (1), fish or flowers (2), so birds. The one with 745 doesn't collect flowers or inventions

Solutions

(6), so fish. The one who collects the inventions theme hasn't 582 stamps (1), so 3,250 and whoever has 582 collects flower stamps. Miranda doesn't collect on fish or inventions and hasn't 582 or 1,090 (2), so she has 2,633 stamps. The woman with bird stamps (5) is thus Charlotte. Harvey hasn't 582 or 3,250 stamps (1), so 745. Charlotte hasn't stamps from Belgium (4) the USA or New Zealand (5) or Great Britain (6), so Australia. Glen hasn't 582 (1), so 3,250 and Anthony has 582 stamps. Glen doesn't collect from the USA (1), Great Britain or New Zealand (6), so Belgium. Miranda's aren't from Great Britain or the USA (4), so New Zealand. The stamps from Great Britain aren't collected by Anthony (6), so Harvey. Anthony collects stamps from the USA.

Thus:

Anthony, USA, flowers, 582 stamps;
Charlotte, Australia, birds, 1,090 stamps;
Glen, Belgium, inventions, 3,250 stamps;
Harvey, Great Britain, fish, 745 stamps;
Miranda, New Zealand, transport, 2,633 stamps.

No 145

Randolph who bought floral paper had one fewer roll than Nicholas (clue 2) and Trevor had one fewer roll than the person with polka dot paper (clue 5), who thus wasn't Nicholas. The person who bought polka dot paper wasn't Patience (5), so Jocelyn. The one with zigzag paper bought one fewer roll than the person with wavy paper (1), who thus wasn't Nicholas (one more than floral, 2). The person with wavy paper wasn't Patience (1), so Trevor. No-one bought 7 rolls (grid). Thus the person who bought 8 rolls wasn't Nicholas or Randolph (2), Trevor or Jocelyn (5), so Patience. Thus she didn't buy zigzag paper (1), so that with stripes and Nicholas bought the zigzag paper. Nicholas bought one more than Randolph (2) and one fewer than Trevor who (5) bought one fewer than Jocelyn; so Nicholas bought 4, Randolph 3, Trevor 5 and Jocelyn 6 rolls. The person 5th in the queue wasn't Nicholas (2), Patience (3), Randolph (4) or Trevor (5), so Jocelyn. Trevor was 4th (5), Randolph wasn't 3rd (4), so Nicholas was 1st (2), Randolph 2nd and Patience 3rd.

Thus:

First, Nicholas, zigzag, 4 rolls;
Second, Randolph, floral, 3 rolls;
Third, Patience, stripes, 8 rolls;
Fourth, Trevor, wavy, 5 rolls;
Fifth, Jocelyn, polka dots, 6 rolls.

No 146

By elimination, pieces 21 and 25 (clue 3) both contain A. Pieces 2 and 18 (clue 1) both contain C. Pieces 4 and 36 (2) both contain E, so 39=G and 32=D. In line 1-49, the D is in 17 (6). In row 1-7, the D is in 5 (4). Piece 1 contains either F or B, as does piece 41. Thus piece 6 (4) contains A, 49=E, 9=G and 33=C. In row 43-49, the D is in 48. Piece 43=B (5). In 7-43, 13=C. By elimination, 1=F and 41=B, so 3=B, 44=A, 47=G and

45=C. Piece 15=G, 29=A, 8=D and 22=C. In 3-45, the G is in 24 and in 6-48 it's in 34. In 5-47, the B is in 26. Piece 27=F and 28=D. Piece 20=E, 16=B and 19=F, 30=F, 31=E and 35=B. Piece 40=A and 38=F, so 12=E, 10=A and 14=F.

Thus:

F	C	B	E	D	A	G
D	G	A	B	E	C	F
G	B	D	C	F	E	A
C	E	G	A	B	F	D
A	F	E	D	C	G	B
E	D	F	G	A	B	C
B	A	C	F	G	D	E

No 147 *R & J miscommunication*

The girl who posted on Saturday isn't Laurel (clue 1), Morag (clue 4), Sheree (5) or Marie (6), so Caitlin. Laurel posted on Wednesday (2). The girl who lives in Spain posted on Friday (1). Sheree lives in Hong Kong (5) and Morag in Morocco, so Marie lives in Spain. Sheree posted on Tuesday (5) and Morag on Thursday. Caitlin doesn't live in Gibraltar (3), so Canada. Thus Laurel lives in Gibraltar. Marie wrote to Laurel (6), so (3) Morag wrote to Caitlin. Caitlin wrote to Marie (6). Sheree thus wrote to Morag and Laurel to Sheree.

Thus:

Caitlin, Marie, Saturday, Canada;
Laurel, Sheree, Wednesday, Gibraltar;
Marie, Laurel, Friday, Spain;
Morag, Caitlin, Thursday, Morocco;
Sheree, Morag, Tuesday, Hong Kong.

No 148

Remember throughout that each woman used 3 different colours (intro). Harriet used yellow (clue 5), so Beatrix didn't (clue 4). Noelle didn't use yellow (3), so the 3 women who did are Harriet, Fenella and Lyndsey. Both Beatrix and Noelle used navy (6), so Lyndsey (3) and Harriet (4) didn't; thus the other woman who used navy is Fenella. The woman whose hat has a yellow brim didn't make a cream or green bobble (2), so either navy or red, thus she isn't Harriet (5 and above). Harriet's yellow piece isn't the bobble (5), so it's the main colour of her hat. The woman who made the red bobble didn't use navy wool (1), thus isn't Beatrix, Noelle or Fenella (above), so Lyndsey. By elimination, Fenella made the yellow bobble. The navy bobble wasn't made by Noelle (6), so Beatrix. The woman whose hat is mainly brown made the green bobble (2), so (by elimination) she's Noelle and Harriet made the cream bobble. The brim of Harriet's hat isn't red (5), so purple. Since Noelle used green, Lyndsey didn't (3), so Lyndsey's main colour is orange. By elimination, Fenella's main colour is navy and Beatrix's is green. Thus the woman who knitted the navy brim is Noelle. The one who knitted the yellow brim isn't Fenella (yellow bobble, above), so Lyndsey. Harriet used cream (bobble, above), thus Beatrix's brim isn't cream (4), so red and Fenella's is cream.

298

Solutions

Thus (main, bobble, brim):
Beatrix, green, navy blue, red;
Fenella, navy blue, yellow, cream;
Harriet, yellow, cream, purple;
Lyndsey, orange, red, yellow;
Noelle, brown, green, navy blue.

No 149 <♈>

Mike's surname is Coates or Crane (clue 4), so Chris's husband is Philip (clue 3). Philip isn't Mr Jarvis (4), so (3) Mr Wise. Debbie married Mr Jarvis (5), so Ella married Mr Crane (1). Her surname was either Delaney or Adamson (1), so Penny's was Walters (2) and she's married to Richard. Debbie Jarvis married Paul (4) and (5), her surname was Adamson, so (1) Ella's was Delaney. Miss Collins married Gordon (6), so she's Grace, Chris's surname was Payne and Ella married Mike. Gordon's surname isn't Anderton (6), so Coates. Richard is Mr Anderton.

Thus:
Chris, Payne, Philip, Wise;
Debbie, Adamson, Paul, Jarvis;
Ella, Delaney, Mike, Crane;
Grace, Collins, Gordon, Coates;
Penny, Walters, Richard, Anderton.

No 150

No-one came in at 4.45 (grid). The person who came at 5.15 wasn't Jane or Norman (clue 2), Sally (clue 3) or Martin (5), so Vera and *Rook's Lair* was returned at 5.00 (1). Vera didn't return *Jaded Jackdaw* (5), so Martin didn't come at 5.00. Sally returned *Wally's Dream* (3), so the person who came at 5.00 is Jane (2) and Norman came at 4.30. Vera didn't return *Little Aspirations* (4), so *The Journey*. Martin came at 4.15 (5) and *Jaded Jackdaw* was returned at 4.30 by Norman, so Sally came at 4.00 and Martin borrowed *Little Aspirations*. Martin's book was 5 weeks overdue (3), so Vera's 6 weeks (4), Jane's 4 weeks (1), Norman's 3 weeks (5) and Sally's 2 weeks overdue.

Thus:
Jane, 5.00, *Rook's Lair*, 4 weeks;
Martin, 4.15, *Little Aspirations*, 5 weeks;
Norman, 4.30, *Jaded Jackdaw*, 3 weeks;
Sally, 4.00, *Wally's Dream*, 2 weeks;
Vera, 5.15, *The Journey*, 6 weeks.

No 151

6	4	1	8	2	4
9	5	7	1	5	3
7	6	5	4	3	2
1	7	9	8	6	8
7	8	5	3	4	6
2	9	2	9	1	3

No 152

Jasmine's surname is Mayne (clue 1) and Kenny had a salad sandwich (clue 3), so Bates who had a ham sandwich and isn't Alice or Shane (5) is Daniel. The one who had chicken isn't Jasmine (1) or Shane (4), so Alice. She had pea soup (3). Watson had tomato soup and isn't Kenny (3), so Shane. Alice's surname isn't Durrell (4), so Grove. Kenny's is Durrell. Daniel didn't have mulligatawny (2) or potato (5), so mushroom soup. Kenny's soup wasn't mulligatawny (2), so potato. Jasmine had mulligatawny, but not an egg sandwich (2), so cheese. Shane had the egg sandwich.

Thus:
Alice, Grove, chicken, pea;
Daniel, Bates, ham, mushroom;
Jasmine, Mayne, cheese, mulligatawny;
Kenny, Durrell, salad, potato;
Shane, Watson, egg, tomato.

No 153

The person who picked 3 pears isn't Lynn (clue 1), Jerry or Matthew (clue 2), June or William (3). Jerry didn't pick 4 pears (2), so Dolly didn't pick 3 (1), thus Dermot did, not with 8 apples (3), so 7. June picked 8 apples (3). No-one picked 7 pears. The one with 8 pears wasn't Jerry or Lynn (1), Matthew (2) or June (3). Jerry didn't pick 9 (2), so Dolly didn't pick 8 (1), thus William did. June picked 6 pears (3). Matthew picked one fewer apple than whoever picked 5 pears (3), so (4) Matthew picked 4 pears. William picked 6 apples (2). Dolly picked 9 pears (1) and Jerry 10, so Lynn 5. Lynn picked 5 apples (2). Matthew picked 4 apples (3). Jerry picked 3 apples (1), so Dolly picked 2 apples.

Thus:
Dermot, 7 apples, 3 pears;
Dolly, 2 apples, 9 pears;
Jerry, 3 apples, 10 pears;
June, 8 apples, 6 pears;
Lynn, 5 apples, 5 pears;
Matthew, 4 apples, 4 pears;
William, 6 apples, 8 pears.

No 154

Remember throughout the quantities as listed on the grid and the fact that each player held 3 different quantities of cards (clue 4). The man with 6 cards on the 2nd deal and 10 on the 3rd isn't Paul (clue 2), Leslie or Eric (1) or Fred (3), so Norman, who thus hadn't 6 or 10 on the 1st (4). The man with 5 on the 3rd wasn't Eric (1) Paul (2) or Fred (3), so Leslie and (1) Eric had 7 on the 3rd, so not 7 on the 2nd. The man with 11 on the 3rd wasn't Fred (3), so Paul and Fred had 9. Paul had 10 on the 1st (3), so Leslie had 8 (1) and Eric 6 on the 1st. Fred hadn't 9 on the 1st (4), so 5 and Norman had 9. Eric had 5 on the 2nd (1) and Leslie 7. Fred hadn't 9 on the 2nd (4), so 8 and Paul had 9 on the second.

Thus (1st deal, 2nd deal, 3rd deal):
Eric, 6, 5, 7;
Fred, 5, 8, 9;
Leslie, 8, 7, 5;
Norman, 9, 6, 10;
Paul, 10, 9, 11.

Solutions

No 155

Remember throughout that each picture is made up of 4 different parts (intro). Mrs Edgar's head is with Mr Norton's body (clue 1) and Miss Plodd's head is with Mr Overton's legs (clue 2). Thus (by elimination) Mr Overton's feet and Miss Nixon's body (3) are with Mr Norton's head; and Mr Overton's body is with Miss Nixon's head. Miss Plodd's head thus has Mrs Edgar's body and Mr Overton's head has Miss Plodd's body. Miss Plodd's legs and Mr Norton's feet (4) are thus with Miss Nixon's head, Mr Norton's head is with Mrs Edgar's legs, Mrs Edgar's head is with Miss Nixon's legs and Mr Overton's head is with Mr Norton's legs. Miss Plodd's feet are with Mrs Edgar's head, Miss Plodd's head is with Mrs Nixon's feet and Mr Overton's head is with Mrs Edgar's feet.

Thus (head, body, legs, feet):
Mrs Edgar, Mr Norton, Miss Nixon, Miss Plodd;
Miss Nixon, Mr Overton, Miss Plodd, Mr Norton;
Mr Norton, Miss Nixon, Mrs Edgar, Mr Overton;
Mr Overton, Miss Plodd, Mr Norton, Mrs Edgar;
Miss Plodd, Mrs Edgar, Mr Overton, Miss Nixon.

No 156

Daniel lives on the 4th floor (clue 4). Bridie doesn't live on the 7th (clue 3), so (1) on the 6th and Janine on the 5th. Daniel has lived there either for 6 years and Louisa for 3 years (4) or for 9 years and Louisa for 6 years; ie either Daniel or Louisa has been there for 6 years. So Janine has been there for 2 years (2) and the person in No 19 for one year. The person at No 19 isn't Bridie (3), so Ian. Bridie hasn't lived there for 9 years (3), so 3. Daniel has been there 9 and Louisa 6 years. Louisa is at No 5 (4). The person at No 13 isn't Bridie (3) or Daniel (5), so Janine. Since Daniel lives on the 4th floor, his flat number isn't eight lower than Bridie's (3). So Daniel lives at No 3 and Bridie at No 11, Ian lives on the 7th floor (3) and Louisa on the 3rd.

Thus:
Bridie, Flat 11, 6th, 3 years;
Daniel, Flat 3, 4th, 9 years;
Ian, Flat 19, 7th, 1 year;
Janine, Flat 13, 5th, 2 years;
Louisa, Flat 5, 3rd, 6 years

No 157

There is no 8, so card O wasn't 10th (clue 2), thus the card called 10th was either E or J. The card called 1st is next to and left of the card called 2nd (3) and the cards called 1st and 15th (last) are of the same value. F wasn't 1st or 2nd (3). If E was 2nd, then J was 15th (3) and there's no 10th card (above). H wasn't 1st (2), so I wasn't 2nd (3). Since there are no 8s or 10s, the 2nd card wasn't J or O. There's only one 3, so N wasn't 2nd (3). Nor was L 2nd (4), thus (3) O was 13th, B 2nd, A 1st and E 15th. J was 10th (2) and I 12th. C was called next-but-one before H (2), so C was 4th (1) and D 8th; and H was 6th (2). F was 5th (4). L wasn't 9th (1), so 11th (4) and M was 9th. Neither K nor N was 7th

(immediately after H, 2), so G was 7th. N wasn't 3rd (4), so 14th and K was 3rd.
Thus:
1st A, 2nd B, 3rd K, 4th C, 5th F, 6th H, 7th G, 8th D, 9th M, 10th J, 11th L, 12th I, 13th O, 14th N, 15th E.

No 158

No-one lives 2½ miles away (grid), so either the moped-rider lives 2 miles away and the woman who arrives at 7.30 is 3 miles away (clue 2) or the moped-rider lives one mile away and the woman who arrives at 7.30 is 2 miles away; ie the woman 2 miles away either rides a moped or arrives at 7.30. Leonie arrives 5 minutes later than the moped rider (2), so Leonie doesn't live 2 miles away. May arrives at 7.50 (1), so isn't the moped rider, thus doesn't live 2 miles away. The woman 2 miles away isn't Avril (3) and Gerda who drives a car doesn't arrive at 7.30, so isn't 2 miles away. Thus Dawn lives 2 miles from the store. Gerda arrives 5 minutes later than Dawn (3) and Leonie 5 minutes later than the moped-rider (2), who thus isn't Dawn. So Avril rides the moped and (above) Dawn is the woman who arrives at 7.30. Gerda arrives at 7.35 (3). Leonie arrives at 7.45 (2) and Avril at 7.40. Avril lives one mile away (2) and Gerda 1.5 miles (3). The woman who travels on foot (walks) is May (3) who lives 3½ miles away. Leonie lives 3 miles away. Dawn doesn't travel by bus (1), so bicycle. Leonie uses the bus.
Thus:
Avril, 7.40am, 1 mile, moped;
Dawn, 7.30am, 2 miles, bicycle;
Gerda, 7.35am, 1½ miles, car;
Leonie, 7.45am, 3 miles, bus;
May, 7.50am, 3½ miles, on foot.

No 159

The woman in lighting is 30 (clue 3) and May is 33 (clue 4), so the woman in footwear is 29 (5) and Gerda is 31. Avril is in the toy department (1). Gerda isn't in haberdashery (5), so stationery. By elimination, May works in haberdashery and Avril is 32. The employee of 6 months is 29 (2). Dawn isn't 30 (3), so she's 29 and Leonie is 30 and has worked there for one year. Avril has been there for 3 years and Gerda for 2 (1), so May has been an employee for 18 months.
Thus:
Avril, toys, 32 years old, 3 years;
Dawn, footwear, 29 years old, 6 months;
Gerda, stationery, 31 years old, 2 years;
Leonie, lighting, 30 years old, 1 year;
May, haberdashery, 33 years old, 18 months.

No 160

Tuesday's omelette was cheese (clue 4), so either the asparagus omelette was served on Monday, the green pepper omelette on Wednesday and the bacon omelette on Friday (clue 2), or the asparagus was on

Solutions

Wednesday, the green pepper on Friday and the bacon on Sunday. In other words, Wednesday's was either green pepper or asparagus and Friday's either bacon or green pepper. Amber cooked the green pepper omelette and Marlene the asparagus (2), so either Amber or Marlene was visited on Wednesday. Honor didn't make the cheese omelette (4), so either Tammy cooked on Thursday and Honor on Friday (1) or Tammy cooked on Friday and Honor on Saturday, ie Friday's cook was either Honor or Tammy. Thus Amber's green pepper omelette was served on Wednesday, Marlene's asparagus on Monday (2) and the bacon omelette on Friday. The bacon omelette wasn't made by Tammy (1), so Honor and Thursday's visit was to Tammy. Tuesday's visit wasn't to Suzanne (3) or Gail (4), so Polly. Saturday's wasn't to Suzanne (3), so Gail and Suzanne were visited on Sunday. Gail's omelette wasn't onion or tomato (4), so pea and ham. Thus Tammy's was onion (1) and Suzanne's was tomato.

Thus:

Monday, Marlene, asparagus;
Tuesday, Polly, cheese;
Wednesday, Amber, green pepper;
Thursday, Tammy, onion;
Friday, Honor, bacon;
Saturday, Gail, pea and ham;
Sunday, Suzanne, tomato.

No 161

Fern washed on Tuesday (clue 3) and Amanda on Friday (clue 6). No-one ironed on Wednesday (grid), so Jason didn't wash on Tuesday (2), thus he isn't the partner of Fern who (3) ironed on Friday. So Jason did his ironing on Tuesday (1) and Candy washed on Wednesday. Morgan washed and ironed on one day (4), so isn't Fern's partner. Kurt did the washing the day before ironing (5), so isn't Fern's partner. Fern's partner isn't Oliver (3), so Lance. Morgan washed and ironed on either Monday or Saturday (4). His partner isn't Pauline (4), so (by elimination) she's Rosa. Jason's partner isn't Candy (1) or Pauline (2), so Amanda. Pauline ironed on Saturday (2). So Morgan/Rosa washed and ironed on Monday, Candy ironed on Thursday and Pauline washed on Saturday. Kurt's partner (5) is thus Candy. Oliver's partner is Pauline.

Thus (washing, ironing):

Jason, Amanda, Friday, Tuesday;
Kurt, Candy, Wednesday, Thursday;
Lance, Fern, Tuesday, Friday;
Morgan, Rosa, Monday, Monday;
Oliver, Pauline, Saturday, Saturday.

No 162

RxY is less than 52 (clue 14) and is equivalent to YxYxY (clue 4), so D+S equals either 8 or 27. If D+S=8, Y=2 and S would be at least 9 (8), so D+S=27, Y=3 and R=9 (4). D is less than 14 (6), so S is either 16 or 25 (8) and D either 11 or 2. If D=11 and S=16, then H=4 (8), F=2 (6) and B is less than 5 (13), so B=1, also G=22

(6) so P=6 (2). But then IxI=7 (10), which isn't possible. So D isn't 11. Thus D=2 (14), S=25 and H=5 (8). K=7 (1), G=26 (2) and P=1, F=13 (6), I=4 (10) and B=15. A is either 6 or 8 (7), as is Z (9), so L and V are 18 and/or 24 (7 and 9). If A=6, J would also be 24 (13). So A=8, J=22 (13), L=24 (7), Z=6 and V=18 (9). E and/or W are 10 and/or 14 (12). X is at most 23 (3), so X=21, E=10, N=11 and W=14 (12). M=12 and Q=23 (11). U=17 and T=19 (5). O=20 (15), so C=16.

Thus:

A=8; B=15; C=16; D=2; E=10; F=13; G=26; H=5; I=4; J=22; K=7; L=24; M=12; N=11; O=20; P=1; Q=23; R=9; S=25; T=19; U=17; V=18; W=14; X=21; Y=3; Z=6.

No 163 *Odyssey Homecoming*

Arthur lives at No 5 (intro). David and his wife Katie aren't the parents of Emma or Beatrice (clue 1), Adam or Derek (clue 2), so Carl. They don't live at No 1 (1), No 2 or No 3 (2), so No 4. Margaret at No 2 isn't the mother of Adam or Derek (2) or Emma (1), so Beatrice. Beatrice's father is Grant (1). Frank and Adam aren't at No 3 (2), so No 1. Frank's wife isn't Lesley (1) or Ingrid (2), so Joanne. Ingrid and Derek aren't at No 3 (2), so No 5. The family at No 3 are Harry, Lesley and Emma.

Thus:

No 1, Frank, Joanne, Adam;
No 2, Grant, Margaret, Beatrice;
No 3, Harry, Lesley, Emma;
No 4, David, Katie, Carl;
No 5, Arthur, Ingrid, Derek.

No 164

Neil didn't wash the teeshirt (clue 1), beach-towel (clue 3), trousers (4) or a jumper (5), so shorts. The beach-towel washed by either Roy or Valerie didn't turn things pink (3), brown (1), blue (2) or green (4), so grey. The item which turned things pink was also washed by either Roy or Valerie (3). The teeshirt was washed by either Claire or Donna and didn't turn things brown (1) or green (4), so blue. Thus it was washed by Donna (2) and Neil washed 6 garments which (4) are now green. Claire's item turned things brown, so (1) Donna washed the teeshirt. Whoever washed the trousers washed 5 items (4), so this wasn't Claire (1). Thus Claire washed the jumper and (5) Roy washed 11 items. By elimination, Valerie washed the trousers, so Roy washed the beach-towel and (5) Valerie's items turned pink. Donna washed 8 articles (1) and Claire 10.

Thus:

Claire, jumper, 10 garments, brown;
Donna, teeshirt, 8 garments, blue;
Neil, shorts, 6 garments, green;
Roy, beach-towel, 11 garments, grey;
Valerie, trousers, 5 garments, pink.

No 165

Bread was taken at either 2.00 or 2.30 (clue 1) as was milk (clue 4). The dogs who went at 8.30, 11.00 and/or 11.30 are Jack (1), Bobby (2) and Fido who went with

Solutions

the eggs (3), so Butch and/or Sukie went at 2.00 or 2.30. Bobby went with Mrs Perry's delivery (2), so the dog who went with Mr Argent's delivery at either 8.30 or 11.00 (1) is Fido and Jack at either 11.00 or 11.30. Jack wasn't taken with the bread (1), sugar (3) or milk (4), so the tea. Either Butch or Sukie was taken with the bread (1) and milk (4), so Bobby was taken with the sugar. The milk was for Mr Dent (4). Jack (tea, above) wasn't taken with Miss Cooper's delivery (5), so Mr Tring's. Butch wasn't taken with Miss Cooper's (5), so Mr Dent's and Sukie was taken with Miss Cooper's. Thus Sukie went at 2.00 (5) and Butch at 2.30. By elimination, the bread went to Miss Cooper, so Jack was taken at 11.00 and Fido at 8.30. Bobby was taken out at 11.30.

Thus:

Bobby, 11.30am, Mrs Perry, sugar;
Butch, 2.30pm, Mr Dent, milk;
Fido, 8.30am, Mr Argent, eggs;
Jack, 11.00am, Mr Tring, tea;
Sukie, 2.00pm, Miss Cooper, bread.

No 166

No 167

Bowl A isn't Hal's (clue 1), Caroline's (clue 2), Damien's (3) or Ferdinand's (4), so either Edna's or Glenda's. Caroline's is thus B (2). Glenda's isn't C (1), so (2) A and Edna's is C. Glenda adds chocolate (2). The person who adds banana isn't Ferdinand, Edna or Hal. Caroline (bowl B) doesn't add banana (4). Thus Damien adds banana. Edna doesn't add syrup (2), so Damien's bowl is E (3 and 4) and Ferdinand has treacle (3). Hal owns bowl D and has syrup. Edna doesn't have raisins (2), so strawberries. Caroline has raisins.

Thus:

Bowl A, Glenda, chocolate;
Bowl B, Caroline, raisins;
Bowl C, Edna, strawberries;
Bowl D, Hal, syrup;
Bowl E, Damien, banana;
Bowl F, Ferdinand, treacle.

No 168

The 6oz of bull's-eyes and 6oz of coffee fudge were bought by either Sara or Rachel (clue 6) together with the 4oz of bull's-eyes and 8oz of coffee fudge. Thus Sara didn't buy 6oz of mint creams, so Barbara did (clue 3) and Sara bought 4oz of mint creams. By elimination, Rachel bought 4oz of bull's-eyes, so 6oz of coffee fudge; and Sara bought 6oz of bull's-eyes and 8oz of coffee fudge. Norma bought 8oz of fruit chews (5). No treacle toffee was bought by Eve (2) or Barbara (4), so Rachel bought 8oz of treacle toffee and Norma 4oz. The 4oz of humbugs weren't bought by Barbara (1), so Eve and Barbara bought 4oz of aniseed balls. By elimination, Barbara bought 8oz of liquorice toffee and Eve 8oz of aniseed balls. Eve bought 6oz of coffee creams and Norma 6oz of humbugs.

Thus (4ozs, 6ozs, 8ozs):

Barbara, aniseed balls, mint creams, liquorice toffee;
Eve, humbugs, coffee creams, aniseed balls;
Norma, treacle toffee, humbugs, fruit chews;
Rachel, bull's-eyes, coffee fudge, treacle toffee;
Sara, mint creams, bull's-eyes, coffee fudge.

No 169

Raymond's wife is Rebecca (clue 4) and Ruth ate the Mexican meal (clue 5). Ryan ate Italian food, but not with Raisa or Roma (6), so Rosie. Richard ate at Antonio's (3). Raisa went to The Oak Tree, but not with Rupert (2), so Robert. Rupert didn't go to Alfonso's or La Contessa (1), so The Kitchen. He didn't go with Ruth (5), so Roma. Richard went with Ruth. La Contessa serves Chinese food (1), so Ryan's Italian meal (6) was at Alfonso's and Raymond went to La Contessa. The Thai meal wasn't at The Oak Tree (2), so The Kitchen. The Oak Tree serves Indian food.

Thus:

Raymond, Rebecca, La Contessa, Chinese;
Richard, Ruth, Antonio's, Mexican;
Robert, Raisa, The Oak Tree, Indian;
Rupert, Roma, The Kitchen, Thai;
Ryan, Rosie, Alfonso's, Italian.

No 170

The 2002 resolution lasted for 6 months (clue 2) and Colin's for either 2 or 3 months. Tony's was last made in 2003 (clue 4). The 6-month resolution concerned snacks and wasn't made by Yolande (5) or Delores (1), so Owen. The resolution on swearing lasted for 4 months (1) and Delores kept hers for one month. The 2004 resolution on sweets wasn't made by Delores or Colin (4), so Yolande. The 2001 resolution which lasted for 2 months (3) was thus Colin's and (2) Delores' resolution concerned alcohol and was last made in 2005. The swearing resolution which (1) lasted for 4 months was thus Tony's and Colin's concerned smoking. Yolande's lasted for 3 months.

Solutions

Thus:
Colin, smoking, 2001, 2 months;
Delores, alcohol, 2005, 1 month;
Owen, snacks, 2002, 6 months;
Tony, swearing, 2003, 4 months;
Yolande, sweets, 2004, 3 months.

No 171
Cards total 81 (intro), so the 10 is missing. Card L isn't the 2 (clue 3), so E isn't the ace (clue 2). If E is the 2, then L is the 4 and H is the 8 (2), which isn't possible (3). So E is the 3, L is the 6 and H is the queen. D is the 9 (3). C isn't the 8 (3), so B isn't the 4 (1). B isn't the ace (1), so B is the 2 and C is the 4. F is the 8 (3), so K is the 5 (4). Card I is the 7 (5). J isn't the ace or jack (1), so the king. G is the jack (5) and A is the ace. H is a diamond or a heart (2), as is F (intro). E isn't a club (2), so a spade and G is a club. K isn't a diamond, so (intro) K is a heart, as is A and C and I are diamonds. B isn't a spade (4), so B and L are clubs and D and J are spades. H isn't a diamond (1), so a heart. F is a diamond.
Thus:
AH 2C 4D 9S
3S 8D JC QH
7D KS 5H 6C

No 172
The boy aged 11 who tried on Friday (clue 3) isn't Stuart (clue 5), so Gerry and the child aged 10 tried on Thursday (4). The 12-year-old used 26 bricks but not on Monday (5) or Tuesday (4), so Wednesday. Jemima tried on Monday (2), so Stuart on Tuesday (5), Trixie used 24 bricks (1), so Melody is 12 and Trixie tried on Thursday. Stuart used 28 bricks (4). Gerry didn't use 32 (3), so 30 and Jemima used 32. Stuart isn't 9 (5), so 8. Jemima is 9.
Thus:
Gerry, Friday, 11 years old, 30 bricks;
Jemima, Monday, 9 years old, 32 bricks;
Melody, Wednesday, 12 years old, 26 bricks;
Stuart, Tuesday, 8 years old, 28 bricks;
Trixie, Thursday, 10 years old, 24 bricks.

No 173 *Odyssey Homecoming*
Unwin is married to Edwina (clue 2). Denise's daughter is Penny (clue 5) and Carol's is Roberta (7). Queenie's father is Terry who isn't married to Felicity or Belinda (1), so Annie. Felicity's son is Joe (1). Liam's father is Wally who isn't married to Carol (6) or Denise (5), so Belinda. Their daughter isn't Naomi (Harry's sister, 2) or Olivia (8), so Melanie. Since Harry's sister is Naomi (2), they're Edwina's children and Joe's sister is Olivia. Annie's son isn't Graham or Ian (3), so Kevin. Penny's brother isn't Graham (4), so Ian and Roberta's is Graham. Their father isn't Stan (7). Stan's son isn't Ian (3), so Joe. Vernon's wife isn't Denise (4), so Denise is married to Xerxes and Carol to Vernon.

Thus:
Stan, Felicity, Joe, Olivia;
Terry, Annie, Kevin, Queenie;
Unwin, Edwina, Harry, Naomi;
Vernon, Carol, Graham, Roberta;
Wally, Belinda, Liam, Melanie;
Xerxes, Denise, Ian, Penny.

No 174
By elimination, the letter in 11 and 41 (clue 3) is A and pieces 15 and 48 (clue 4) contain E. Thus 20=F and 27=G, so (2) 2=G. Pieces 1 and 19 contain C (1). In diagonal 1-49, the F isn't in 9 (5), so 33. In 1-49, the G is in 49 and the B is in 17. Pieces 9 and/or 25 contain D and/or E, so piece 37 contains neither. Thus 37=F and (by elimination) in 7-43, 7=A. So 21=D and in 1-7, the F is in piece 3. Piece 16=A, so the A in 29-35 is in 29. Thus 43=D, so 25=E, 9=D and 31=G. In 3-45, the E is in 10, 45=C and 38=D. So 44=B and 47=A. In 2-44, 30=E and 23=C. In 8-14, 12=G, 8=F and 14=C. So 22=B, 36=G, 40=B, 39=C, 4=B, 32=D, 5=E, 26=D, 28=F and 35=B.
Thus:

C	G	F	B	E	D	A
F	D	E	A	G	B	C
E	A	B	G	C	F	D
B	C	A	E	D	G	F
A	E	G	D	F	C	B
G	F	D	C	B	A	E
D	B	C	F	A	E	G

No 175
David's briefcase held either his lunch or washing (clue 5), thus the grey briefcase with either the newspaper or gym kit is Walter's (clue 3) and David's is green (5). Mr Stoner is either James or Keith (4), thus his briefcase is black and (7) Mr Hale with the newspaper is Walter. Mr Macleod's briefcase contained washing (1), so the gym kit was in the beige briefcase. Mr Cameron's is green or tan (4), thus Mr Woodleigh's is beige. Tom's surname is Cameron (6), so David's is Macleod and Tom's briefcase is tan. James isn't Mr Woodleigh (2), so Mr Stoner. Keith is Mr Woodleigh. James's briefcase held books (2), so Tom's contained his lunch.
Thus:
David, Macleod, green, washing;
James, Stoner, black, books;
Keith, Woodleigh, beige, gym kit;
Tom, Cameron, tan, lunch;
Walter, Hale, grey, newspaper.

No 176

B	A	C	B	A	C
C	A	A	C	B	B
A	B	C	A	B	C
C	B	B	A	C	A
B	C	A	B	C	A
A	C	B	C	A	B

Solutions

No 177

Cora watched *Gosford Park* (clue 1) and whoever watched *Peter Pan* drank tea (clue 6). Roger drank lager but didn't see *Titanic* or *Doctor Doolittle* (3), so *Pulp Fiction*; thus he ate Indian curry. The person with fish and chips drank lemonade (4) and Alice drank cola (5). Edward's meal was Chinese (7). Alice didn't eat pizza (5), so doner kebab. Edward didn't drink tea (7), so white wine. Cora thus drank lemonade and Janet watched *Peter Pan* and ate pizza. Edward didn't watch *Doctor Doolittle* (1), so *Titanic*. Alice saw *Doctor Doolittle*.

Thus:

Alice, *Doctor Doolittle*, doner kebab, cola;
Cora, *Gosford Park*, fish and chips, lemonade;
Edward, *Titanic*, Chinese, white wine;
Janet, *Peter Pan*, pizza, tea;
Roger, *Pulp Fiction*, Indian curry, lager.

No 178

Craig repaired the Ford on Wednesday (clue 2). The cars fixed on Thursday and Friday aren't the Fiat (clue 3) or Peugeot (5), so (1) Mr Chester repaired the Vauxhall on Friday and the Rover was fixed on Thursday. Adrian thus worked on Thursday and the Fiat was fixed on Tuesday (3), so the Peugeot on Monday. Theo worked on Tuesday (5), thus he's Mr Chambers (4). The Peugeot owner isn't Mr Kent (5) or Mr Barton (6), so Mr Johnson. Adrian is Mr Barton (3) and Mr Kent worked on Wednesday. George didn't fix the Peugeot (6), so the Vauxhall. The Peugeot belongs to Bill.

Thus:

Adrian, Barton, Rover, Thursday;
Bill, Johnson, Peugeot, Monday;
Craig, Kent, Ford, Wednesday;
George, Chester, Vauxhall, Friday;
Theo, Chambers, Fiat, Tuesday.

No 179

Jacqueline's reason for being online was homework (clue 4) and Jerry's was the weather (clue 5). Cathy's wasn't to find a map (1) or read the news (3), so shopping. She didn't spend 75 minutes online (4), so 60 (1) and the person attracted to the holiday site spent 45 minutes online. Jessica spent 50 minutes online (4), so Jacqueline 75 minutes. Moira spent 45 minutes online (2) and Jerry 35 minutes. Moira had wanted a map (1), so Jessica had wanted the news and (5) ended up on the auction site. Thus Jacqueline visited the puzzles site (2). The chat site visitor was thus Jerry (3) and Cathy was attracted to the healthcare site.

Thus:

Cathy, shopping, 60 minutes, healthcare;
Jacqueline, homework, 75 minutes, puzzles;
Jerry, weather, 35 minutes, chat;
Jessica, news, 50 minutes, auction;
Moira, map, 45 minutes, holiday.

No 180 *Thank you Ma'm*

The $120,000 robbery was from a bank (clue 1) and the $160,000 robbery was in 2005. Thus the $40,000 robbery was from the warehouse in South Africa (clue 6) and the $120,000 robbery was in 2002. The robbery in Peru netted $200,000 (2), so the 2004 robbery in Canada (4) netted $80,000. The jewellery shop robbery was in 2001 (5), thus netted $200,000. The robbery from the casino netted $160,000 (3) and the robbery in Wales netted $120,000, so the casino robbery was in Austria and the Canadian robbery was from a museum. The warehouse robbery was in 2003.

Thus:

Bank, 2002, Wales, $120,000;
Casino, 2005, Austria, $160,000;
Jewellery shop, 2001, Peru, $200,000;
Museum, 2004, Canada, $80,000;
Warehouse, 2003, South Africa, $40,000.

No 181

The traffic cop is in the United Kingdom (clue 3). The auto theft cop isn't in Brazil (clue 3), Pakistan or Australia (5), so New Zealand. The cop from homicide is in Brazil (5). O'Leary in Australia (4) isn't in the robbery squad (2), so vice squad. The robbery squad cop is in Pakistan. The man in Brazil isn't Wyndrake (1), so (3) Steinbeck. The robbery squad cop isn't Andrews or Goodman (2), so Wyndrake. The auto theft cop isn't Goodman (6), so Andrews and Goodman is the traffic cop. Wyndrake is from South Dakota (1) and Goodman is from Missouri (6). O'Leary is from Utah (4). Steinbeck is from Alaska (3) and Andrews from Texas.

Thus:

Officer Andrews, Texas, auto theft, New Zealand;
Officer Goodman, Missouri, traffic, United Kingdom;
Officer O'Leary, Utah, vice, Australia;
Officer Steinbeck, Alaska, homicide, Brazil;
Officer Wyndrake, robbery, Pakistan.

No 182 *Speckled Band*

Martin is Scott (clue 3) and Peter is researching *Macbeth* (clue 4), so Oliver is the man (6) surnamed Collins and researching *Julius Caesar*. The man (6) researching *King Lear* and reading Hardy is Martin. Nancy is reading Dickens (1). The student surnamed Marlowe is reading Carroll and isn't Lorna (7), so Peter. The one surnamed Barrie is reading Tolkien (2), so Lorna's surname is Barrie and Nancy's is Stoker. Oliver is reading Austen. Nancy is researching *The Tempest* (5). Lorna is researching *Romeo and Juliet*.

Thus:

Lorna, Barrie, J R R Tolkien, *Romeo and Juliet*;
Martin, Scott, Thomas Hardy, *King Lear*;
Nancy, Stoker, Charles Dickens, *The Tempest*;
Oliver, Collins, Jane Austen, *Julius Caesar*;
Peter, Marlowe, Lewis Carroll, *Macbeth*.

Solutions

No 183

2	1	6	8	4	2
3	4	5	6	7	8
1	8	4	1	5	3
9	7	3	2	6	9
5	3	2	4	7	6
7	9	1	5	8	9

No 184

The student who got 60% in algebra got either 35% or 40% in geometry (clue 3), so the one who got 50% in algebra got 70% in geometry (clue 1) and whoever got 50% in trigonometry got 50% in geometry. Edina didn't get 50% in trigonometry (2), so she got 40% in geometry (5) and Sheila got 60%. Sheila's mark in trigonometry was thus not 50%, so (6) 60% and Edina got 80% in trigonometry. Barry got 40% in algebra (2), so Sheila got 35% (3) and Julie 50% in algebra (plus 70% in geometry, above). Samuel got 55% in both algebra and trigonometry (4), so Edina got 30% in algebra and Barry got 50% in trigonometry. By elimination, Samuel got 85% in geometry.

Thus (algebra, geometry, trigonometry):
Barry, 40%, 50%, 50%;
Edina, 30%, 40%, 80%;
Julie, 50%, 70%, 70%;
Samuel, 55%, 85%, 55%;
Sheila, 35%, 60%, 60%.

No 185 *Gift of magic*

Fiona has an interview (clue 1), Gabrielle went to Hair Quality (clue 2) and Iona is visiting her aunt (3). The woman attending a retirement party went to Miranda's Salon (4) and isn't Hannah (5), so Jackie. Hannah chose Purple Haze (5). The Snip Shop customer who chose Pink Perfection isn't Iona (3), so Fiona. Jackie didn't choose Chestnut Charm or Ebony Black (2), so Bouncy Blonde. Gabrielle didn't choose Chestnut Charm (2), so Ebony Black. Iona chose Chestnut Charm. The woman whose hair was done for her wedding didn't go to Top Knotch or Hair Quality (6), so Tracey's Tresses. Thus she's Hannah, Iona went to Top Knotch and Gabrielle is going to a Christening.

Thus:
Hair Quality, Gabrielle, Ebony Black, Christening;
Miranda's Salon, Jackie, Bouncy Blonde, retirement;
The Snip Shop, Fiona, Pink Perfection, interview;
Top Knotch, Iona, Chestnut Charm, visit to aunt;
Tracey's Tresses, Hannah, Purple Haze, wedding.

No 186

The letter with a value of 1 isn't T or A (clue 4). In clues 1, 4, 7 and 9, T+X=A, AxT=S, S+X=U and PxU=Y, so the only solution is that X=1, T=3, A=4, S=12, U=13, P=2 and Y=26. J=11 (2). W has a value of at least 16 (3) and at most 20 (5) and R has a value of more than 20, so (3) the value of H is either 5, 6, 7, 8 or 9, as (5) is that of E. Thus the value of V (6) is either 10, 14, 16 or 18 and that of E is either 5, 7, 8 or 9. Three times E

thus equals B (6 and 8), so E is either 5, 7 or 8 and B is either 15, 21 or 24. Thus (10) V=10, B=15 and N=25. E=5 (6). G+L=20 (16), so their values are 6 and/or 14. Since J=11 (above), the value of L isn't 14 (12). Thus G=14 (16), L=6 and (12) Z=19. In clues 3 and 5, H=7, W=18 and R=23. The value of F isn't 24 (14), so O=9 (13) and F=16. D=8 and Q=24 (14). I=22 (11). Since P=2 (above), K=17 (15) and M=21. By elimination (intro), C=20.

Thus:
A=4, B=15, C=20, D=8, E=5, F=16, G=14, H=7, I=22, J=11, K=17, L=6, M=21, N=25, O=9, P=2, Q=24, R=23, S=12, T=3, U=13, V=10, W=18, X=1, Y=26, Z=19.

No 187 *Odyssey*

The trip to Brentville took 60 minutes (clue 2) and Madeleine made the 55-minute trip (clue 4), so Zoë's trip to Ayre's Junction took 45 minutes (5) and Dave's took 30 minutes. Dave read a magazine (3) and Bob did the crosswords (6). The High Point traveller snoozed (1). Dave didn't go to Middleton (5), so Woodbury. Zoë didn't read a novel (5), so she had the newspaper. Bob didn't go to Middleton (6), so Brentville, thus Alan's journey took 80 minutes. Madeleine went to Middleton (6) and Alan to High Point. Madeleine read a novel.

Thus:
Alan, High Point, 80 minutes, snooze;
Bob, Brentville, 60 minutes, crosswords;
Dave, Woodbury, 30 minutes, magazine;
Madeleine, Middleton, 55 minutes, novel;
Zoë, Ayre's Junction, 45 minutes, newspaper.

No 188

The only times 'half-an-hour longer' are 1½ hours and 2¼ hours (grid), so these relate to the batches for the eldest son (clue 2) and youngest son (clue 4). Neither was made on Thursday (4). Thursday's batch didn't take one hour (3) or 2½ (4), so 1¾ hours. The youngest son's took 2¼ (4), so the eldest son's took 1½ hours (2) and Tuesday's took one hour. No baking was done on Wednesday, so (3) the ginger cakes (day before Madeira) took 1½ hours. They weren't made on Monday (2), so Friday and (3) the Madeira on Saturday. The cherry cakes for a neighbour (1) were made on Tuesday and the seed cakes for a daughter on Thursday. The batch for the vicar's wife thus took 2½ hours. She didn't make it on Saturday (5), so Monday, thus (by elimination) the vicar's wife got chocolate cakes and Saturday's batch was for the youngest son.

Thus:
Cherry cakes, 1 hour, Tuesday, neighbour;
Chocolate cakes, 2½ hours, Monday, vicar's wife;
Ginger cakes, 1½ hours, Friday, eldest son;
Madeira cakes, 2¼ hours, Saturday, youngest son;
Seed cakes, 1¾ hours, Thursday, daughter.

Solutions

No 189

October's picture was taken in Sweden (clue 1) and April's picture is of fisherman (clue 2), so June's is of a sunset (6), July's is from Barbados and August's is from the USA and (5) is of trees. The market photo taken by Louis (3) isn't from Sweden (1), so Barbados and the beach scene photo was taken in Sweden. Viv's isn't of the sunset (6). So Johnny's photo from Japan (6) was taken in June (sunset, above) and Viv's is of trees. The photo of fisherman is thus from Holland, so (4) it was taken by Mortimer. Reggie's is of a beach scene.

Thus:

Beach scene, Reggie, Sweden, October;
Fishermen, Mortimer, Holland, April;
Market, Louis, Barbados, July;
Sunset, Johnny, Japan, June;
Trees, Viv, USA, August.

No 190

The card called 14th wasn't F (clue 3), so D wasn't 12th. If F was 3rd, then D was called 1st (3) and 6th (1). So F wasn't 3rd. M wasn't called 6th (1), so H was 10th, G 12th, N 3rd and K 6th. No other card has a value between those of E and G, so F wasn't called 4th (2). Thus B was 4th (2), D 5th and E 15th. F was called 7th (3), O 14th and C 2nd. J wasn't 1st or 13th (4). If J was 9th, then (only cards A, I, J, L and M are left) there aren't two cards of the same suit left to have been called 8th and 13th. Card I wasn't 13th (4), so J wasn't 11th. Thus J was 8th (4) and A 13th. M was 1st (4). The card called 9th wasn't L (3), so I and L was called 11th.

Thus:

1st M, 2nd C, 3rd N, 4th B, 5th D, 6th K, 7th F, 8th J,
9th I, 10th H, 11th L, 12th G, 13th A,
14th O, 15th E.

No 191

The men who left at 3.50 and 4.00 ('ten minutes earlier than') are Wesley (clue 2) and/or Malcolm (clue 4), so Joseph left at 3.30 (1) and Bryn at 3.00. Stan left at 4.10. Joseph ate chicken sandwiches (4). The man who left at 4.00 ate either ham (2) or cheese (4). Bryn arrived at 10.50 (3), so stayed for 4 hours and 10 minutes and whoever ate ham sandwiches also stayed for 4 hours and 10 minutes, arriving ten minutes later than the man who ate beef sandwiches (2). No-one left at 3.10 (grid), so the man who ate ham sandwiches didn't arrive at 11.00. Thus the man who ate ham arrived at 11.50 and left at 4.00 and the one who ate beef arrived at 11.40. Wesley left at 3.50 (2), so Malcolm at 4.00. Stan ate cheese and arrived at 11.00 (4) and Joseph at 11.20. Wesley arrived at 11.40 (beef, above), so Bryn had bacon sandwiches.

Thus:

Bryn, 10.50am, 3.00pm, bacon;
Joseph, 11.20am, 3.30pm, chicken;
Malcolm, 11.50am, 4.00pm, ham;
Stan, 11.00am, 4.10pm, cheese;
Wesley, 11.40am, 3.50pm, beef.

No 192

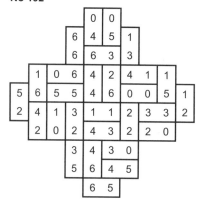

No 193

Each woman wore two different colours (intro). No woman is 23 (grid). Judith's skirt wasn't red (clue 5) and the 24-year-old's jumper wasn't green (clue 1) or blue (4), so (6) orange, as was Judith's skirt. The 25-year-old's jumper was green (1), thus her skirt wasn't green: so Kath's jumper wasn't green (3), thus Kath is either 22 and Noelle is 21 or she's 26 and Noelle is 25. Mandy is one year younger than the woman in the blue jumper (4), so Mandy is also either 21 or 25 and the woman in the blue jumper is 22 or 26 (and isn't Kath, above). The 24-year-old isn't Judith (6), so Laura. The woman one year older than Mandy (4) is thus Judith, so (5) Mandy's skirt was red. Judith's jumper was blue (4 and above), as was Laura's skirt (2). The 25-year-old's skirt (not green, above) and Kath's jumper (3) were both red. So Mandy is 25 and (4) Judith 26. Kath is 22 and Noelle 21 (3). Noelle wore the yellow jumper, but not a black skirt (7), so green. Kath wore a black skirt.

Thus (jumper, skirt):

Judith, 26 years old, blue, orange;
Kath, 22 years old, red, black;
Laura, 24 years old, orange, blue;
Mandy, 25 years old, green, red;
Noelle, 21 years old, yellow, green.

No 194 *Most Dangerous Game*

Remember throughout that each picture is made of 4 different parts (intro). The pig's tail is in the same picture as the dog's head (clue 4), so the goat's head, which is with the lamb's body but not the dog's tail (2) is with the cow's tail. The dog's legs are with the goat's body (3), so the goat's head is (by elimination) with the pig's legs. The lamb's tail isn't with the pig's head (1), so the cow's. Thus the dog's head is with the cow's body, so they're with the lamb's legs. The pig's head isn't with the dog's legs/goat's body (3), so with the dog's body, thus also with the goat's tail/cow's legs. The dog's tail is thus with the lamb's head, thus the goat's body/dog's legs are with the cow's head; and the lamb's head is with the pig's body/goat's legs.

Solutions

Thus (head, body, legs, tail):
Cow, goat, dog, lamb;
Dog, cow, lamb, pig;
Goat, lamb, pig, cow;
Lamb, pig, goat, dog;
Pig, dog, cow, goat.

No 195

A	B	C	A	C	B
C	C	B	B	A	A
B	A	A	B	C	C
B	B	C	C	A	A
A	A	B	C	B	C
C	C	A	A	B	B

No 196 *R95 / Mist Red Death*

Six people lay on blue towels, 8 on green, 8 on white, 4 on orange and 4 on red towels (clue 1). The men amounted to 2 on blue towels, 2 on white and 2 on red towels (clue 2). Boys were: 2 on blue towels, 2 on green, 2 on white and 2 on orange towels (3). Women were: 2 on blue towels, 2 on green, 2 on white and 2 on red towels (4). Girls were: 4 on green towels, 2 on white and 2 on orange towels (4). Those in green were: 2 men/blue towels, 2 men/white towels, 2 boys/green towels and 2 boys/white towels (5). Those in red were: 2 men/red towels and 4 girls/green towels (6). Those in yellow were 2 boys/blue towels, 2 boys/orange towels and 2 women/blue towels (7). Those in navy blue were 2 women/white towels and 2 girls/white towels (8). Those still unaccounted for, wearing purple (9) are: 2 women/green towels, 2 girls orange towels and 2 women/red towels.

Thus:
Six sunbathers wore purple.

No 197 *odyssey*

Fran lives in Innthorpe or Redport (clue 2), so (clue 3) the woman who lives in Puzzleton is Wendy, who drove to Tanbridge. Either Gina or Sandra travelled on Thursday (1) and either Ellen or Fran travelled on Tuesday (6). Wednesday's traveller lives in either Benmoor or Whitbury (5) and Friday's went to either Raymouth or Bearton, so Wendy travelled on Monday. Ellen went to Pulbury or Southam (4), so (6) Fran went to Pulbury on Tuesday, thus Ellen went to Southam and (4) lives in Whitbury. Friday's traveller didn't go to Southam (5), so Ellen went on Wednesday and Bearton was visited on Friday. Fran lives in Innthorpe (2), so Gina lives in Redport and travelled on Thursday. Sandra lives in Benmoor and travelled on Friday. Gina went to Raymouth.

Thus:
Ellen, Whitbury, Southam, Wednesday;
Fran, Innthorpe, Pulbury, Tuesday;
Gina, Redport, Raymouth, Thursday;
Sandra, Benmoor, Bearton, Friday;
Wendy, Puzzleton, Tanbridge, Monday.

No 198

By elimination, the letter in 14 and 25 (clue 2) is D. The letter in 23 and 42 is G (clue 3). The letter in 1 and 37 (1) is either C or B, as is the letter in 41, so in diagonal 1-49, the C and/or B are 1 and/or 41, so 17 and/or 33 are F and/or G, thus 19 and 31 are not F or G and 6 is not C or B. In 36-42 the C and/or B are in 37 and/or 41. So, 40=D and 44=D (5). In 15-21, 20=D. In 1-7, 3=D. The letter in 31 isn't F (above), so (4) 31=E, 28=E, 38=A, 36=E. Thus 13 isn't A (7), so in 7-43, 19=A. In 15-21, 18=E and there is an E in either 5 or 6 and one in either 47 or 48, so Es in either 5 and 48 or 6 and 47, thus (6) 5=E and 48=E. If 7=F, then in 1-7, 6 isn't C or B (above), so 6=A and 1 and 2 are C or B, as is 37 (above), so in 2-44, 16=F, thus 17=G, 15=B. Then 1=C, 37=C (1), 41=B, 13=G, so (diagonal) 43 isn't G and there is nowhere for G in 1-43. Thus 7=B, 35=F, 33=G, 17=F, 16=B, 15=G, 37=C, so 1=C (1), 43=F, 13=G, 10=C, 45=G, 30=A, 2=F, 6=A, 22=A, 8=B, 11=A, 12=F, 26=C, 27=F, 47=B, 46=C, 32=B, 34=C, 41=B.

Thus:

C	F	D	G	E	A	B
B	E	C	A	F	G	D
G	B	F	E	A	D	C
A	G	B	D	C	F	E
D	A	E	B	G	C	F
E	C	A	F	D	B	G
F	D	G	C	B	E	A

No 199

No-one lost 5 sheets (grid). The woman who has lost 6 sheets hasn't lost 7 towels (clue 2), 6 towels (clue 3) or 5 towels (4), so (5) 4 towels and Trudy has lost 3 towels. The woman who has lost 3 sheets hasn't lost 7 towels (2), 6 towels (3) or 5 towels (4), so (Trudy). The woman who lost 7 towels also lost 4 sheets (2). The woman who lost 6 sheets didn't lose 6 pillowcases (5). The woman who lost 6 pillowcases isn't Trudy (2), so didn't lose 3 sheets. Thus the one who lost 6 pillowcases also lost 7 sheets (4) and the woman who lost 5 towels lost 8 sheets. By elimination, the woman who lost 7 towels also lost 6 sheets, so Sue lost 6 sheets (3). The woman who lost 12 pillowcases lost 6 sheets (1) and Lola 8 sheets. Trudy didn't lose 14 pillowcases (5), so the woman who lost 7 towels lost 8 pillowcases (2) and Trudy 10 pillowcases. By elimination, Lola lost 14 pillowcases. Sue lost the same number of sheets as the number of towels lost by Deirdre (1), so Deirdre lost 6 towels (plus 6 pillowcases, above). Mel lost 8 pillowcases (plus 4 sheets, above).

Thus (pillowcases, sheets, towels):
Deirdre, 6, 7, 6;
Lola, 14, 8, 5;
Mel, 8, 4, 7;
Sue, 12, 6, 4;
Trudy, 10, 3, 3.

Solutions

No 200 *R8J*

The couple who met at the bakery took the No 82 (clue 1) and those who met at the café took the No 61 (clue 4). Marcia took the No 53 (3). Estelle who met her boyfriend at the bus stop didn't take the No 77 (2), so No 99. The girl who met her boyfriend at 5.42 isn't Estelle (2), Marcia or Amy (3) or Colleen (5), so Daphne. The girl who met her boyfriend at 5.34 isn't Marcia or Amy (3) or Colleen (5), so Estelle. The girl who took the No 61 and met her boyfriend at the café wasn't Daphne (4) or Colleen (5), so Amy. Amy's meeting was 2 minutes before Marcia's (3) and Colleen's was 2 minutes before that at the shopping mall (5). Thus the woman at the shopping mall wasn't Marcia, so Daphne. Colleen's meeting was thus at 5.40, Marcia's at 5.38 and Amy's at 5.36. Marcia thus met her boyfriend on a street corner and Colleen was at the bakery, so Daphne took the No 77 bus.

Thus:
Amy, café, 5.36pm, No 61;
Colleen, bakery, 5.40pm, No 82;
Daphne, shopping mall, 5.42pm, No 77;
Estelle, bus stop, 5.34pm, No 99;
Marcia, street corner, 5.38pm, No 53.

No 201 *Short Stories*

No-one joined in July (grid). The woman who joined in June isn't Sara (clue 1), Cara (clue 3), Lara (4) or Tara (5), so Fara. The one who joined in September isn't Cara (3), Lara (4) or Tara (5), so Sara. The woman who bought 24 books joined in May (3) and Cara in April. Lara joined in May (4) and Fara is interested in crime, so Tara joined in August (5) and Sara is interested in wildlife. Lara's interest isn't thrillers (2) or gardening (4), so romance. No-one bought 18 books (grid), so Tara bought 12 (5) and Sara 15. The woman interested in thrillers bought 27 books (2), so she's Cara and Tara's interest is in gardening. Fara bought 21 books.

Thus:
Cara, thrillers, April, 27 books;
Fara, crime, June, 21 books;
Lara, romance, May, 24 books;
Sara, wildlife, September, 15 books;
Tara, gardening, August, 12 books.

No 202 *The Necklace*

The only possible total for £159.00 is 3 weeks at £53.00 per week, so this is owed by Mr Barber (clue 2) and a total of £160.00 is 4 weeks at £40.00 per week, which is owed by the tenant of Cracky Cottage. Miss Keele rents Dampe Cottage (clue 1). Mr Barber's £53.00 per week isn't for Mildew Cottage (1) or Sliproof Cottage (3), so Mouldy Cottage. The £50.00 per week rent isn't for Mildew Cottage (1) or Sliproof Cottage (3), so Dampe Cottage. Mrs Napier thus pays £48.00 per week (3) and the rent at Sliproof Cottage is £45.00 per week. The tenant at Sliproof Cottage isn't Mr Parkinson (3), so Mr Davis. By elimination, Mrs Napier lives at Mildew Cottage, so Mr Parkinson at Cracky Cottage.

Mr Davis owes 6 weeks' rent (3). Mrs Napier owes 8 weeks' (3), so Miss Keele 2 weeks' rent.

Thus:
Mr Barber, Mouldy Cottage, £53.00, 3 weeks;
Mr Davis, Sliproof Cottage, £45.00, 6 weeks;
Miss Keele, Dampe Cottage, £50.00, 2 weeks;
Mrs Napier, Mildew Cottage, £48.00, 8 weeks;
Mr Parkinson, Cracky Cottage, £40.00, 4 weeks.

No 203

The 164cm (shortest person) isn't the typist (clue 1), the nurse (clue 4) or the waitress (5), so the clerk and (2) the 41-year-old is 165cm. The 44-year-old isn't 167cm (1) or 166cm. The 56kg (heaviest) woman isn't 167cm or 166cm (4). She isn't 41 (4), so isn't 165cm (above), thus 164cm. The 43-year-old is thus 166cm (4) and the 42-year-old 167cm. Molly is 41 (5). Bessie weighs 54kg (2). The 50kg (lightest) woman is 43 (3), so Molly weighs 52kg and Bessie is 42. Rosa weighs 56kg (5), so she's 44 (above) and Lynne is 43. Molly is the waitress (5). Lynne (166cm, above) isn't a nurse (4), so a typist. Bessie is a nurse.

Thus:
Bessie, 42 years old, 167cm, 54kg, nurse;
Lynne, 43 years old, 166cm, 50kg, typist;
Molly, 41 years old, 165 cm, 52kg, waitress;
Rosa, 44 years old, 164cm, 56kg, clerk.

No 204 *Odyssey*

Quentin's 1st bus wasn't the No 46 or No 47 (clue 3). So Quentin's 1st was the No 48 (clue 2), Stella's 2nd was the No 48, Stella's 1st was the No 49 and whoever got off the No 47 took the No 49 2nd. Jasmine's 2nd was the No 46 (3). Claire's 2nd was the No 49 (1). The person who took the No 46 1st isn't Norman or Pete (4), so Theresa. Norman's 1st wasn't the No 54 (4), so the No 52, Pete's 2nd was the No 54, thus his 1st was the No 56 and the No 56 was Norman's 2nd. Jasmine's was thus the No 54. Theresa's 2nd wasn't the No 47 (1), so the No 52. Quentin's 2nd was the No 47.

Thus:
Claire, No 47, No 49;
Jasmine, No 54, No 46;
Norman, No 52, No 56;
Pete, No 56, No 54;
Quentin, No 48, No 47;
Stella, No 49, No 48;
Theresa, No 46, No 52.

No 205 *The Necklace*

The lilac coat was bought by the woman whose old coat was either beige or brown (clue 4), so the woman who bought boots bought the yellow coat (clue 1). The woman with the lime green coat bought either gloves or a handbag (3), so the one who bought a scarf has the royal blue coat (5) and had either a brown or rust coat; thus (2) it was brown. The lilac coat was bought by the woman whose coat was beige (4). Tina's old coat was thus black (6) and she bought yellow. Lydia bought

308

Solutions

shoes or a handbag (7), thus not the royal blue coat (scarf, above). So her new coat is scarlet (7) and her old one rust. The woman with a grey coat thus bought lime green. Myrna's old coat was beige or brown (3), so Evelyn the lime green coat. Angelina bought gloves or a handbag (2), so Myrna bought the scarf. Angelina's coat was beige, so Lydia bought the shoes. Angelina bought the gloves (3) and Evelyn the handbag.

Thus:

Angelina, beige, lilac, gloves;
Evelyn, grey, lime green, handbag;
Lydia, rust, scarlet, shoes;
Myrna, brown, royal blue, scarf;
Tina, black, yellow, boots.

No 206 *Gift of Magi/The Necklace*

Clarice and Melanie served in consecutively visited shops (clue 2), so either Clarice works in Fletcher's (5) or she sold the washing machine. Thus the woman who sold the fridge in Metson's (1) is Melanie. The assistant in Electrique is thus Clarice (4) and Luke sold the microwave. Clarice sold the washing machine (5). Johnnie didn't sell the freezer (3), so the dishwasher. Philip sold the freezer and (1) works for Walter & Co. Metson's was visited before the shop which sold the microwave (1), which thus isn't Fletcher's (5), so Brand & Co. Fletcher's sold the dishwasher. Fletcher's was visited immediately before Metson's (5), which was visited immediately before Electrique. So (1) Walter & Co was visited 1st, Fletcher's 2nd, Metson's 3rd, Electrique 4th and Brand & Son 5th.

Thus:

Brand & Son, 5th, Luke, microwave;
Electrique, 4th, Clarice, washing machine;
Fletcher's, 2nd, Johnnie, dishwasher;
Metson's, 3rd, Melanie, fridge;
Walter & Co, 1st, Philip, freezer.

No 207

The bathroom tap was fixed on Thursday (clue 5), so the bathroom pipe on Wednesday (clue 2) and the kitchen pipe on Monday, by (4) Arnold. Mrs Walsh's boiler wasn't fixed on Tuesday (6), so the kitchen tap was fixed on Tuesday, by (1) Kevin. The boiler was thus fixed on Friday, so (2) Mr Shaw's call-out was on Thursday. Monday's wasn't Mr Timson's (3) or Mr Richards' (7), so Mrs Yale's. Bill didn't see Mr Timson or Mr Richards (7), so Mr Shaw and Mr Richards' call was on Wednesday. Mr Timson's was on Tuesday. Stephen visited on Wednesday (4) and Roger on Friday.

Thus:

Mr Richards, Stephen, bathroom pipe, Wednesday;
Mr Shaw, Bill, bathroom tap, Thursday;
Mr Timson, Kevin, kitchen tap, Tuesday;
Mrs Walsh, Roger, boiler, Friday;
Mrs Yale, Arnold, kitchen pipe, Monday.

No 208

Cards total 88 (intro), so the 3 is missing. Cards I, J, K and L don't include the king (clue 3), so to total 42 (clue 1) I is the 9, J the 10, K the jack and L the queen. F is the king (3). K is either a club or a spade (5), as are cards A, C and I (intro). B isn't a heart (4), so a diamond, as is L (intro) and D and J are hearts. B thus isn't the 4 (2), so (4) it's the 2 and C is the ace. F (king) isn't a spade (3), so (intro) it's a club and H is a spade. The 4 of hearts is next to and left of a club (2), so it's E. G is a diamond (intro). Card I isn't a club (2), so I and C are spades (intro) and A and K are clubs. D is the 8, A is the 7 and G is the 5 (5), so H is the 6.

Thus:

7C 2D AS 8H
4H KC 5D 6S
9S 10H JC QD

No 209

The woman with the grey car brought flowers (clue 2) and the one with the silver car brought a scarf (clue 3). Dawn's car is red (6), so Mattie whose car isn't white brought chocolates (1) and has a black car. Dawn didn't bring soap (6), so a book and the driver of the white car brought soap. The 1st to arrive brought soap and wasn't Katie (3) or Patsy (4), so Fran. Katie didn't bring the scarf (3), so flowers. Patsy brought the scarf. Patsy arrived earlier than Katie (3), thus (4) Patsy was 3rd and Dawn 2nd. Mattie wasn't 4th (5) and Katie 5th.

Thus:

Dawn, 2nd, red, book;
Fran, 1st, white, scented soap;
Katie, 5th, grey, flowers;
Mattie, 4th, black, chocolates;
Patsy, 3rd, silver, scarf.

No 210

Wilma received one more card than Stephanie (clue 2) and one fewer card than someone (clue 4), so Wilma got 14 cards. Stephanie got 13 cards (2). Marian got 15 cards and 16 parcels (1), so got one more parcel than Valerie (4), who thus got 15 parcels. The woman with 13 invitations wasn't Marian (1), Wilma (2), Stephanie or Jane (3), so Valerie. Thus Wilma didn't get one fewer than Valerie (2), so got 16 invitations. Stephanie got 12 invitations (3) and Valerie got one more parcel than Jane, who thus got 14 parcels. Wilma got 12 parcels (2) and Stephanie 13. Marian didn't get 17 invitations (2), so 19 and Jane got 17. Jane didn't get 17 cards (5), so 18. Valerie got 17 cards.

Thus (cards, invitations, parcels):

Jane, 18, 17, 14;
Marian, 15, 19, 16;
Stephanie, 13, 12, 13;
Valerie, 17, 13, 15;
Wilma, 14, 16, 12.

Solutions

No 211

Wednesday's shopper bought a tea-cosy (clue 4) and Monday's shopper paid £1.50 for an umbrella (clue 5). Tuesday's shopper didn't buy a table-lamp (2) or a book (3), so a jacket. Moira who spent £2.25 shopped either on Wednesday and the table-lamp was bought on Thursday (2) or on Thursday and the table-lamp was bought on Friday; ie Thursday's shopper was either Moira or the person who bought the table-lamp. Caroline who bought a book for £1.75 (3), thus shopped on Friday, the table-lamp was bought on Thursday and Moira shopped on Wednesday. The woman who spent £2.00 bought the table-lamp (3), so the jacket was £1.25. Patricia shopped on Thursday and Sandra on Tuesday (1), so Thelma shopped on Monday.

Thus:

Caroline, Friday, book, £1.75;
Moira, Wednesday, tea-cosy, £2.25;
Patricia, Thursday, table-lamp, £2.00;
Sandra, Tuesday, jacket, £1.25;
Thelma, Monday, umbrella, £1.50.

No 212

The woman born in 1932 has a granddaughter born in 1982 (clue 3), so Bryony was born in 1977 and her grandmother in 1933 (clue 1). Trish's grandmother was born in 1943 (2). Lucy's grandmother is Alison (6) who was thus born in 1942 and Penny's grandmother was born in 1932. Thus Melissa's grandmother was born in 1944. No granddaughter was born in 1979 (grid), thus Sharon's granddaughter born in 1978 (5) isn't Trish (2), so Melissa. Tracey's isn't Penny or Trish (2), so Bryony and Trish was born in 1976, thus Lucy in 1981. Eloise wasn't born in 1943 (4), so 1932 and Margaret in 1943.

Thus:

Alison, 1942, Lucy, 1981;
Eloise, 1932, Penny, 1982;
Margaret, 1943, Trish, 1976;
Sharon, 1944, Melissa, 1978;
Tracey, 1933, Bryony, 1977.

No 213 *Think you Ma'm*

Jasper's delay was due to the truck breakdown (clue 1) and Errol's to a landslide (clue 2). Angela's wasn't due to black ice (1) or cattle (4), so a car accident. The 8.15 announcement didn't cover the delay caused to Jasper (1), Errol (2), Angela (4) or Hazel (5), so Dermot. Hazel's delay was 16 minutes (5). The 14-minute delay wasn't Errol's or Dermot's (2) or Angela's (4), so Jasper's. The 7.30 announcement wasn't about black ice (1), a landslide (2), a car accident (3) or cattle (4), so the truck breakdown and (1) the 8.00 announcement concerned black ice. Thus Hazel's delay was due to black ice and Dermot's to cattle. Dermot's delay was 11 minutes (4) and Angela's 12 minutes, so Errol's was 17 minutes. He didn't hear the 7.55 announcement (6), so Errol heard the one at 7.45 and Angela heard the 7.55 announcement.

Thus:

Angela, 7.55am, car accident, 12 minutes;
Dermot, 8.15am, cattle, 11 minutes;
Errol, 7.45am, landslide, 17 minutes;
Hazel, 8.00am, black ice, 16 minutes;
Jasper, 7.30am, truck breakdown, 14 minutes.

No 214

A	C	B	C	B	A
C	B	A	B	C	A
A	B	C	A	C	B
C	A	B	B	A	C
B	C	A	C	A	B
B	A	C	A	B	C

No 215 *Short stories*

The person who leaves at 3.45 (latest) isn't Marc (clue 1), Benny or Samantha (clue 2), so Rachel (3) and Harold leaves at 3.25. Benny leaves at 3.15 and Samantha at 3.20 (2), so Marc leaves at 3.35 and (1) Rachel reads the *Independent*. No-one arrives at 2.00, so Rachel doesn't arrive at 1.30 (3). The person who arrives at 1.30 doesn't read the *Telegraph* (1), *Times*, (2) or *Guardian* (4), so the *Mirror* and the *Guardian* reader arrives at 1.45. Rachel arrives at 2.30 and Harold at 3.00. Marc arrives at 1.45 (1) and the *Telegraph* reader at 2.15. By elimination, Harold reads the *Times*, so Benny arrives at 2.15 (2) and Samantha at 1.30.

Thus:

Benny, 2.15pm, 3.15pm, *Puzzleton Telegraph*;
Harold, 3.00pm, 3.25pm, *Puzzleton Times*;
Marc, 1.45pm, 3.35pm, *Puzzleton Guardian*;
Rachel, 2.30pm, 3.45pm, *Puzzleton Independent*;
Samantha, 1.30pm, 3.20pm, *Puzzleton Mirror*.

No 216

Five numbers are multiples of E: D (clue 2), I (clue 9), J (10), K (11) and T (13) so E is either 2 or 3. Six numbers are multiples of B: A (1), G (3), Y (7), K (11), M (12) and V (14), so B is also 2 or 3. Thus K=6 (11), C=4 and X=24 (4) and W=16 (5). F=5, O=25 (6), and H=20 (8). A and T are (1 and 13) 8 and/or 12, so (9) I=18 and E=3 so B=2. A=8 (1), D=15 (2), T=12 (13), V=10 (14), Q=7 and J=21 (10), and Y=14 (7). By elimination, G and M are 22 and/or 26 (12 and 3) and P and N are 11 and/or 13. So (15) M=26; and Z and U are 17 and/or 9. N=13 (12), P=11 and G=22 (3). Z=17 (16), R=1 and L=19; and U=9 (15). By elimination, S=23.

Thus:

A=8; B=2; C=4; D=15; E=3; F=5; G=22; H=20; I=18; J=21; K=6; L=19; M=26; N=13; O=25; P=11; Q=7; R=1; S=23; T=12; U=9; V=10; W=16; X=24; Y=14; Z=17.

Solutions

No 217 *The Necklace?*

Cliff holidayed in either India or Majorca (clue 3), so the man who lost his camera in either Egypt or Japan (clue 1) is Vincent and (3) Cliff lost his binoculars. Emile lost his house keys (2). Cliff didn't go to Thailand (3), so the man who went to Thailand lost his sunglasses (4). Emile drank cola or wine (2), so (5) Jess drank lager. Vincent drank cola (1), so Emile drank wine. The man who went to Thailand isn't Jess (5), so Sean. Jess lost a book. Sean didn't drink pale ale (4), so whisky. Cliff drank pale ale. Jess didn't holiday in Egypt (5), so Emile (house keys, above) went to Egypt. Vincent went to Japan (1). Jess went to Majorca (5), so Cliff went to India.

Thus:
Cliff, pale ale, India, binoculars;
Emile, wine, Egypt, house keys;
Jess, lager, Majorca, book;
Sean, whisky, Thailand, sunglasses;
Vincent, cola, Japan, camera.

No 218

Edward at No 5 isn't married to Janet (clue 5), Rhoda or Tessa (clue 6) or Cecily (4), so Vera. Arthur doesn't live at No 9 (4), so Tessa lives at No 6 (2) and Arthur at No 8. Cecily lives at No 9 (4). Mr & Mrs Donaldson live at No 6 (1) and Gordon is at No 7. Colin is at No 9 (3) and Rhoda at No 7. Ivan is at No 6 and Janet is at No 8. Janet's surname is O'Connor (5). Rhoda's isn't Paige or Vine (3), so King. Colin's isn't Paige (3), so Vine and Edward is Mr Paige.

Thus:
Arthur, Janet, O'Connor, No 8;
Colin, Cecily, Vine, No 9;
Edward, Vera, Paige, No 5;
Gordon, Rhoda, King, No 7;
Ivan, Tessa, Donaldson, No 6.

No 219

The card called 6th has a value five higher than that called 14th (clue 2) and is directly next to and right of a card which isn't a club. If card E was called 6th, then (clue 2) D was 4th, which isn't possible (clue 3). So card L was 6th (2), K 4th and N 14th. The 15th (last) card called (3) was either A or I, so the only remaining possibility for the 9th, 10th, 1st and 2nd sequence in clue 1 is that B was 9th, F 10th, M 1st and C 2nd. Since A or I was called 15th (above), O was called 12th (4), H 8th and J 13th. Card E was 3rd (3), D 5th and G 7th. Card I wasn't 11th (4), so 15th. Card A was thus called 11th.

Thus:
1st M, 2nd C, 3rd E, 4th K, 5th D, 6th L, 7th G, 8th H, 9th B, 10th F, 11th A, 12th O, 13th J, 14th N, 15th I.

No 220 *Secret Life Walter Mitty*

The 0900 flight was from gate 16, but not on Friday (clue 2). Flight BB63 from gate 6 wasn't at 1130 (clue 3), so 0930 and Friday's was at 0800. NE33 was at 0900 (1) and the gate 14 flight at 0800. The 1130 departed from gate 4 (4), so the 0730 from gate 9. KB19 left at 0800 (4) and DF46 at 0730 (5). The 1130 flight was taken on Thursday (4) and was CL12, so that on Wednesday departed from gate 6. Monday's left from gate 16 (2) and Tuesday's from gate 9.

Thus:
Monday, NE33, 0900 hours, gate 16;
Tuesday, DF46, 0730 hours, gate 9;
Wednesday, BB63, 0930 hours, gate 6;
Thursday, CL12, 1130 hours, gate 4;
Friday, KB19, 0800 hours, gate 14.

No 221

4	3	2	5	6	1
8	1	4	1	7	2
3	9	2	6	3	7
8	7	6	5	4	3
4	5	8	7	6	9
1	9	2	9	8	5

No 222

Remember throughout that each woman has relatives of three different ages (intro). Veronique's nephew isn't 15 or 17 (clue 2), so 20 (clue 3), Brenda's daughter is 21 and Katrina's nephew is either 22 or 23. Nell's niece is 17 (2) and Selina's daughter is 16. The woman whose nephew is 15 isn't Selina (1) or Brenda (4), so Nell. The woman whose nephew is 17 isn't Selina (1), so Brenda and (4) Veronique's niece is 15. Selina's nephew is 22 (1) and Veronique's daughter is 23. By elimination, Katrina's nephew is 23. Brenda's niece is 20 (5) and Katrina's daughter is 19. Thus Katrina's niece is 22 (5), Selina's niece is 18 and Nell's daughter is 20 years old.

Thus (daughter, nephew, niece):
Brenda, 21, 17, 20;
Katrina, 19, 23, 22;
Nell, 20, 15, 17;
Selina, 16, 22, 18;
Veronique, 23, 20, 15.

No 223

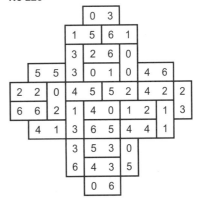

311

Solutions

No 224

Don went to the ABC (clue 1) and Giles to the Palace (clue 2). The Clara Bow film was at the Roxy (4) and the Lillian Gish film was at the Plaza, so Ted saw the Pearl White film (2) at the Gaiety. Ted went on the 18th (5), so Giles on the 20th (2). Virginia went on the 12th (1). The Lillian Gish film wasn't on the 12th (4), so Virginia saw the Clara Bow film and Lynne went to the Plaza. The Charlie Chaplin film wasn't seen by Don (3), so Giles and Don saw the Buster Keaton film. Don didn't go on the 14th (6), so the 16th and Lynne went on the 14th.

Thus:

Don, Buster Keaton, ABC cinema, 16th;
Giles, Charlie Chaplin, Palace cinema, 20th;
Lynne, Lillian Gish, Plaza cinema, 14th;
Ted, Pearl White, Gaeity cinema, 18th;
Virginia, Clara Bow, Roxy cinema, 12th.

No 225

Mrs Flinders spent 10 cents less than Anthea George (clue 3), so Mrs Flinders isn't Coral (10 cents less than Venetia, clue 4) or Lucinda (10 cents less than Mrs Connolly, 5). Nor is Mrs Flinders Venetia (4), so Mrs Flinders is Imogen. Coral spent 10 cents less than Venetia (4) and Lucinda spent 10 cents less than Mrs Connolly (5), so Venetia isn't Mrs Connolly. Thus Coral is Mrs Connolly. The woman who spent €21.92 (least) is thus either Lucinda (5 and above) or Imogen Flinders (3). If Lucinda spent €21.92, then Coral spent €22.02 (5) and Venetia €22.12 (4), so (3) Anthea €22.32 and Imogen €22.22. But Mrs Flinders didn't spend €22.22. Thus Imogen spent €21.92, Anthea €22.02 (3), Lucinda €22.12, Coral €22.22 (5) and Venetia €22.32. Lucinda's surname isn't Hobart (1), so Feighan. Venetia is Mrs Hobart. Coral was served immediately after Imogen (2) who was served immediately after Anthea (3); thus Lucinda was served immediately after Coral (5), so the 1st woman in the queue was either Anthea or Venetia. Venetia spent €22.32 (above), so wasn't 1st (1). Thus Anthea was 1st, Imogen 2nd, Coral 3rd, Lucinda 4th and Venetia 5th.

Thus:

1st, Anthea, George, €22.02;
2nd, Imogen, Flinders, €21.92;
3rd, Coral, Connolly, €22.22;
4th, Lucinda, Feighan, €22.12;
5th, Venetia, Hobart, €22.32.

No 226

In the diagonal 7-43, the D isn't in piece 19 (clue 1), so (by elimination) 13=D and 19=A, thus 1=A (clue 1). In column 5-47 the D isn't in 47 (3), so 40=D; and the C isn't in 47 (3), so 33=C. Piece 24=D (3 and above). In 7-49, 49=D. In 15-21, 18=D. In 5-47 pieces 5 and 47 are F and/or E, thus the letter in piece 4 is F or E (3). So in row 1-7, pieces 3 and 6 contain B and/or G. Thus 43=G and 3=G (2), so 6=B. By elimination, 17=E, thus 31=F, 10=C and 45=B. In diagonal 7-43, 37=E, thus (6)

5=E, 4=F, 47=F (3), 44=C and 46=E. Pieces 11 and 35 contain either G or A (4). Thus in 7-49, 42=B; and in 4-46, 39=C. So 36=F, 41=G, 20=C, 8=E, 15=B, 22=C and 16=G. In 1-49, 9=F. Piece 23=A, 30=B, 28=E, 27=F and 34=E. Piece 32 isn't G (7), so 32=A, thus 11=G, 35=G and 14=A.

Thus:

A	D	G	F	E	B	C
E	F	C	G	B	D	A
B	G	E	D	A	C	F
C	A	D	B	G	F	E
D	B	F	A	C	E	G
F	E	A	C	D	G	B
G	C	B	E	F	A	D

No 227

The old Volgeot was exchanged for a new Daevo (clue 4). The new Dathall was bought at 3.00 but not in exchange for a Daevo (clue 3), or a Dathall (intro) or a Peutsun (2.00, 7), so an old Vauxwoo. The person who bought a new Peutsun didn't have an old Dathall (5) or Peutsun (intro), so an old Daevo. This person is a man (5), but not Mr Malone or Mr Hudson (2), so Mr Bailey. Mr Malone bought a new Vauxwoo (2). Mrs Taylor called at 5.00 (1). The one who bought the new Dathall at 3.00 (3) isn't Miss Jarvis (6), so Mr Hudson. Mr Malone called at 4.00 (2), so Mr Bailey at 1.00 and (by elimination) Miss Jarvis at 2.00. Thus Miss Jarvis bought the new Volgeot, Mrs Taylor bought the new Daevo and Mr Malone part-exchanged the old Dathall.

Thus:

Mr Bailey, 1.00pm, Daevo, Peutsun;
Mr Hudson, 3.00pm, Vauxwoo, Dathall;
Miss Jarvis, 2.00pm, Peutsun, Volgeot;
Mr Malone, 4.00pm, Dathall, Vauxwoo.
Mrs Taylor, 5.00pm, Volgeot, Daevo.

No 228

The 7.00 wake-up call wasn't requested by the person in room 107 (clue 3) and no-one had room 105 (grid), so the 7.00 call was requested by the person in room 103 (clue 2) and Mr Kane had room 107. His call was for 6.15 (4), so (3) Mrs Ivy's was for 7.00. Miss Jones asked for a call at 6.30 (1) and Mr Headley at 6.45, so Mr Loxley wanted the 6.00 call. No-one arrived at 5.35 (grid). The person who arrived at 5.30 didn't have room 109 (2), 103 (3), 107 or 101 (4), so 111. Either Mr Loxley arrived at 5.45 and Mrs Ivy at 5.40 (2) or Mr Loxley arrived at 5.50 and Mrs Ivy at 5.45, ie the person who arrived at 5.45 is Mr Loxley or Mrs Ivy. Mr Loxley's room wasn't 109 (2) or 111 (5.30, above), so 101. Mr Loxley arrived earlier than both the person in room 109 (2) and Mr Kane (4) who was in room 107 (above). Thus Mr Loxley arrived at 5.45, Mrs Ivy at 5.40 (2), Mr Kane at 5.50 and the person in 109 at 5.55. Mr Headley didn't arrive at 5.30 (1), so 5.55 (room 109, above) and Miss Jones was in room 111.

Solutions

Thus:
Room 101, Mr Loxley, 5.45pm, 6.00am;
Room 103, Mrs Ivy, 5.40pm, 7.00am;
Room 107, Mr Kane, 5.50pm, 6.15am;
Room 109, Mr Headley, 5.55pm, 6.45am;
Room 111, Miss Jones, 5.30pm, 6.30am.

No 229

Remember throughout that each woman now has a hat and scarf of the same colour as her gloves. Helga gave her hat to Brenda (clue 2) and Jenny gave her hat to Josephine (clue 6). Diane didn't give her hat to Jenny (3), so to Helga. Helga's scarf was white (1). The owner of yellow gloves had a pink hat (4) and the owner of pink gloves had a yellow hat but not a turquoise scarf (4), so cream or white. If white (Helga, above) then Brenda had the pink hat and (above) has yellow gloves. But then it's Brenda (rather than Diane, above) who gave Helga her hat. So the owner of the pink gloves had a cream scarf and yellow hat. The owner of yellow gloves (who gave a pink hat, 4) had a turquoise or white scarf. If white (Helga, above) then Brenda (2) has pink gloves and gave a yellow hat; but then it's Brenda rather than Diane (above) who gave Helga her hat. Thus the owner of the yellow gloves gave a turquoise scarf and Brenda has cream gloves. Helga's gloves are turquoise, so Diane gave the turquoise hat (3). By elimination, Diane's gloves are white and Brenda gave the white hat. Brenda's scarf wasn't pink (2), so yellow. Diane's scarf was pink, as was Jenny's hat (6). Josephine's gloves are pink (6), so Jenny's are yellow.

Thus (gloves, hat, scarf):
Diane, white, turquoise, pink;
Brenda, cream, white, yellow;
Helga, turquoise, cream, white;
Jenny, yellow, pink, turquoise;
Josephine, pink, yellow, cream.

No 230

Baines had 45% in the 3rd poll (clue 4), so Baines had 46% and Hobbs 49% in the 2nd (clue 3), thus Baines had 43% and Hobbs 41% in the 1st poll. Baines got 47% in the 5th poll (5), so 40% in the 4th. The 1st poll either surveyed 120 and the 4th 125 (1) or the 1st surveyed 125 and the 4th 130, ie the sample of 125 was in either the 1st or 4th poll. Thus the 3rd sampled 130 (4), the 4th 125 and the 1st 120. Thus the 5th sampled 110 (2) and the 2nd 140. Hobbs had 44% in the 4th poll (4) where the difference was thus 4% (Baines had 40%, above). So the 5th poll (Baines had 47%, above) didn't show Hobbs (1) on 42% (a 5% difference). Thus Hobbs had 48% in the 5th poll and 42% in the 3rd.

Thus (Baines, Hobbs):
1st poll, 120 students, 43%, 41%;
2nd poll, 140 students, 46%, 49%;
3rd poll, 130 students, 45%, 42%;
4th poll, 125 students, 40%, 44%;
5th poll, 110 students, 47%, 48%.

No 231

Sid's wife is Hilary (clue 6). Heidi moved to the town that Camilla moved from (clue 5) and Crispin moved to the town that Daisy moved from (3), so Heidi's husband isn't Crispin. Gus moved to Baywood (1). Heidi moved to Fishbrook and her husband isn't Jeremy (5), so Benjamin. Crispin's wife isn't Daisy or Shirley (3), so Camilla who (5) moved from Fishbrook. Jeremy moved from Baywood (1). Crispin moved to the town Daisy moved from (3), so Jeremy's wife isn't Daisy. Thus Jeremy's wife is Shirley and Daisy's husband is Gus. Benjamin and Heidi didn't move from Crowville (2) or Edgeburgh (4), so Dawston. Sid didn't move from Crowville (6), so Edgeburgh. Thus Gus moved from Crowville and (3) Crispin moved to Crowville. By elimination, Jeremy moved to Edgeburgh and Sid moved to Dawston.

Thus:
Benjamin, Heidi, Dawston, Fishbrook;
Crispin, Camilla, Fishbrook, Crowville;
Gus, Daisy, Crowville, Baywood;
Jeremy, Shirley, Baywood, Edgeburgh;
Sid, Hilary, Edgeburgh, Dawston.

No 232

Olive has red shorts (clue 4). Joanne has a blue jumper but not a white skirt (clue 1), blue or white trousers (5), so a blue skirt. Joanne hasn't red or white shoes (6), so white trainers (7) and the woman with white shoes has a white skirt. The latter isn't Pauline (3). Pauline isn't wearing blue trousers (3), so white trousers plus (5) either a red or white jacket. The woman with white shoes and a white skirt (above) isn't wearing a jacket (5), so (6) a white jumper. Thus she isn't Isabel, so Sylvia. Olive isn't wearing a red jacket or white jacket (5), so a blue cardigan. Olive isn't wearing red boots (4) or red shoes (6), so blue trainers. Pauline isn't wearing red shoes (3), so red boots; thus she isn't wearing a white jacket (6), so a red jacket. By elimination, Isabel has a white jacket, blue trousers and red shoes.

Thus:
Isabel, white jacket, blue trousers, red shoes;
Olive, blue cardigan, red shorts, blue trainers;
Joanne, blue jumper, blue skirt, white trainers;
Pauline, red jacket, white trousers, red boots;
Sylvia, white jumper, white skirt, white shoes.

No 233

The Revd King is planning a Sunday school (clue 1) and Revd Ogden has a congregation of 64 (clue 4). The preacher with a congregation of 42 who is planning a youth club isn't the Revd Linton (6) or the Revd Marsh of St Stephen's (7), so he's the Revd Nairn. Bible classes are planned at St Paul's (4), but not by the Revd Ogden, so the Revd Linton. St Luke's has a congregation of 86 (3), so (by elimination) its rector is the Revd King. The Revd Marsh has a congregation of 75 (7) and the Revd Linton has 53. The crèche isn't planned for All Saints' or St Anthony's (2), so St

Solutions

Stephen's. The mothers' group will be at St Anthony's (5) and the youth club at All Saints'.
Thus:
All Saints', Revd Nairn, youth club, 42 people;
St Anthony's, Revd Ogden, Mothers' group, 64 people;
St Luke's, Revd King, Sunday school, 86 people;
St Paul's, Revd Linton, bible classes, 53 people;
St Stephen's, Revd Marsh, crèche, 75 people.

No 234
The celebrity surnamed Westwood donated boots (clue 1), the one surnamed Rushmore donated jeans and Kate donated stockings (clue 2). Tom Adamson (3) didn't give the shirt, so a teddy bear. Judy is in *Bet You Can't!* and didn't give the boots (1). The star of *The Love Match* gave a shirt (3), so Judy gave jeans. The one surnamed Stein is in *Joking Apart* (4), so (by elimination) gave stockings and the person surnamed Jackson gave a shirt. The latter isn't Sindy (5), so Adam and Sindy's surname is Westwood. She isn't in *Wild Wanders* (5), so *House Huntin'*. Tom is in *Wild Wanders*.
Thus:
Adam, Jackson, *The Love Match*, shirt;
Judy, Rushmore, *Bet You Can't!*, jeans;
Kate, Stein, *Joking Apart*, stockings;
Sindy, Westwood, *House Huntin'*, boots;
Tom, Adamson, *Wild Wanders*, teddy bear.

No 235 Odyssey Homecoming
The man arriving on Monday is landing at Stanwick (clue 1) and Joe is coming back on Tuesday (clue 5). The man landing at Gatrow will arrive the day before the man from Ecuador (4), who thus isn't Joe (day after Stanwick). George has been to Dubai (2). The man from Austria isn't landing on Tuesday (3) and Joe hasn't been to Canada (6), so to Barbados. The man from Austria is landing at Luchester (3). Joe isn't landing at Mansted or Heathton (5), so Gatrow. The man from Ecuador will land on Wednesday (4), so (3) he's Patrick and the man from Austria will arrive on Friday. Dave hasn't been to Canada (6), so Austria. Simon has been to Canada. Patrick isn't landing at Heathton (5), so Mansted. Simon is returning on Monday (7), so George on Thursday.
Thus:
Dave, Austria, Luchester, Friday;
George, Dubai, Heathton, Thursday;
Joe, Barbados, Gatrow, Tuesday;
Patrick, Ecuador, Mansted, Wednesday;
Simon, Canada, Stanwick, Monday.

No 236
No-one lives at No 15 or No 19 (grid). The woman at No 14 doesn't hate cooking or cleaning windows (clue 1), dusting (clue 2) or vacuuming (6), so ironing. Mrs Dean lives at No 16 (4), so Mrs White lives at No 14 (5) and the woman who loves cooking is at No 18. Mrs Frost who hates cooking lives at No 17 (1) and

the woman who hates cleaning windows is at No 18. Mrs Dean loves ironing and hates dusting (2), so the woman at No 20 hates vacuuming. Since Mrs Frost hates cooking, Mrs Browne doesn't love cooking (3), so she doesn't live at No 18. Thus Mrs Browne is at No 20 and Mrs Davis at No 18. Mrs Browne loves cleaning windows (3). Mrs Frost loves vacuuming (3), so Mrs White loves dusting.
Thus:
No 14, Mrs White, dusting, ironing;
No 16, Mrs Dean, ironing, dusting;
No 17, Mrs Frost, vacuuming, cooking;
No 18, Mrs Davis, cooking, windows;
No 20, Mrs Browne, windows, vacuuming.

No 237 The Necklace
The woman who shopped on Saturday didn't spend $320 or $380 (clue 2) and the one who shopped on Sunday didn't spend $380. The one who spent $380 shopped the day before whoever spent $330 (clue 4) and the day after whoever spent $320. Thus the Sunday shopper didn't spend $320 or $330 so (2) Saturday's spend wasn't $330 or $340. Tuesday's spend wasn't of $320 or $380 (3). Thus $380 was spent on Thursday (4), $330 on Friday and $320 on Wednesday. The $370 spend wasn't on Saturday (2) or Tuesday (3), so Monday. The woman who shopped the day before Bernadette spent $40 more than Bernadette (5), so Bernadette didn't spend $330 ($370 was spent on Monday and $330 Friday, above). If Bernadette spent $340, then the $380 spend was the day before the $340 (5). But (above) $380 was spent on Thursday and $330 on Friday. So Bernadette spent $320 and (5) $360 was spent on Tuesday. Thus $350 was spent on Saturday and (2) $340 on Sunday. Kirsty shopped on Monday (2) and Cassie on Thursday (3). Geraldine spent less than Susan (1), but more than Lois, so (3) Joyce shopped on Tuesday and Susan spent $350. Geraldine thus shopped on Sunday and Lois on Friday.
Thus:
Bernadette, Wednesday, $320;
Cassie, Thursday, $380;
Geraldine, Sunday, $340;
Joyce, Tuesday, $360;
Kirsty, Monday, $370;
Lois, Friday, $330;
Susan, Saturday, $350.

No 238
C	C	A	B	B	A
A	B	C	A	B	C
B	B	A	A	C	C
B	A	B	C	C	A
A	C	B	C	A	B
C	A	C	B	A	B

No 239
Penelope gave lilies (clue 3) and Rob gave roses (clue 4). The person who gave theatre tickets and

Solutions

carnations isn't Quentin or Tina (1), so Sean. The one who gave asters and wine isn't Tina (3), so Quentin. Tina gave freesias. Rob called on Monday (4). Either Quentin called on Thursday and Sean on Friday (1) or Quentin called on Friday and Sean on Saturday, ie Friday's caller was either Quentin or Sean. So the biscuits were given on Monday (5) and the bracelet on Tuesday. The bracelet wasn't given by Penelope (2), so Tina. Penelope gave chocolates and (6) didn't call on Saturday, so Thursday. Thus Quentin called on Friday (1) and Sean on Saturday.

Thus:

Monday, Rob, roses, biscuits;
Tuesday, Tina, freesias, bracelet;
Thursday, Penelope, lilies, chocolates;
Friday, Quentin, asters, wine;
Saturday, Sean, carnations, theatre tickets.

No 240 RtJ

The woman in blue who left at 9.50 took longest to get to the church (clue 4), so Audrey left at 10.20 (1) and the woman who left at 10.15 took the shortest time and arrived at 10.25, so took 10 minutes. Joan took more than half an hour (2), so didn't get to the church at 10.10. Thus Constance in cream arrived at 10.10 (2) and Joan in turquoise at 10.45. The woman in blue (4) didn't arrive at 10.10 (after 10 minutes) and the shortest travel time was 10 minutes (above), so the woman who left at 10.05 didn't arrive at 10.10. Thus the woman who left at 9.55 arrived at 10.10. Joan thus left at 10.05 (and took 40 minutes). Audrey's dress wasn't pink (1), so lemon. Gail's wasn't blue (3), so Melanie wore blue and Gail pink. Gail left at 10.15. Melanie didn't arrive at 10.40 (4), so 10.35 and Audrey arrived at 10.40.

Thus:

Audrey, 10.20am, 10.40am, lemon;
Constance, 9.55am, 10.10am, cream;
Gail, 10.15am, 10.25am, pink;
Joan, 10.05am, 10.45am, turquoise;
Melanie, 9.50am, 10.35am, blue.

No 241

Olivia's surname is Marchant (clue 2) and Ellen went to Oregon (clue 3), so the woman (1) surnamed Jenkins who went to Idaho is Carla who (3) also went to Maine. Ellen's surname isn't Richards or Thomkins (3), so Underwood. Joseph's isn't Thomkins (5), so Richards and Martin's is Thomkins. Martin went to Virginia (4). Olivia didn't go to New Hampshire or Florida (2), so Georgia. The person who went to both Florida and Washington (2) is Joseph. Ellen went to New Hampshire. Olivia didn't go to Nevada (6), so California. Martin went to Nevada.

Thus:

Ellen, Underwood, New Hampshire, Oregon;
Joseph, Richards, Florida, Washington;
Carla, Jenkins, Maine, Idaho;
Martin, Thomkins, Virginia, Nevada;
Olivia, Marchant, Georgia, California.

No 242

The person who found 13 cans isn't Seamus, Fran or Moira (clue 2) or Gina (clue 5), so Kenny (3) and Nigel found 10. Nigel found 2 more bottles than Moira (3) and 2 fewer than Gina (1). Fran found twice as many packets as Gina found bottles (1), so Gina didn't find 6 bottles, thus Nigel didn't find 4. So Nigel found 6 bottles, Moira 4 (3), Gina 8 bottles and Fran 16 packets. Fran found 9 cans and Moira 7 (2). Seamus counted 8 cans and Fran 7 bottles (2), so Gina found 12 cans and 10 packets (5). Moira counted 18 packets and Kenny 14 (3), so Nigel 8 (4) and Seamus 6 packets. Kenny found 3 bottles (3) and Seamus 2 bottles.

Thus (bottles, cans, packets):

Fran, 7, 9, 16;
Gina, 8, 12, 10;
Kenny, 3, 13, 14;
Moira, 4, 7, 18;
Nigel, 6, 10, 8;
Seamus, 2, 8, 6.

No 243

Cards total 82 (intro), so the 9 is missing. Card D is a spade (clue 1), so B and L are clubs (intro) and J is a spade. C isn't a diamond (clue 1), so C and I are hearts (intro) and A and K are diamonds. Thus card I is the 2 (4), E is the 10 and A is the 3. The jack of clubs (5) is thus G, C is the 8 and D is the king. E is a spade (intro). Thus the queen of diamonds is K (3) and L is the 5. H is the 7 (1), so the 4 of hearts (2) is F and H is a diamond. Since the king is a spade (above), card J isn't the ace (2), so the 6 and B is the ace.

Thus:

3D AC 8H KS
10S 4H JC 7D
2H 6S QD 5C

No 244

No 18 has one pint (clue 4), so No 23 has 4 pints (clue 6) and No 29 2 pints. Mr Nutton is at No 29 (1) and ordered eggs (6). Mr Franks at No 15 (5) has 5 pints and potatoes were delivered to No 23. By elimination, No 17 has 3 pints. Miss Barton who ordered bread doesn't live at No 18 (4), so No 17. Mr Franks ordered cream (2), so the cheese went to No 18. Mrs Weller lives at No 23 (3) and Mrs Anderson at No 18.

Thus:

No 15, Mr Franks, 5 pints, cream;
No 17, Miss Barton, 3 pints, bread;
No 18, Mrs Anderson, 1 pint, cheese;
No 23, Mrs Weller, 4 pints, potatoes;
No 29, Mr Nutton, 2 pints, eggs.

No 245 Mask Red Death

Loxbury Manor's ghost is the grey lady (clue 3). The April (earliest) investigation was at Hanbury Heights (clue 6) and wasn't that of a witch or child, so (1) the black dog and the Roman soldier was investigated in

Solutions

May. The Dixter Hall investigation was in September (4), Mrs Naseby's in November and that into the child was in August. Dr Collins' investigation at the Ace Supermarket didn't involve the child (5), so the Roman soldier. By elimination, the witch haunts Dixter Hall and the child is at Oldcastle Abbey, so the Loxbury Manor ghost was investigated in November. Mr Tyler's investigation was in September (2) and Dr Morton's in August, so Miss Parkinson investigated the ghost at Hanbury Heights.

Thus:
Ace Supermarket, Dr Collins, May, Roman soldier;
Dixter Hall, Mr Tyler, September, witch;
Hanbury Heights, Miss Parkinson, April, black dog;
Loxbury Manor, Mrs Naseby, November, grey lady;
Oldcastle Abbey, Dr Morton, August, child.

No 246

Axel's surname is Danbury (clue 6). Mr Marks isn't Anton or Roger (clue 1) or Will (3), so Francesco. Mr Zarné isn't Anton or Roger (1), so Will. Anton joined the year before Francesco (5), who joined the year before the man from France (3) who joined the year before Will. Roger is from Russia (4), so isn't in the above sequence of four men, thus he started either before or after them. So (4) he joined in 2001 and the man from Japan in 2002. By elimination, Anton started in 2002, Francesco in 2003 (5), the man from France in 2004 and Will in 2005. Axel is from France. Francesco is from England (6), so Will is from Germany. Anton (Japan, above) isn't surnamed Grosliche (2), so Wang. Roger is Mr Grosliche.

Thus:
Anton, Wang, 2002, Japan;
Axel, Danbury, 2004, France;
Francesco, Marks, 2003, England;
Roger, Grosliche, 2001, Russia;
Will, Zarné, 2005, Germany.

No 247

No man is out for 1 hour and 15 minutes (grid), so either the man who walks around the lake is out for 1 hour 30 minutes and Robert for one hour (clue 4), or the man who goes to the lake is out for one hour and Robert for 30 minutes, ie the man out for one hour is either the one who goes to the lake or Robert. Adam goes to the harbour (2), so isn't out for one hour. The man who leaves at 9.00 goes to the shop and is out for 30 minutes (1), so Adam is out for 1 hour 45 minutes (2) and the man out for 1 hour 30 minutes leaves at 8.45. The man who walks in the streets is out for 15 minutes longer than Colin (3), so Colin is out for either 30 or 45 minutes. The man who walks in the streets gets home half an hour later than Colin (3), so (since he's out 15 minutes longer than Colin) he leaves his home 15 minutes later than Colin. The man who walks in the streets is out for either 45 minutes or one hour (3 and above), so doesn't leave at 8.45 and Colin doesn't leave at 9.00. So Colin is out for 45 minutes

and (by elimination) the man out for one hour walks in the streets. By elimination, Colin walks in the park. The man who goes to the lake is thus out for 1 hour 30 minutes, so (4) Robert is out for one hour. Tim doesn't go to the shop (1), so the lake. Steven goes to the shop. Robert goes out later than Adam (4) and 15 minutes later than Colin (3 and above), so Adam goes out at 8.00, Robert at 8.30 and Colin at 8.15.

Thus:
Adam, harbour, 8.00pm, 1 hour 45 minutes;
Colin, park, 8.15pm, 45 minutes;
Robert, streets, 8.30pm, 1 hour;
Steven, local shop, 9.00pm, 30 minutes;
Tim, lake, 8.45pm, 1 hour 30 minutes.

No 248

Robert won 2nd prize (clue 2) and 5th place went to the writer surnamed Norton (clue 4). Miss Elwood (thus female) wasn't awarded 1st or 4th place (3), so 3rd and wrote *I Can't Recall* (1). George's surname is Player (2) and Robert's isn't Garner, so Purvis. Robert wrote *The Rose Tree* (5) and Harriet's entry was 1st. Thus Abigail is Miss Elwood, George's entry was 4th and John's was 5th. By elimination, Harriet's surname is Garner. John wrote *Time After Time* (1). *Starstruck* wasn't written by George (2), so Harriet. George wrote *Call to Arms*.

Thus:
Abigail, Elwood, *I Can't Recall*, 3rd;
George, Player, *Call To Arms*, 4th;
Harriet, Garner, *Starstruck*, 1st;
John, Norton, *Time After Time*, 5th;
Robert, Purvis, *The Rose Tree*, 2nd.

No 249 *The Lesson*

The African entry will be 5th (clue 5) and Petunia is appearing 2nd (clue 6), so Andreas will be 3rd (4), the South American entry 4th and *Worldly Love* either 1st or 2nd. *Yours Forever* won't be 2nd (6), so 3rd and Jasmine will sing *My Gift* 5th. The Asian entry is *Peace to You* and won't be 1st (3), so 2nd. Thus *Worldly Love* will be 1st (above) and *A Lonely Love* 4th. Honor will sing 4th (1), so Marcus 1st. Andreas isn't representing North America (6), so Australasia. Marcus will represent North America.

Thus:
Andreas, Australasia, *Yours Forever*, 3rd;
Honor, South America, *A Lonely Love*, 4th;
Jasmine, Africa, *My Gift*, 5th;
Marcus, North America, *Worldly Love*, 1st;
Petunia, Asia, *Peace To You*, 2nd.

No 250

Donna's baby arrived at 9.30 (clue 4) and Harmony at 1.59 (clue 5), so either Rose's baby arrived at 1.59 and Amanda at 3.32 (2) or Rose's baby at 3.32 and Amanda at 9.30, ie the baby born at 3.32 is either Rose's or Amanda. Camille's baby is Larry (3), so wasn't born at 3.32. Mrs Levine whose baby was born at 3.32 (6) is either Rose or Amanda's mother.

Solutions

Carolyn's surname is Hawkins (1) and Julia's mother is Ms Walton. Camille's surname isn't Reeves (3), so Fiske, thus she gave birth at 1.03 (2). Julia wasn't born at 11.15 (1), so 9.30. Thus Amanda was born at 3.32 (2) and Rose's baby at 1.59. Carolyn's baby was thus born at 11.15 and is Michael. Rose's surname is Reeves and Marnie gave birth at 3.32.

Thus:

1.03am, Camille, Fiske, Larry;
1.59am, Rose, Reeves, Harmony;
3.32am, Marnie, Levine, Amanda;
9.30am, Donna, Walton, Julia;
11.15am, Carolyn, Hawkins, Michael.

No 251

Marilyn Monroe's body has John Wayne's legs (clue 1) and Doris Day's body is with Oliver Hardy's feet (4), but not with Frank Sinatra's legs, so Marilyn Monroe's legs. Oliver Hardy's head is with Doris Day's legs (3), so Oliver Hardy's body is with Frank Sinatra's legs. Doris Day's legs/Oliver's head aren't with John Wayne's body (3), so Frank Sinatra's. Thus John Wayne's body is with Oliver Hardy's legs. Marilyn Monroe's body and John Wayne's legs aren't with Frank Sinatra's feet (1), so Doris Day's, thus (by elimination) they're with Frank Sinatra's head. Doris Day's body is (by elimination) with John Wayne's head. Marilyn Monroe's head isn't with Frank Sinatra's feet (2), so John Wayne's, thus (by elimination) they're with Oliver Hardy's body and Frank Sinatra's legs. Frank Sinatra's body is thus with Marilyn Monroe's feet; and Doris Day's head is with John Wayne's body and Frank Sinatra's feet.

Thus (head, body, legs, feet):

Doris Day, John, Oliver, Frank;
Oliver Hardy, Frank, Doris, Marilyn;
Marilyn Monroe, Oliver, Frank, John;
Frank Sinatra, Marilyn, John, Doris;
John Wayne, Doris, Marilyn, Oliver.

No 252

2	5	1	3	8	1
7	6	5	4	3	2
3	9	2	5	9	3
9	8	7	6	5	4
6	7	1	7	8	2
1	4	9	8	4	6

No 253 *The Odyssey*

Neil is wearing No 10 (clue 4). The man in the blue vest is wearing either No 8 or No 10 (clue 2), Keith is wearing either No 7 or No 9 and the man in the black vest is wearing either No 6 or No 8. In other words, the man wearing No 8 has either a blue or black vest. So either the man in green is wearing No 6, Oliver No 5 and Lenny No 7 (3) or the man in green is wearing No 7, Oliver No 6 and Lenny No 8. If the man in black is

wearing No 6, then (above) the man in green is wearing No 7 and Oliver is wearing No 6. But Oliver's vest isn't black (2). So the man in black is wearing No 8, Keith is wearing No 9 (2) and the man in blue is wearing No 10. Keith's vest isn't yellow (3) or white (5), so red. If Oliver is wearing No 6, then Lenny is wearing No 8 (3), leaving no place for Joel (1). So Oliver is wearing No 5, the man in green is wearing No 6 and Lenny is No 7 (3). Lenny's vest isn't yellow (3), so white and Oliver's is yellow. Joel's vest isn't green (1), so black (No 8, above). Mitch is wearing No 6.

Thus:

No 5, Oliver, yellow;
No 6, Mitch, green;
No 7, Lenny, white;
No 8, Joel, black;
No 9, Keith, red;
No 10, Neil, blue.

No 254

Remember throughout that the three members of a family have names starting with different letters (intro). Amelia's daughter isn't Christina (clue 1) and Daphne's daughter isn't Christina (clue 2). Elaine's husband and Christina's mother have names starting with the same letter (4) and Elaine's husband isn't Frank, so Christina's mother isn't Felicity: thus she's Brenda and Elaine's husband is Bob. Amelia's daughter is Emma (1) and Clara's husband is Edmund. Daphne's husband is Craig. Bella's mother isn't Daphne or Clara (2) and isn't Amelia (above), so Daphne's daughter is Florence (2), Christina's father is Fred and Bella's mother is Felicity. By elimination, Amelia's husband is Daniel and Alan is Felicity's husband (and Bella's father, above). Edmund's daughter isn't Augusta (5), so Diane. Augusta's father is Bob.

Thus:

Amelia, Daniel, Emma;
Brenda, Fred, Christina;
Clara, Edmund, Diane;
Daphne, Craig, Florence;
Elaine, Bob, Augusta;
Felicity, Alan, Bella.

No 255

The 22-year-old was boring (clue 4). The 44-year-old wasn't stuck-up (clue 1), didn't smell awful (2) and wasn't very ugly (3), so was self-centred. The 33-year-old didn't smell awful (2) and wasn't very ugly (3), so was stuck-up and (1) is Nadine. Maureen is 44 (3) and the very ugly woman is 39, so the one who smelled awful is 28 and (2) the 22-year-old was Thursday's date. The date with Delores was on Friday. Maureen's date wasn't on Monday (5). She's 11 years older than Nadine, so Anita's date was on Thursday (1) and Maureen's on Tuesday. Nadine's date wasn't on Monday (6), so Wednesday. Kristel was Monday's date and (3) isn't 39, so 28. Delores is 39 years old.

Solutions

Thus:
Anita, Thursday, 22 years old, boring;
Delores, Friday, 39 years old, very ugly;
Kristel, Monday, 28 years old, smelled awful;
Maureen, Tuesday, 44 years old, self-centred;
Nadine, Wednesday, 33 years old, stuck-up.

No 256
Emily donated the vase (clue 1) and Patricia gave the printer (clue 2). Howard bought vegetables (2). Albert either gave the footstool (4) or bought the footstool and, if the latter, then (7) he gave vegetables. Ray and Dean either gave the cake and/or bought the cake (5). The person who gave a barometer and bought a book (3) isn't Laurence, so Tilly. Emily bought the barometer (1). Albert either donated or bought the footstool (4), so the item donated by Howard and bought by Patricia (2) is the clock. The person who donated vegetables and bought a footstool (7) wasn't Ray or Dean (5). The book bought by Tilly (above) wasn't donated by Laurence (6) or Dean (8), so Ray. Thus Dean donated the cake and Ray bought it (5). Laurence didn't donate the footstool (6), so the vegetables; thus he bought the footstool (7) and (4) Albert donated it. Albert bought the printer (4) and Dean bought the vase.
Thus (gave, bought):
Albert, footstool, printer;
Dean, cake, vase;
Emily, vase, barometer;
Howard, clock, vegetables;
Laurence, vegetables, footstool;
Patricia, printer, clock;
Ray, book, cake;
Tilly, barometer, book.

No 257
Lesley's surname is either Gordon or Wishman (clue 2), so Sandra is the woman who shopped at Fashion House, surnamed either Holford or Mitchell (clue 4). Lesley shopped at Ella's Boutique (2). Gloria shopped at Town Girl (1). Either Harriet or Gloria bought the coat (3), so Sandra bought a jacket (1) and Gloria a suit. Harriet bought the coat (3) and is either Mitchell or Wishman. Mrs Abbott isn't Lesley, so (5) Mrs Abbott shopped at Kent & Moore and (by elimination) she's Bonita and Harriet shopped at Jayne's. Bonita bought a skirt (5), so Lesley bought a dress. Miss Gordon isn't Harriet (above), so Miss Gordon shopped at Town Girl (6). So she's Gloria, Sandra's surname is Holford, Lesley's is Wishman and Harriet's is Mitchell.
Thus:
Bonita, Abbott, skirt, Kent & Moore;
Gloria, Gordon, suit, Town Girl;
Harriet, Mitchell, coat, Jayne's;
Lesley, Wishman, dress, Ella's Boutique;
Sandra, Holford, jacket, Fashion House.

No 258 Odyssey
Judy lives in Marsham (clue 2) and Deanna in Tunfield (clue 5). Lynda visited Judy and drove to Marsham (2), Judy drove to Arkbourne (3) and Deanna to Cosbrook (5). The woman who drove to Tunfield (to see Deanna) wasn't Magdalene or Charlene (4), so Phoebe. Magdalene visited Phoebe (4) who thus lives in Holbury or Winford. The woman who lives in Holbury drove to Winford (1), so she's either Charlene or Magdalene. Thus Phoebe lives in Winford and Magdalene lives in Holbury and (by elimination) Charlene drove there to visit her. The woman who lives in Arkbourne isn't Linda (3), so Judy visited Charlene there and Linda lives in Cosbrook.
Thus:
Charlene, Arkbourne, Magdalene, Holbury;
Deanna, Tunfield, Linda, Cosbrook;
Judy, Marsham, Charlene, Arkbourne;
Linda, Cosbrook, Judy, Marsham;
Magdalene, Holbury, Phoebe, Winford;
Phoebe, Winford, Deanna, Tunfield.

No 259
Shelagh is 21 (clue 4). The 18-year-old isn't Tamara (clue 1), Dora (5) or Jenny (6), so Ava whose pullover (1) is too small. The long sleeves are on the green pullover (5), so Dora isn't 19. The 19-year-old isn't Jenny (6), so Tamara who (2) got the cream pullover. The pink pullover is Jenny's (6). Dora's isn't white or green (5), so brown. By elimination, Ava's is white and Shelagh's is green. Thus Dora is 22 (5), so Jenny is 20. Tamara has a jumper with odd sleeves (6). The neck is tight on Jenny's pullover (3), so the sleeves are tight on Dora's pullover.
Thus:
Ava, 18 years old, white, too small;
Dora, 22 years old, brown, sleeves tight;
Jenny, 20 years old, pink, neck tight;
Shelagh, 21 years old, green, long sleeves;
Tamara, 19 years old, cream, odd sleeves.

No 260
The child in grey trousers isn't Willy, Billy or Jilly (clue 3) or Milly (clue 4), so Dilly. Dilly's jacket isn't brown or maroon (3), beige or scarlet (8), so blue. Her jumper isn't orange or white (7), pink or yellow (8), so cream. Neither Jilly or Milly has a maroon jacket (1) or scarlet jacket (6). Milly's jacket isn't brown (4), so beige and Jilly's is brown. The child in purple trousers isn't wearing a maroon jacket (1), beige jacket (2) or scarlet jacket (5), so brown. The child in a maroon jacket isn't wearing crimson trousers (1) or green trousers (5), so black trousers: not with a pink or white jumper (1) or a yellow jumper (2), so an orange jumper. Jilly's jumper isn't white (4) or yellow (6), so pink. Milly's isn't yellow (6), so white. The child in a scarlet jacket isn't wearing crimson trousers (5), so green. Willy's trousers aren't green (3), so his jacket is maroon and Billy's is scarlet. Milly's trousers are crimson and Billy's jumper is yellow.

Solutions

Thus:
Billy, scarlet, yellow, green;
Dilly, blue, cream, grey;
Jilly, brown, pink, purple;
Milly, beige, white, crimson;
Willy, maroon, orange, black.

No 261 *The Necklace*

The woman 1st in line isn't the one immediately in front of Denise (clue 5), nor was Denise 1st in line. Denise wasn't 3rd or 4th (clue 4), so 5th. The woman who spent $3.80 isn't the one who spent twenty cents more than the woman who wanted a bread roll (1), so the woman who wanted a bread roll spent $3.70. Thus she isn't Denise (3). Nor did Denise want a sausage roll (3), chocolate eclair (4) or Swiss roll (5), so a doughnut. Denise didn't spend $4.00 (2), $3.60 (4) or $3.90 (5), so $3.80. The woman who spent $3.70 didn't spend 10 cents more than Debbie (3), so Debbie didn't spend $3.60. The woman who spent $3.60 isn't Dinah (2) or Delia (4), so Dora. Debbie didn't spend $3.70 or $4.00 (3), so $3.90. Dinah didn't spend $4.00 (2), so $3.70 and Delia spent $4.00. The woman who wanted a chocolate eclair didn't spend $3.60 and wasn't Delia (4), so the one who wanted the eclair spent $3.90. The only place for Delia in clue 1 is as the woman 2nd in the queue. In clue 2, Debbie's place is as the woman 3rd in line. Dora's place in clue 3 is as the woman who wanted a sausage roll. By elimination, Delia wanted a Swiss roll. Dora ($3.60, above) wasn't 4th in the queue, so 1st and Dinah was 4th.

Thus:
Debbie, third, chocolate eclair, $3.90;
Delia, second, Swiss roll, $4.00;
Denise, fifth, doughnut, $3.80;
Dinah, fourth, bread roll, $3.70;
Dora, first, sausage roll, $3.60.

No 262 *The Odyssey*

The person whose bus is at 7.55 takes 15 minutes to get to work (clue 1), thus not 10 minutes longer than anyone else, so Nigel's bus doesn't arrive at 7.45 (clue 4), so at 7.30 and whoever gets the 7.40 bus has a journey time 10 minutes longer than Andy's. Rosie gets the No 28 at 7.45 (2) and the commuter with the 30-minute journey time gets a bus at 8.00. The latter isn't Claudine (2), so Andy. Thus the person with the 40-minute journey gets the 7.40 bus (4 and above). Dirk's journey isn't 40 minutes (3), so Claudine's bus is at 7.40 and Dirk's is at 7.55. Claudine's bus has a number five higher than Andy's (4), which is five higher than Dirk's (3), so Claudine's is the No 23, Andy's is the No 18 and Dirk's is the No 13. Nigel's is the No 33, so (5) his journey takes 25 minutes and Rosie's takes 10 minutes.

Thus:
Andy, No 18, 8.00am, 30 minutes;
Claudine, No 23, 7.40am, 40 minutes;
Dirk, No 13, No 7.55am, 15 minutes;
Rosie, No 28, 7.45am, 10 minutes;
Nigel, No 33, 7.30am, 25 minutes.

No 263 *The Odyssey (time)*

Pig A (furthest left) isn't orange (clue 1), white (clue 3), blue (4) or red (5), so green. The pig with $16.00 is next to and left of the pig with $14.00 (2), so the pig with $16.00 isn't Donny's (3) or Peter's (5) and the one with $14.00 isn't white (3) or red (5). The one with $16.00 isn't Veronica's (1), Jodie's (2), Donny's (3) or Peter's (5), so Ronald's. No pig contains $14.50 (grid). The pig with $13.50 doesn't belong to Veronica (1), Donny (3) or Peter (5), so Jodie. It isn't orange (1), white (3) or blue (4), so red. Peter's is D and contains $14.00 (5) and pig C contains $16.00 (2). Veronica's contains $15.00 (1) and C is orange. Thus Peter's pig is blue and pig B is white. By elimination, Donny's contains $15.50, so pig C is Ronald's. Donny's is A (3), so Veronica's is B.

Thus:
A, Donny, green, $15.50;
B, Veronica, white, $15.00;
C, Ronald, orange, $16.00;
D, Peter, blue, $14.00;
E, Jodie, red, $13.50.

No 264

B	C	C	B	A	A
A	A	C	B	B	C
A	B	A	C	C	B
C	B	A	C	A	B
C	C	B	A	B	A
B	A	B	A	C	C

No 265 *The Lesson*

The Cliffhangers signed with Virgo Records and reached No 15 (clue 3) and The Moonmen signed with Folydor (clue 6), so The Hagglers reached No 2 (2) and Musiqua signed with GCO. The Moonmen achieved a higher position than the band with Plum Music (6), so the Hagglers are with Cemtella and Jay and the Rooks are with Plum Music. The Hagglers were predicted to reach No 17 (4), so The Cliffhangers were predicted to reach No 22 (3). The Moonmen didn't reach No 18 or No 20 (6), so No 3, thus (1) they were predicted to reach No 12 and (6) Jay and the Rooks were predicted to reach No 2. Musiqua were predicted to reach No 15. Musiqua didn't reach No 18 (5), so No 20. Jay and the Rooks were at No 18.

Thus (predicted, actual):
The Cliffhangers, Virgo Records, No 22, No 15;
The Hagglers, Cemtella, No 17, No 2;
Jay and the Rooks, Plum Music, No 2, No 18;
The Moonmen, Folydor, No 12, No 3;
Musiqua, GCO, No 15, No 20.

Solutions

No 266

Joel has 14 tickets at $1.10 (clue 2) and hasn't 18 of any ticket (grid), so he has 10 at $1.30 for the 19 July draw (clue 1) and 12 at $0.50 for the prize of a holiday. The $1.10 tickets are for the raffle on 9 June (2) and the car is the prize for the raffle on 12 May. The $0.50 tickets aren't for the raffle on 16 March (4), so 28 September. The 20 tickets aren't for the raffle on 9 June (4), so 12 May, thus those for the raffle on 16 March cost $0.90 and those for the 12 May raffle cost $0.70. By elimination, he has 16 tickets for the raffle on 16 March. The latter is for the food hamper (3) and the prize for the 9 June raffle is a computer. The prize for the 19 July raffle is a television.

Thus:

16 March, food hamper, 16 tickets, $0.90 each;
12 May, car, 20 tickets, $0.70 each;
9 June, computer, 14 tickets, $1.10 each;
19 July, television, 10 tickets, $1.30 each;
28 September, holiday, 12 tickets, $0.50 each.

No 267

The person who walked for 24 minutes wasn't Barbara (clue 1), Charles (clue 3), David or Gwen (4), so Trevor. The one who walked for 22 minutes wasn't Charles (3), David or Gwen (4), so Barbara. The one who walked for 20 minutes wasn't Charles (3) or Gwen (4), so David. No-one left at 2.30 (grid), so David didn't leave at 2.00 (3). Thus David left at 3.00 (2) and the person with the black umbrella at 4.00. The latter is Trevor (1). David's umbrella isn't green (3), so Charles walked for 16 minutes and Barbara's umbrella is green and she left at 3.30. Gwen walked for 14 minutes and (4) her umbrella is red. David's isn't grey (3), so blue. Charles has a grey umbrella, so didn't leave at 2.00 (1). Thus Gwen left at 2.00 and Charles at 1.30.

Thus:

Barbara, 3.30pm, 22 minutes, green;
Charles, 1.30pm, 16 minutes, grey;
David, 3.00pm, 20 minutes, blue;
Gwen, 2.00pm, 14 minutes, red;
Trevor, 4.00pm, 24 minutes, black.

No 268 *The Odyssey*

The card from Mel didn't arrive on Friday or Saturday (clue 1), Monday or Thursday (clue 4), so Tuesday. Thus the card next to and left of the one from Tony arrived on Monday and wasn't sent by Jeff (4) or Craig (6), so Vivienne. The card from Thailand is further left than Vivienne's (3), which is next to and left of the one from Tony (4), which is next to and left of the one from Jeff (2), which is next to and left of the card which came on Saturday. So the one from Thailand is A, Vivienne's is B, Tony's C, Jeff's D and E came on Saturday. By elimination, A is from Mel and E from Craig. Vivienne's isn't from Norway (1), Scotland or Cyprus (5), so Hawaii. Jeff's isn't from Scotland or Cyprus (5), so Norway. The one which came on Saturday isn't from Scotland (5), so Cyprus. Card C is from Scotland and came on Friday (5) and Jeff's came on Thursday.

Thus:

A, Mel, Thailand, Tuesday;
B, Vivienne, Hawaii, Monday;
C, Tony, Scotland, Friday;
D, Jeff, Norway, Thursday;
E, Craig, Cyprus, Saturday.

No 269

Pieces 1 and 32 contain D (clue 1). In 1-49, pieces 9 and 33 contain either C and/or E, so piece 49=B. Pieces 31 and 40 contain E (clue 4), so 33=C and 9=E. The letters in 11, 20 and 36 are all either C or B (2). In 43-49, E=48. If 11, 20 and 36 contain B (2), then there is nowhere for a B in diagonal 7-43, so they all contain C. Thus 38 and 23 (3) contain D. In 36-42, 39=B, 37=G and 42=F. Thus 18=A, 46=G and 43=A. In 43-49, 47=D. Thus 19=B, 13=D, 21=D, 15=E, 16=F, 35=A, 24=C, 28=E, 14=G, 2=A, 44=C, 45=F, 10=A, 3=B, 26=A, 12=F, 5=G, 6=F, 8=B, 22=G, 29=F, 27=B and 34=G.

Thus:

D	A	B	E	G	F	C
B	E	A	C	F	D	G
E	F	G	A	B	C	D
G	D	C	F	A	B	E
F	B	E	D	C	G	A
C	G	D	B	E	A	F
A	C	F	G	D	E	B